UNIVERSAL LAWS NEVER BEFORE REVEALED:

KEELY'S SECRETS

Understanding and Using the Science of Sympathetic Vibration

by Dale Pond
John Keely
Nikola Tesla
Edgar Cayce
Clara Bloomfield-Moore
Lawrence Oliphant
Louise Off
Henry Wood
R. Harte
Dr. Hall
Henry Hudson

Edited by Dale Pond

The Message Company

NEW REVISED EDITION

LIBRARY OF CONGRESS CATALOG CARD NUMBER: 94-77879
ISBN: 1-57282-003-9 (Paperback)
Cover Design by Janice St. Marie
Book Design by James Berry

Publisher's Cataloging in Publication

Universal laws never before revealed : Keely's secrets : understanding
 and using the science of sympathetic vibration / by Dale Pond ...
 [et al.] ; edited by Dale Pond. -- 2nd ed., new rev. ed.
 p. cm.
 Includes bibliographical references and index.
 Preassigned LCCN: 94-77879.
 ISBN: 1-57282-003-9 (pbk.)

 1. Keely, John Ernest Worrell, 1827-1898. 2. Vibration. 3.
Keely motor.   I. Pond, Dale.

 QC231.U65 1995   620.2
                          QBI95-20616

Published and distributed by:

The Message Company
4 Camino Azul
Santa Fe, NM 87505
505-474-0998

Printed in the United States of America
Printed on acid-free recycled paper using soy ink.

ACKNOWLEDGEMENTS

I wish to thank all those who have helped directly and indirectly in the preparation of this work. Especially those lonely geniuses of old who bore the brunt of derision and ridicule, never faltering in the thankless task of bringing the Light of Understanding to the Minds of Men. With special gratitude to the memory of Mrs. Clara Sophia Jessup Bloomfield-Moore in her courage and strength to stand by such a Man as John Ernst Worrell Keely, even in the face of public scorn, and humiliation. No less thanks go to The Theosophical Society* for their Light-Bearing efforts, The Rosicrucian Order AMORC*, for their centuries of thankless toil and to the Association for Research and Enlightenment and its employees for their support and encouragement. No less do we thank those unnamed ones who have withstood the fury of ignorance of past ages in order that Man may Evolve to his rightful place. It is with truth and humility that "The few carry the many."

This book contains a vast collection of material on Keely and his work. In it has been included all the pictures and charts known to exist as of this date. I have also included all that we have been able to decipher of this wonderful new science and philosophy. There will be more discoveries and these will be published at a later date. The discoveries mentioned here demonstrate that Keely's science of *Sympathetic Vibratory Physics* is a wholistic approach to science and nature and reveals a wonderful order and simplicity.

It is hoped readers will find a number of ideas and methods in these pages which they can apply to their current scientific work and research.

Dale Pond

*Author's Note: There has been a great deal of discussion concerning the motives and belief systems of these two organizations. It is taken herein that the *original* intent and purpose of these groups was the preservation and disseminations of *real TRUTH* from the ancient days to the present. We, as human beings, can now more properly partake and use the forces and knowledge contained in their *original* knowledge bases. It is further recognized that these organizations may have more or less "lost their way" during the past two or three centuries. Perhaps the present day motivations and directions being assigned to them are in error – perhaps not. It is not to these I give thanks but to their original intent and accomplishments. For, it is, I believe, through the efforts of these *original* organizations that certain specific and valid information was indeed preserved and brought through the centuries of ignorant persecution that we, through Keely's efforts (and others'), may understand and use same. *Dale Pond*

ABOUT THE AUTHOR/EDITOR

Dale Pond is truly a renaissance man with a diversified background in chemistry, physics, mechanical engineering, computers, mathematics, acoustics, hydrodynamics, geometry, music, and common law.

His vast experience includes technical writing, inventing, lecturing, corporate training, business, manufacturing, publishing and authoring scientific and philosophical journals and books.

At the leading edge of new paradigm thinking, he has been able to show that vibration is the principle underlying all things. Vibration is the link between spirit and matter - the magic key for creating new worlds and universes.

As an internationally renowned lecturer, Dale has presented workshops and seminars at the Swiss Association for Free Energy Conference, the International Keely Conferences, Sound and Vibration Conference, International Symposium on New Science, International Forum on New Energy, United States Psychotronics Association Conference, the Alchemy of Sound Conference and many others.

Other books by Mr. Pond:

Sympathetic Vibratory Physics - A Compendium of Terms and Phrases
Sympathetic Vibratory Physics Certification and Training Course - Level I
Nikola Tesla's Earthquake Machine
HyperVibes (a Hypercard research reference library for SVP)
A History of the American Constitutional or Common Law
Our American Common Law
The Physics of Love
John Keely's Musical Dynasphere

Table Of Contents

Universal Laws Never Before Revealed.. Keely's Secrets

ILLUSTRATIONS

Universal Laws Never Before Revealed.. Keely's Secrets

KEELY'S ACOUSTIC THEORETICAL CHARTS

Disintegration of Stone

1888

A short time ago the mining world in America was seized with an inexplicable excitement. The value of gold mines in particular suddenly rose. Mines long since abandoned on account of the expense of working, awoke, and rubbing their eyes made their way again into the stock list. Presently it leaked out that a syndicate of the longest-headed and wealthiest mining capitalists were quietly buying up all the cheap and apparently worthless gold mines they could hear of, and people at once concluded that something was up. Then everyone of a speculative turn, very knowingly began to buy worthless gold mining shares at ever-increasing prices, and when the little speculators had gorged themselves to the full extent of their financial capacity, they asked: What next? No one knew exactly what he was after; and everyone looked to the Syndicate for the next move; but the Syndicate smilingly put its hands in its pockets and whistled! After the fever came prostration. The small fry had not, like the Syndicate, bought to hold, so they got first uneasy, then alarmed, and finally panic-stricken. The tide of credulity turned and began to run out even more quickly than it had set in, and thousands of the unlucky, but greedy little grudgeon of the Stock Exchange were left stranded in a short time by the receding tide of speculation, kicking and gasping in the mortal agonies of financial asphyxia. The panic is easily accounted for by the general laws that govern the movements of the Stock Exchange; but not so the action of the syndicate. The problem remains: Why did the long-headed millionaires buy up worthless mines? That is the point of interest, and the explanation thereof is as follows:---

A few weeks before the panic occurred, twelve solid men - millionaires - met by appointment in a certain laboratory in Philadelphia to witness an exhibition of the disintegration of quartz by a new method. They were mining magnates, who had a tremendous interest in getting the gold out of quartz rock quickly and cheaply. The inventor obliged them by simply touching some blocks of quartz with a little machine he held in his hand; and as he touched each block it instantly crumbled into atomic dust, in which the specks of gold it had contained stood out like boulders in a bed of sand. Then the twelve solid men solidly said: Mr. Keely, if you will in the same manner disintegrate some quartz for us in its natural place, we will each of us give you a cheque for --- dollars. So off they all went to the Katskill mountains, and there the twelve solid men pointed out a reef of quartz on the side of a mountain, as solid as themselves; and Mr. Keely took out his little machine and said: Gentlemen, please take the time. In eighteen minutes there was a tunnel in that quartz mountain eighteen feet long and four and a half feet in diameter. Then Mr. Keely quietly returned to Philadelphia with his cheques in his pocket, and the twelve solid men went from New York to San Francisco to gather in the seemingly worthless stock of mines long disused because of the working expense, thus producing the disastrous effect upon the mining world, which we have just seen. (All these men bound themselves to secrecy; and this is the first time that this incident has been made public.)

How was the quartz disintegrated?-- That is one of Keely's secrets.

The disintegration of the rock is, however, a very small and accidental effect of that tremendous force that lies behind the secret. Indeed, that particular application of the force was a chance discovery. One day the inventor was studying the action of currents of ether playing over a floor upon which he had scattered fine sand,---the ether was rolling the sand into ropes,---when a block of granite, which was used for fastening back a door, disintegrated under his eyes. He took the hint, and in a few days he had made a vibratory disintegrater.

Who is this man, and what is this force? to whom, or to which, boring a tunnel into the mountain side is mere child's play? Surely, were such things true, science would long ago have filled the world with the renown of such a man---the man who has discovered a force in nature compared to which all known motor or mechanical forces are like the scratch of a nail, or the breath of a child. Surely the press, the platform, and even the pulpit would have resounded with the glad tidings of so great a victory over the stubborn powers of nature, a victory which goes so far towards making man the master of things in this material plane!

Those who argue like that know little of modern science and its votaries. An Anglican bishop never ignored a dissenting preacher with more dignified grace than the professor of orthodox science ignores the heterodox genius who has the audacity to wander beyond the limitations which received opinion has placed upon the possibilities of nature. The fact is that men of science have persistently ignored, and know absolutely nothing about, the great department of nature into which Keely penetrated years ago, and in which he has now made himself at home. Not long ago a Fellow of the Royal Society of Edinburgh, Major Ricarde-Seaver, went to Philadelphia to convince himself as to the nature of Keely's discovery. He returned, saying that Keely was working with, and had the apparent command over forces, the nature, or even the very existence, of which was absolutely unknown to him, and so far as he is aware, to modern science.

Beyond disintegration lies dispersion, and Keely can just as easily dissolve the atoms of matter as disintegrate its molecules. Dissolve them into what? Well,---into ether, apparently; into the hypothetical substratum which modern scientists have postulated, and about whose nature they know absolutely nothing but what they invent themselves, but which to Keely is not a hypothesis, but a fact as real as his own shoes; and which ether, indeed, seems to be the protoplasm of all things. As to the law of gravity, it appears very like a delusion, in the light of Keely's experiments, or, at least, but one manifestation of a law of very much wider application---a law which provides for the reversion of the process of attraction in the shape of a process of repulsion. One of Keely's little scientific experiments is to put a small wire round an iron cylinder that weighs several hundred weight, and when the force runs through the wire, to lift the cylinder up on one finger and carry it as easily as if it were a piece of cork. Not long ago he moved, single-handed, a 500 horse-power vibratory engine from one part of his shop to another. There was not a scratch on the floor, and astounded engineers declared that they could not have moved it without a derrick, to bring which in operation would have required the removal of the roof of the shop. Of course it is but a step in advance of this to construct a machine which, when polarized with a negative attraction, will rise from the earth and move under the influence of an etheric current at the rate of 500 miles an hour, in any given direction. This is, in fact, Keely's air ship.

Lately, he has applied his force to optics, and by means of three wires placed across the lens of a microscope he makes its magnifying power equal to that of the great telescope in the Lick observatory - the largest in the world. Why don't all astronomers and opticians run to look through Keely's microscope, and to examine into the process? Perhaps if Galileo were alive he might express an opinion!

But, the reader may naturally exclaim, how long has this been going on, and we to know nothing about it? Mr. Keely is now over 60 years of age, and he has worked since he was a boy, at times, upon various inventions before his discovery of ether. For the last 18 years he has been constantly employed with experiments upon the ether; for eighteen long years he has worked day and night, with hand and brain, in the face of discouragements that would long ago have killed the owner of a less heroic soul; and he has worked almost single handed. Slander, ridicule, open accusations of fraud, charlatanry, insanity---everything evil that it could enter the head of the knave of the heart of the fool to conceive, every mean insinuation, every malicious lie that prejudice, bigotry, ignorance, self-conceit, vested interests, greed, injustice, dishonesty, and hypocrisy could concoct---these have been the encouragement which, so far, the world has bestowed upon the discoverer of the profoundest truths and laws of nature that have ever been imparted to the profane, or even hinted at, outside of the circle of Initiates. And now it has been proved in a hundred ways, and before thousands of persons competent to judge of the merits of his machines, that he has really discovered previously unknown forces in nature, studied them, mastered some of their laws, invented, and almost perfected, apparatus and machinery that will make his discoveries of practical application in a hundred ways---now that he has actually done all this, how does the world treat him? Does Congress come forward with a grant to enable him to complete his marvelous work? Do men of science hail him as a great discoverer, or hold out the hand of fellowship? Do the people do honour to the man whose sole entreaty to them is to receive at his hands a gift a thousand times more precious to them than steam engine or telegraph? It is a literal fact that the world to-day would tear Keely to pieces if it had the power to do so, and if he fell exhausted in the terrible struggle he has so long maintained, his failure to establish his claims would be received with a shout of malignant

delight from nearly every lecture hall, pulpit, counting-house, and newspaper office in the so-called civilized world! The world has hardly ever recognized its benefactors, until it has become time to raise a statue to their memory; 'in order to beautify the town.' Jealousy, stupidity, the malignity which is born of conscious inferiority, are at this moment putting in Keely's road every impediment which law and injustice can manufacture. Two hundred years ago he would have been burned, a century since he would have been probably mobbed to death, but thank God we are too civilized, too humane to burn or mob to death those who make great discoveries, who wish to benefit their fellow men, or whose ideas are in advance of their age - we only break their hearts with slander, ridicule, and neglect, and when that fails to drive them to suicide, we bring to bear upon them the ponderous pressure of the law, and heap upon them the peine forte et dure of injunctions, and orders, and suits, to crush them out of a world they have had the impertinence to try to improve and the folly to imagine they could save from suffering without paying in their own persons the inevitable penalty of crucifixion. Had it not been for the obligations incurred by Mr. Keely, writes Mrs. Bloomfield-Moore in the Philadelphia Inquirer, of Jan. 20th of this year, in accepting the aid of the Keely Motor Company - in other words, had scientists, instead of speculators, furnished him with the means necessary to carry on his 'work of Evolution,' the secrets which he has so carefully guarded would now have been public property, so little does he care personally for financial results. As it is, those who have witnessed his beautiful experiments in acoustics and sympathetic vibration were often too ignorant to comprehend their meaning, and, consequently, even after expressing gratification to him, went away from his workshop to denounce him as a Cagliostro, while others, competent to judge, have refused to witness the production of the ether, as Sir William Thomson and Lord Raleigh refused when they were in America a

Universal Laws Never Before Revealed.. Keely's Secrets

few years since. The company here mentioned has been a thorn in the inventor's side ever since it was organized. It has been bulled and beared by greedy speculators, in whose varying interests the American newspapers for years have been worked, the results of which the inventor has had to bear. For many years the Company has contributed nothing towards Mr. Keely's expenses or support, and in the opinion of many lawyers it is virtually dead. How far it is entitled to his gratitude may be gathered from the fact, as stated in Mrs. Bloomfield-Moore's article above quoted, that when Mr. Keely abandoned his old generator of etheric force, baffled in his attempts to wrest from nature one of her most carefully guarded secrets, harassed by his connection with the Keely Motor Company, some of the officers and stockholders of which had instituted law proceedings against him, which threatened him with the indignity of imprisonment, he destroyed many of his marvelous models, and determined that, if taken to prison, it should be his dead body and not himself.

When the history of his discoveries and his inventions come to be written there will be no more pathetic story in the annuals of genius than that of John Worrell Keely. The world hereafter will find it hard to believe that in the last quarter of the 19th century a man with an insight into the secret workings of nature, and a knowledge of her subtler forces, which, whenever it is utilized, will relieve mankind from much of the grinding toil that now makes bitter the existence of the vast majority of mortals, that such a man should have been left to starve, because in all the ranks of Science there was not found one man capable of understanding his colossal work - because in all the ranks of religion there was not found one man able to realize the enlarged conception of Deity immanent in Keely's great thoughts - because in all the ranks of commerce, of speculation, of literature, of art, there was not found one man large enough, generous enough, unselfish enough, to furnish money for a purpose that did not promise an immediate dividend.

It is to a woman, not a man, that the eternal honour is due of having come to Keely's rescue, and saved humanity from once more disgracing itself by doing genius to death with brokenhearted want and neglect. That woman's name will go down the centuries inseparably connected with Keely's discoveries. Probably no more romantic incident ever happened in the history of invention than the connection between this wealthy and large-minded woman and this slandered and persecuted genius, and no stranger one than the way in which she was led, by a series of most unfortuitous events, to offer her aid. From that day this lady has been not only his benefactor, but also his co-worker, trusted friend, and courageous defender. With the exception of his friend, those who have occupied themselves with Keely's discoveries have confined their attention to its commercial value. This was to be expected, for Science now is the hand-maid of trade, and Religion has become the fawning follower of Science. There is, however, a higher aspect to Keely's discoveries, and that their value as contributions to man's knowledge of Nature and natural laws. So far as that is concerned, Keely's success is an accomplished fact. His work, explaining his whole system, is now in the Press, and were he to die tomorrow he will be just as great a figure in the world's history as he would be were a thousand speculators to clear ten million dollars apiece by his inventions. Fancy honouring Copernicus or Galileo because the yelping jackals of speculation, who were their contemporaries, grew fat by feeding on their brains!

Whether Keely's inventions will be commercial success at present is another matter. The force, or, rather forces, which Keely handles, are the same as those known under other names in Occultism, and it is the belief of Occultists that these forces cannot be introduced into the practical life of men, or fully understood by the uninitiated, until the world is fit to receive them with benefit to itself - until the balance of the good and the evil they work is decidedly on the side of the good. Keely himself is persuaded that the world will derive almost unmixed benefit from his discoveries; but an Occultist would prefer to say that inventions and discoveries are disclosed to man, rather than to credit genius with the elaboration of ideas - disclosed, that is to say, through the brain of the ostensible inventor by one of the higher powers that guide the destinies of humanity. The discoveries of Keely have an occult side, which perhaps he himself may not fully perceive, but it is upon that side that it depends whether those discoveries themselves are fitted, by reason of sympathetic vibration of a still more inner ether than Keely has publicly spoken of, to harmonize with the mass chord of our present civilization, and manifest in the material life of man. Occultists believe that there are intelligent powers behind the visible things and events of life, which powers alone can say So far shalt thou go, and no further; but they do not believe that these powers act as a deus ex machina, for in themselves they are part of the natural order of things, and act in and through material and immaterial nature. We at present in our normal state of consciousness know these powers only as forces and laws, and when we become conscious of them as intelligent entities, we perceive at the same time that they themselves are governed by higher wills and intelligences, which act through them, as they act through us, and are to them their forces and their Laws.

*Occultists see in everything the (to us) eternal action of two opposing powers or principles, which are ever seeking equilibrium, and never find it, for behind them there is a definite tendency towards that which we call progress, which tendency gives the preponderance to one of these powers, and thus prevents the establishment of equilibrium, in other words of stagnation and death. Now all great discoveries are manifestations of one of these powers or forces only, and, however good in themselves, tend to disturb the equilibrium of terrestrial life more than is required for the normal rate of universal progress; and therefore they produce a disproportion of parts, and the opposite power or force gathers strength to resist and check the exaggeration. Already, in the estimation of an ever-growing number of thinking men, the inventions and discoveries of the present century have proved themselves a curse rather than a blessing. The have raised the world's standard of comfort, and at the same time they have lowered the power of purchasing these very comforts, a desire for which they have generated. The advantages that accrue from steam and from machinery have not been distributed, but have become the property of a small minority. Year by year competition is becoming fiercer, and labor more arduous and continual, and men are growing more and more like living machines, and the helpless slaves of machinery and of institutions. An operative, in these days of steam power, has less liberty than a slave ever had, ex-

---

* Franck, in Die Kabballa, says: We learn, by the last three Sephiroth, that the Universal Providence, that the Supreme Artist, is also Absolute Force, the all-powerful Cause; and that, at the same time, this cause is the generative element of all that is. It is these last Sephiroth that constitute the natural world, or nature in its essence and in its Active principle, Natura naturans. This passage is quoted in Isis Unveiled (Vol.I,p.40), the authoress adding: "This Kabalistic conception is thus proved identical with that of the Hindu philosophy. Whoever reads Plato and his Dialogue Timaeus, will find these ideas as faithfully re-echoed by the great philosopher." They are all, in fact echoes of the archaic Secret Doctrine of the Occultists; and it is somewhat singular (pour le dire en passant) that the newspaper press so persistently refers to Theosophy as a new, or new-fangled, religion or philosophy, whereas the ideas now called theosophical are the oldest in the world, and may be found, more or less disguised or mutilated, and under many different forma and names, in all the great philosophical and religious sytems of antiquity. One is forced to conclude that the complaint, so often heard, that competition now compels young people to earn their bread while they ought still to be at school, applies with a good deal of force to a certain class of writers for the press.

Universal Laws Never Before Revealed.. Keely's Secrets

cept in one particular - he has full liberty to starve, or to work himself to death, neither of which privileges an owner would allow him. Keely, however, thinks his discoveries will restore this disturbed equilibrium.

The direct effect of modern discoveries and inventions has been the rise of the commercial and economic system; and the inevitable consequence of that system has been to deepen the gulf between the poor and the rich. The natural effect of this is an antagonism between the two poles of society, which has its roots deep down in human nature and human passions, and this antagonism is becoming better recognized, and growing in intensity, year by year, in so much that it is almost universally felt that the only possible outcome from it is a social overturning, the date of the actual occurrence of which will depend chiefly upon the activity of the schoolboards, and the thoroughness of their work. Hardly a thinking man of the present day but foresees, sooner or later, a great social cataclysm, in which all mere political and financial considerations will be as straws in a whirlwind. Now, it would seem that Keely's discoveries tend to develop power over material nature in the same direction in which that power has been growing during the last hundred years. If it be a power into the exercise of which there enter no moral considerations whatever, then it is applicable alike for good purposes and for evil; and it will be as ready to the hand of the bad man as to that of the good. Were such inventions given to the world in their completeness, the whole of the enormous power they gave over human life and destines would, it would seem, fall into the possession of the same small minority who at present control the power conferred by our present inventions and discoveries - the capitalists. If so, that section of the community would then, under our present institutions, obtain almost absolute power over the great majority - those who depend upon their labor for their support. The capitalists who owned the tremendous powers implied in a monopoly of Keely's inventions would be practically the absolute masters of the people; and obedience to their will would be far more really, than even now, the condition upon which those who were not capitalists also would be allowed the means of continued existence.

Occultists believe that the world is not yet ready for the appearance of such tremendous forces on the stage of human life. Mankind is too selfish, too cruel, too stupid, too pitiless, too animal, to be entrusted with what, in sober reality, are minor divine powers. Such powers could not at present be employed for the benefit of mankind and for the advancement of the race; on the contrary, they would tend to the further brutalization and virtual enslavement of the poor, and also to the further materialization and moral degradation of One the rich. In a word, the human qualities of justice, mercy, love, generosity, unselfishness, have not yet grown strong enough in the race, and the animal qualities of revenge, anger, jealousy, tyranny, hatred, selfishness, are still too powerful in man to make the acquisition of almost absolute power over nature, and over one another, anything but a curse to mankind. It would be less disastrous to give dynamite cartridges to monkeys for playthings.

For this reason Occultists, in general, do not regard Keely's discoveries as likely to succeed in the commercial sense. And at present things have certainly a look that is in accordance with that opinion. The powers that might be expected to intervene in order to prevent Keely's inventions from becoming factors in human life, are, as has been said, through human means, and the stolid stupidity of the scientists in regard to Keely's discoveries, the bovine indifference of theologians, the silly ridicule of the press, the hostility of vested interests, the suicidal greed of some of the largest shareholders, and the paralyzing influence of the law, which apparently lends itself in this case to those whose object is simple robbery. All these things seem very like the operation of the higher controlling powers, acting with a consciousness other than our consciousness for the attainment of ends that transcend our narrow calculations.

Be this as it may, Keely's discoveries, and Keely's personality also, have a peculiar interest for Theosophists, for the force with which he is working is without doubt the ether of the ancient philosophers, which is one aspect of the Akasa, the underlaying great force in nature, according to the Secret Doctrine, a force whose existence has been recognized from time immemorial under various fanciful names, and whose property is sound, whether audible or inaudible to us; or, in more modern language, whose characteristics are vibration and rhythm. It corresponds to the seven-fold Vach of Hindu Philosophy, and is the raison d'etre of spells and Mantrams. It is the basis of harmony and melody throughout Nature. This force is alluded to many times in Madame Blavatsky's Isis Unveiled. On page 139, vol I., we read: The Akasa is a Sanscrit word which means sky, but it also designates the imponderable and intangible life principles, the astral and celestial lights combined together, and which two form the anima mundi, and constitute the soul and spirit of man; the celestial light forming his nous, pneuma, or divine spirit, and the other his psyche, soul, or astral spirit. The grosser particles of the latter enter into the fabrication of his outward form, the body. The Akasa is connected on the one hand with physical matter and on the other with WILL, that intelligent, intangible, and powerful something which reigns supreme

over all inert matter. Of the Akasa in this respect we read on page 144, vol,I., of Isis Unveiled: The mysterious effects of attraction and repulsion are the unconscious agents of that will; fascination, such as we see exercised by some animals, by serpents over birds, for instance, is a conscious action of it, and the result of thought. Sealing-wax, glass, and amber, when rubbed, *i.e.*, when the latent heat which exists in every substance is awakened, attract light bodies; they exercise unconscious-

ly Will; for inorganic as well as organic matter, however infinitesimally small it may be, possesses a particle of the divine essence in itself... What is, then, this inexplicable power of attraction but an atomical portion of that essence that Scientists and Kabalists equally recognize as the 'principle of life' - the Akasa? Granted that the attraction exercised by such bodies may be blind; but as we ascend higher the scale of organic beings in nature, we find this principle of life developing attributes and faculties which become more determined and marked with every rung of the endless ladder. Man, the most perfect of organized beings on earth, in whom matter and spirit - i.e., Will - are the most developed and powerful, is alone allowed to give a conscious impulse to that principle which emanates from him, and only he can impart to the magnetic fluid opposite and various impulses without limit as to the direction. Isis Unveiled was published nearly eleven years ago; and in her forthcoming work, The Secret Doctrine, the authoress enters more fully into this and other matters only sketched or hinted at in her former volumes.

It is the fact that Keely is working with some of the mysterious forces included under the name Akasa that makes his discoveries interesting to Theosophists. It is the fact that he has shown magnificent courage and fixity of purpose under every kind of opposition, and the fact also that he has been supported all through by the generous belief that his discoveries will be of inestimable benefit to mankind that make his personality of interest. If he can succeed in making his marvelous discoveries pay dividends, science may begin to give attention to them; for men of science, like other men, require a sign before they can accept as truth the things that are beyond their comprehension, and the value of a scientific discovery is now determined by its market value.

R. Harte (Sec. T.P.S.)
July, 1888

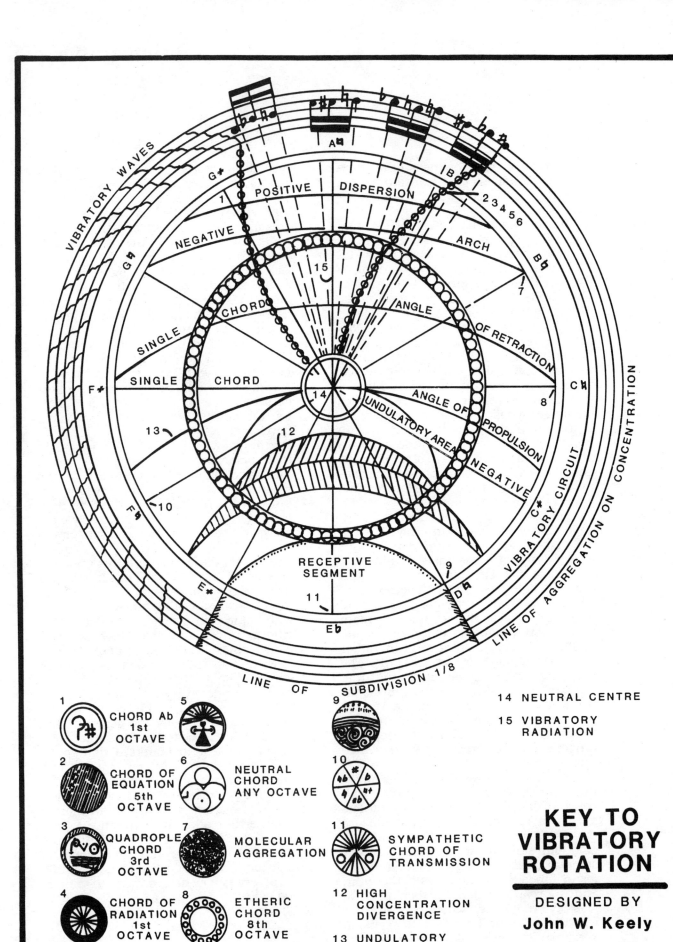

KEY TO VIBRATORY ROTATION

DESIGNED BY
John W. Keely

JANUARY 1886

1 CHORD Ab 1st OCTAVE

2 CHORD OF EQUATION 5th OCTAVE

3 QUADROPLE CHORD 3rd OCTAVE

4 CHORD OF RADIATION 1st OCTAVE

5

6 NEUTRAL CHORD ANY OCTAVE

7 MOLECULAR AGGREGATION

8 ETHERIC CHORD 8th OCTAVE

9

10

11 SYMPATHETIC CHORD OF TRANSMISSION

12 HIGH CONCENTRATION DIVERGENCE

13 UNDULATORY AREA POSITIVE

14 NEUTRAL CENTRE

15 VIBRATORY RADIATION

Etheric Force Identified as Dynaspheric Force

Clara Jessup Bloomfield-Moore

"Science is to know things."

Herodotus.

"Knowledge is developed by experience from innate ideas."

Plato

"Truth is not attained through reflection, but through immediate intuition. We neither originate thought nor its form. "

Aryan Teachings

"It may be said that if all things come from only one cause or internal source, acting within itself, then motion and matter must be fundamentally and essentially one and the same, and we look upon matter as being latent force and upon force as being free matter. "

Franz Hartmann, M.D.

JOHN WORRELL KEELY---the discoverer of compound inter-etheric force, as operating in the animal organism, man - is a great thinker, and a great student of the capabilities of nature in offering to man's intelligence the means whereby he may discover for himself the secrets she often veils without entirely concealing.

The result of more than twenty years of persistent effort to apply this force to the operation of machinery has, at last, been enabled to produce continuity of motion in his engine; but, up to this time, he has not so mastered this subtle force as to control reversions. The development of his various discoveries has been one uninterrupted work of evolution, reaching, within the last year, he thinks, the sphere of perfect vibratory sympathy, both theoretically and practically. The proof of this is found in the fact that he now transmits vibrations along a wire, connected at one end with the vibratory machine which is the source of power, and at the other end with the engine or cannon, as the case may be, which is operated by such vibratory power. Until recently, comparatively speaking, Keely stored force, as he generated it, in a receiver; and experiments were made by him in the presence of thousands, at various times, for the purpose of testing the operations of this force, liberated in the presence of his audience and stored up in this small receiver. The editor of the Scientific Arena thus describes what took place at one of these exhibitions, when he was present:---"The confined vapor was passed through one of the small flexible tubes to a steel cylinder on another table, in which a vertical piston was fitted so that its upper end bore against the underside of a powerful weighted lever. The superficial area of this piston was equal to one-half of a square inch, and it acted as a movable fulcrum placed close to the hinged end of the short arm of this lever, whose weight alone required a pressure of 1,500 pounds to the square inch against the piston to lift it.

After testing the pressure by several small weights, added to that of the lever itself, in order to determine how much power had already been accumulated in the receiver, the maximum test was made by placing an iron weight of 580 pounds, by means of a differential pulley, on the extreme end of the long arm of the lever. To lift this weight, without that of the lever supporting it, would require a pressure against the piston of 18,900 pounds to the square inch, counting the difference in the length of the two arms and the area of the piston, which we, as well as several others present, accurately calculated. When all was ready, and the crowded gathering had formed as well as possible to see the test, Keely turned the valve-wheel leading from the receiver to the flexible tube, and through it into the steel cylinder beneath the piston, and simultaneously with the motion of his hand the weighted lever shot up against its stop, a distance of several inches, as if the great mass of iron had been only a cork. Then, in order to assure ourselves of the full 25,000 pounds to the square inch claimed, we added most of our weight to the arm of the lever without forcing the piston back again.

After repeating this experiment till all expressed themselves satisfied, Keely diverted his etheric gas to the exciting work of firing a cannon, into which he placed a leaden bullet about an inch in diameter. He conveyed the force from the receiver by the same kind of flexible copper tube, attaching at one end of it to the breech of the gun. When all was again in readiness he gave a quick turn to the inlet valve, and a report like that of a small cannon followed, the ball passing through an inch board and flattening itself out to about three inches in diameter, showing the marvelous power and instantaneous action of this strange vapor.

The difficulty encountered by Keely in his old generator of etheric force grew out of the fact, in part, that the vaporic power produced was so humid that he could not, when he attempted to utilize it, obtain its theoretical value in work. This difficulty has been entirely overcome by dispensing with the water which he used in liberating etheric force, by his old generator; and, by this departure, he has attained a success beyond that which we anticipated by himself, when he abandoned his original line of experiment. Ignorant, indeed, of the nature of Keely's work must those men be who accuse him of "abandoning his base" or "principle," each time that he discovers his mistakes:---using them as stepping-stones to approach nearer and still nearer to his goal. Reproaching him, even, for keeping his own counsel, until certainty of success rendered it prudent for him to make known that he had changed his field of experiment from positive attraction to negative attraction, he had

succeeded in his efforts to produce continuity of motion. Equally ignorant are those, who would wrench by force his secrets from him before the time is ripe for their disclosure. Let us suppose that Faraday, when he discovered radiant matter in 1816, had formed a "Faraday Phospho-Genetic Radiant Company," to enable him to experiment: fully cognizant of all that Crookes has since discovered, and had taken for his base in experimenting the principle involved in Crookes' discovery. Not succeeding at first, we will suppose that the Company became clamorous for returns, and demanded that his secret principle should be made public. Had he been driven into making known, who would have credited what Crookes is now able to prove? The effect would have been upon the Faraday Company the same as if a balloon were punctured just as it was soaring heavenward. The same with the Keely Motor Company, had Keely obeyed the order of the Court in 1882, and made his marvelous secret public. It would have collapsed. Therefore, he has maintained his secret in the interests of the stockholders of the Keely Motor Company with a firmness worthy of a Christian martyr. The one person to whom alone Keely then disclosed it thought him under a delusion, until he had demonstrated its soundness. When he said, in all solemnity, "Now, I feel as if you and I were the god and goddess of this world," the effect upon the hearer was no more than it would have been had a patient in a hospital for the insane spoken the words. Charles B. Collier, Keely's patent lawyer, writes as follows, concerning the difficulties attendant upon "the supposed duty" of his client's imparting his "secrets," as ordered by the Court to do, some time since:---

If to-day, for the first time in your lives, you saw a harp attuned and being played upon, you would hardly expect, without considerable time and study, to be able to reproduce the harp, attune its strings in proper relation to each other, and to play upon it so as to produce the harmonies which you had listened to. Mr. Keely's work is analogous

Etheric Force Indentified as Dynaspheric Force

to the illustration which I have presented, inasmuch as he is dealing with the subject of sound, or acoustics, but in a much more involved form than as applied simply for the production of harmonies for the delight of the ear. Mr. Keely's engine is analogous to the mechanism of the human ear, in the respect that it is a structure operated upon, and its notion induced by vibration; and to the end of securing and attaining, in and by it, uniformity or regularity of motion, there must be perfect unison or synchronism, as between it and his structure which is the prime source of vibration. To attain this perfect unison or synchronism, has involved unparalleled research and experiment upon his part---experiments that have varied from day to day. No one, in my opinion, who had not stood by his side, as his shadow, watching every experiment, could have kept fully abreast of him. To pursue my simile, I may say that his harp (engine) is not yet perfectly attuned ("graduated"); when it is so, it will produce nothing but harmony (regularity of motion), and his work will be finished.

At such time, I doubt not that he will be able to give to Mr. Boekel, myself or another, the scale with which to reconstruct and attune another apparatus so as to produce like results with it; but to go over the ground that he has gone over, to explore the wilderness in which he has been the pioneer, in other words, the study, to a full understanding of them, of his experiments and researches, as recorded in his writings and illustrated in the beautiful charts which he has produced, will be a work rather for scientists than for mechanicians or engineers

Mr. Keely's "Theoretical Expose'" is in preparation for the press; and, when these volumes are issued, we may look for a change of attitude towards him in all men who hold themselves ready to abandon preconceived notions, however cherished, if they be found to contradict truths; which, Herbert Spencer says, is the first condition of success in scientific research. The Rev. J. J. Smith, M.A., D.D., tells us that the only way the

great problem of the universe can ever be scientifically solved is by studying, and arriving at just conclusions with regard to the true nature and character of force. This has been Mr. Keely's life study; and he is able to demonstrate all that he asserts.

The author of No. 5 of the pamphlets issued by The Theosophical Publication Society, "What is Matter and What is Force, " says therein, "The men of science have just found out 'a fourth state of matter,' whereas the occultists have penetrated years ago beyond the sixth, and therefore do not infer, but know of, the existence of the seventh, the last. "This knowledge comprises one of the secrets of Keely's so-called "compound secret." It is already known to many that his secret includes "the augmentation of energy, "the insulation of the ether," and the "adaptation of dynaspheric force to machinery."

Laurence Oliphant writes: Recent scientific research has proved conclusively that all force is atomic --- that electricity consists of files of particles, and that the interstellar spaces contain substances, whether it be called ether or astral fluid (or by any other name), which is composed of atoms, because it is not possible to dissever force from its transmitting medium. The whole universe, therefore, and all that it contains, consists of matter in motion, and is animated by a vital principle which we call God.

"Science has further discovered that these atoms are severally encompassed by an ethereal substance which prevents their touching each other, and to this circumambient, inter-atomic element they have given the name of dynasphere; but, inasmuch as has further been found, that in these dynaspheres there resides a tremendous potency, it is evident that they also must contain atoms, and that these atoms must in their turn be surrounded by dynaspheres, which again contain atoms, and so on *ad infinitum.* Matter thus becomes infinite and indestructible, and the force which pervades it persistent and everlasting.

"This dynaspheric force, which is

Universal Laws Never Before Revealed.. Keely's Secrets

also called etheric, is conditioned as to its nature on the quality of the atoms which form its transmitting media; and which are infinite both in variety and in their combinations. They may, however, be broadly divided into two categories; *viz.* the sentient and the non-sentient atoms. Dynaspheric force, composed of non-sentient atoms, is the force that has been already mechanically applied by Mr. Keely to his motor; and which will probably ere long supersede the agencies now used for locomotive, projectile, and other purposes. When the laws which govern it come to be understood, it will produce materially a great commercial and industrial revolution. There is no hard and fast line between the animal and vegetable creation, so there is a graduated scale of atoms, between which although animated by the divine life are not sentient, and those which are as highly developed, relatively to them, as man is to a cabbage."

"The most remarkable illustration of the stupendous energy of atomic vibratory force is to be found in that singular apparatus in Philadelphia --- which for the last fifteen years has excited in turn the amazement, the skepticism, the admiration, and the ridicule of those who have examined it --- called 'Keely's Motor.'" ... "in the practical land of its origin, it has popularly been esteemed a fraud. I have not examined it personally, but I believe it to be based upon a sound principle of dynamics, and to be probably the first of a series of discoveries destined to revolutionize all existing mechanical theories, and many of the principles upon which they are founded. Those who are sufficiently unprejudiced to connect the bearings of this discovery, of what must be dynaspheric force, with phenomena which have hitherto been regarded as supernatural by the ignorant, will perceive how rapidly we are bridging over the chasm which has divided the seen from the unseen, obliterating the distinction between 'matter' and what has most erroneously been called 'spirit.'"

In 1882 a woman, coversing with Mr. Keely, said, "You have opened the door into the spirit world." He an-swered, "do you think so? I have sometimes though I might be able to discover the origin of life." At this time Mr. Keely had given no attention whatever to the occult bearing of his discovery; and it was only after he had pursued his researches, under the advantages which his small Liberator afforded him for such experiments, that he realized the truth of this women's assertion. It was then, in 1887, that a "bridge of mist" formed itself before him, connecting the laws which govern physical science with the laws which govern spiritual science, and year by year this bridge of mist has solidified, until now he is in a position to stand upon it, and proclaim that its abutments have a solid foundation --- one resting in the material and visible world, and the other in the spiritual and unseen world; or, rather, that no bridge is needed to connect the two worlds, one law governing both in its needed modifications.

"The physical thing," writes a modern scientist, "which energizes and does work in and upon ordinary matter, is a separate form of matter, infinitely refined, and infinitely rapid in its vibrations, and is thus able to penetrate through all ordinary matter, and to make everywhere a fountain of motion, no less real because unseen. It is among the atoms of the crystal and the molecules of living matter; and, whether producing locked effects or free, it is the same cosmic thing, matter in motion, which we conceive as material energy, and with difficulty think of as only a peculiar form of matter in motion."

Oliphant, commenting upon this view of energy, says: "This is nothing more or less than what we have been in the habit of calling 'spirit.'" ... "Mind is also composed of this extraordinary matter; so is will; so is every emotion." Jacob Boehme calls it "heavenly substantiality," and Swendenborg calls it "natural and spiritual atmospheres, composed of discrete substances of a very minute form." Professor Crookes has invented the word "protyle." Professor Cones calls it "soul-stuff," or biogen; while Occultists call it "astral fluid."

Etheric Force Indentified as Dynaspheric Force

To all who are conversant with Mr. Keely's theories a similarity of views will be evident.

The President of the British Association, Sir Henry Roscoe, in his address before that body, said: "In nature there is no such thing as great or small; the structure of the smallest particle, invisible even to our most searching vision, may be as complicated as that of any of the heavenly bodies which circle round our sun." As to the indivisibility of the atom, he asks this question: "Notwithstanding the properties of these elements have been studied, and are now known with a degree of precision formerly undreamt of, have the atoms of our present elements been made to yield?" He continues: "A negative answer must undoubtedly be given, for even the highest of terrestrial temperatures, that of the electric spark, has failed to shake any one of these atoms in two."

This is an error, for it is well known by those who are fully acquainted with the principle involved in Keely's inventions that the intense vibratory action which is induced in his "Liberator" has accomplished what the retort of the chemist has failed to do, what the electric spark has left intact, and what the inconceivably fierce temperature of the sun and the volcanic fires has turned over to us unscathed. The mighty Genii imprisoned within the molecule, thus released from the chains and fetters which Nature forged, has been for years the the tyrant of the one who rashly intruded, without first paving the way with the gold which he has since been accused of using in experiments with reckless and wanton waste! For more than a score of years has Keely been fighting a hand-to-hand fight with this Genii; often beaten back by it, paralyzed at times, even, by its monstrous blows; and only now so approaching its subjugations as to make it safe to harness it for the work that is calling for a power mightier than steam, safer and more uniform in operation than electricity; a power which, by its might and beneficence, will ameliorate the condition of the masses, and reconcile and

solve all that now menaces our race; as it was never menaced before, as has been said.

The structure of the air molecule, as believed in by Keely, is as follows: --- Broken up, by vibratory action, he finds it to contain what he calls an atomic triplet. The position of a molecule, on the point of a fine cambric needle sustains the same relation to the point of the needle that a grain of sand sustains to a field of ten acres.

Although, as Sir H. Roscoe has said, "In nature there is no such thing as great or small," the human mind cannot conceive such infinitesimal minuteness. We will, then, imagine a molecule magnified to the size of a billiard ball, and the atomic triplet magnified to the size of three marbles, in the triangular position, within that molecule, at its center; unless acted upon by electricity, when the molecule, the billiard ball, becomes oblate, and the three atoms are ranged in a line within, unless broken up by the mighty force of vibratory action. Nature never gives us a vacuum; consequently, the space within the

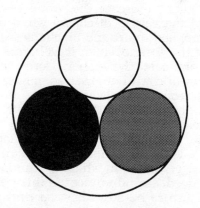

molecule not occupied by the atomic triplet must be filled with something. This is where the Genii- "the all-prevading ether"---has made its secret abode through untold eons, during which our world has been in course of preparation for its release, to fulfill its appointed task in advancing the

Universal Laws Never Before Revealed.. Keely's Secrets

progress of the human race.

Step by step, with patient perseverance which some day the world will honour, this man of genius has made his researches, overcoming the colossal difficulties which have raised up in his path what seemed to be insurmountable barriers to further progress: but never before has the world's index finger so pointed to an hour when all is making ready for the advent of the new form of force that mankind is waiting for. Nature, always reluctant to yield her secrets, is listening to the demands made upon her by her master, necessity. The coal mines of the world cannot long afford the increasing drain made upon them. Steam has reached its utmost limits of power, and does not fulfill the requirements of the age. Electricity holds back, with bated breath, dependent upon the approach of her sister colleague. Air ships are riding at anchor, as it were, waiting for the force which is to make aerial navigation something more than a dream. As easily as men communicate with their offices from their homes by means of the telephone, so will the inhabitants of separate continents talk across the ocean. Imagination is palsied when seeking to foresee the grand results of this marvelous discovery when once it is applied to art and mechanics. In taking the throne which it will force steam to abdicate, dynaspheric force will rule the world with a power so mighty in the interests of civilization, that no finite mind can conjecture the results. Laurence Oliphant, in his preface to "Scientific Religion," says: "A new moral future is dawning upon the human race - one, certainly, of which it stands much in need." In no way could this new moral future be so widely, so universally, commenced as by the utilizing of dynaspheric force to beneficial purposes in life, thus revealing to all men another phase of God's "underlying purpose."

In 1746, when Franklin's attention was drawn to the phenomena of electricity, little more was known on the subject than Thales had announced two thousand years before. Von Kleist

in Leyden, Collinson in London, and others in as widely-separated cities in Europe, were experimenting in the same field of research. What our last century has done toward subduing this tyrant which Franklin succeeded in bringing down to earth, from the clouds, the next century will see surpassed beyond man's widest conjectures, should Keely's utilization of this unknown force of nature bestow upon humanity the costless motive power, which he anticipates it will. Reynolds predicted that those who "studied the mysteries of molecular vibration would win the victorious wreaths of successful discovery." After such discoveries as Mr. Keely has made in this field of research, it matters not to him whether he succeeds commercially or not. His work of discovery commenced when, as a boy of twelve, he held the seashells to his ear as he walked the shore and noted that no two gave forth the same tone. From the construction of his first crude instrument, his work of evolution progressed slowly for years; but within the last five years he has made giant strides towards the "Dark Tower" which is his last fortress to take. When he is ready, "Dauntless the slug-horn to his lips" he will set; and the world will hear the blast, and awaken from its slumber into new life.

Molecular vibration is thus seen to be Keely's legitimate field of research; but more than once has he had to tear down portions of the vibratory scaffolding which aided him in the building up of his edifice of philosophy; therefore, he is ever ready to admit that some of the present scaffolding may have to be removed. The charge of "abandoning his base," recently brought against him by one of the editors of The New York Times, could only have been made by one who is utterly ignorant of the subject upon which he writes. Under the heading "A Cool Confession," this editor asserts that Keely has "given up the Keely Motor as a bad job," and that he admits that he is a "bogus inventor" and a "fraud." This is not true.

What Keely does admit is that, baffled in applying vibratory force to mechanics, upon his first and second lines of experimental research, he was obliged either to confess a commercial failure, or to try a third departure from his base or principle; seeking success through another channel of experiment. While experimenting upon this third line, until his efforts were crowned with success, he kept his secret from all men; with the approbation of the one who furnished the money for these experiments. There is a time when silence is golden; and the charge made by the same editor that Keely had been "receiving money from the Keely Motor Company on false pretences from the time that he abandoned his original plans," could only have been made by one who knows nothing of the facts of the case: for years have passed away since the Keely Motor Company broke its contract with him, and since it has furnished him with any money for his experiments.

But let Keely speak for himself in reference to his work: --- *"In considering the operation of my engine, the visitor, in order to have even an approximate conception of its modus operandi, must discard all thought of engines that are operated upon the principle of pressure and exhaustion, by the expansion of steam or other analogous gas which impinges upon an abutment, such as the piston of a steam-engine. My engine has neither piston nor eccentrics, nor is there one grain of pressure exerted in the engine, whatever may be the size or capacity of it.*

"My system, in every part and detail, both in the developing of this power and in every branch of its utilization, is based and founded on sympathetic vibration. In no other way would it be possible to awaken or develop this force, and equally impossible would it be to operate my engine upon any other principle.

"All that remains to be done is to secure a uniform speed under different velocities and control reversions. That I shall accomplish this is absolutely certain. Some few years ago, I contemplated using a wire as a connective link between two sympathetic mediums, to

evolve this power as also to o. ate my machinery --- instead of tubular connections as heretofore employed --- I have recently succeeded in accomplishing successfully such change. This, however, is the true system; and henceforth all my operations will be conducted in this manner---that is to say, the power will be generated, my engines run, my cannon operated, through a wire.

"It has been only after years of incessant labour, and the making of almost enumerable experiments, involving not only the construction of a great many most peculiar mechanical structures, and the closest investigation and study of the phenomenal properties of the substance "ether," per se, produced, that I have been able to dispense with complicated mechanism, and to obtain, as I claim, mastery over the subtle and strange force with which I am dealing.

"When my present process of adjustment is completed, the force, the mechanism, and all that pertains to it, will be explained in a theoretical exposition of the subject, with appropriate diagrams, which I shall publish to the world; through the medium, and my patents, when taken out, a knowledge of all that is required for its commercial employment will be more easily acquired than is the necessary skill required to enable one to safely operate a steam-engine.

"My power will be adapted to engines of all sizes and capacities, as well to an engine capable of propelling the largest ship as to one that will operate a sewing machine. Equally well and certain is it that it will be adapted as a projectile force for guns and cannons of all sizes, from the ordinary shoulder-piece to the heaviest artillery."....

When Keely in 1887 obtained continuity of motion (for a time) in his engine he thought that his last difficulty had been overcome: but, up to the present time, he has not succeeded in governing its speed nor in controlling reversions. He has, however, again reduced in size the instrument with which he produces force. From 1882 to 1884 the "Generator" was a structure six feet long and correspondingly wide

Universal Laws Never Before Revealed.. Keely's Secrets

and high; but, failing in his attempt to make an automatic arrangement upon which its usefulness in mechanics depended, Keely found a new standard for research in an experiment often made by himself, but never before successful, which resulted in the production of a machine in 1885 which he named a "Liberator" --- not so large as a lady's small round work-table. Continuing his labor of evolution Keely within one year made such astonishing progress, from experiments with this beautiful piece of vibratory mechanism, as to combine the production of the power, and the operation of the cannon, his engine and his disintegrator in a machine no larger than a dinner plate, and only three or four inches in thickness. This instrument was completed in 1886, up to which time his experiments had been conducted upon a principle of sympathetic vibration, for the purpose of liberating a vapour or etheric product. His later experiments have been confined to another modification of the vibratory sympathy; and the size of the instrument used now, '88, for the same purposes is no larger than an old-fashioned silver watch, such as we see in Museum collections. The raising of a lever with an apparent uplifting expansive force of between 20,000 and 30,000 pounds to the square inch, the running of the engine, the firing of the cannon, are conducted without one ounce of pressure in any part of the apparatus, and without the production or presence of what has been known as Keely's ether. The force is now transmitted along a wire (of platinum and silver), and when the lever is lowered there is no exhaustion, into the atmosphere of the room, of any up-lifting vapor, as was always the case when ether was used in this experiment; nor is there any vapor impinging upon the piston under the lever to raise it.

Mr. Keely has named this new modification of the one force in nature "Negative Attraction," which to the uninitiated does not suggest as much as it would had he called it "Exploded Humbug."

The two forms of force which he has been experimenting with, and the phenomena attending them, are the very antithesis of each other. Keely does not feel the shadow of a doubt as to his eventual success in producing engines of varying capacities; small enough, on the one hand, to operate sewing machines with, and large enough, on the other hand, to propel the largest ships that plough the seas. Every fact and feature surrounding the case warrants the belief, notwithstanding the incredulity of all who have not witnessed the progress of Mr. Keely, step by step, that his success will be complete, and his work stand as the most colossal example of the survival of the fittest, in the process of inventive evolution. Cox says: "not one of the great facts which science now accepts as incontrovertible truths but was vehemently denied by the scientists of its time:---declared to be *a priori* impossible, its discoverers and supporters denounced as fools and charlatans, and even investigation of it refused as being a waste of time and thought." "History repeats itself," and Amiel's definition of science gives the key to the incredulity of scientists in reference to Mr. Keely's discovery; for if, as Amiel has said, "science is a lucid madness occupied with tabulating its own hallucinations," it is not strange that men of science should refuse to investigate what they consider the hallucinations of others.

It is an undisputed fact that "too much has been conceded to science, too little to those sublime laws which make science possible." But the one law which regulates creation, and to which

---

* A system of pendulums tuned to swing the various ratios of the musical scale, form a "Silent Harp" of extraordinary interest. This "Silent Harp," D.C.Ramsay, of Glasgow, has shown to his students of harmony for many a year. A pen, placed by means of a universal-jointed arrangement between any two pendulums of this "Silent Harp," so as to be moved by a blend of their various motions, writes, with all the precision of gravitation, a portrait of the chord which two corresponding strings of a sounding harp would utter to the ear. This spiral writing ia a Pendulograph; exquisite forms such as no human hand could trace.

all other laws are made subservient, keeping in harmony the systems upon systems of worlds throughout space, developing sound and colour, animal and vegetable growth, the crystallization of minerals, is the hidden law, which develops every natural science throughout the universe; and which both Kepler and Newton anticipated would be revealed in our age. "You can even trace the poles in sound," writes Mrs. F. J. Hughes, a niece of Darwin, in her work upon the "Evolution of Tones and Colours." The experiments made by Mrs. Watts Hughes, at the annual Reception of the Royal Society, and the Pendulograph* writings by Andrew of Belfast, have a bearing upon Keely's discovery; illustrating the workings of this hidden law of nature.

Of all women Mrs. Hughes approaches nearest to the theories of Mr. Keely. Concerning them she writes to a friend well versed in music, as music is taught: - "From ignorance of the present Science of Musicians, which you know so thoroughly, it is easier for me to grasp his meaning, than for you. I have lately been proving by scriptural types how Nature's laws in the lower creation develop by fifths below and by fourths above the key-note, the two meeting in one harmony: art mingling both, creating discords, and undulating them into harmony. Dr. C. Martin says: - 'Musicians must have discords; the ear is educated to them: but every one must allow that the nearer Art follows nature, the more perfect it is.' Mrs. Hughes adds: "I think Keely must have caught the center where both laws unite, or act upon Nature's law only."

Of the law of periodicity, Hartmann writes: *Its actions have long ago been known to exist in the vibrations producing light and sound, and it has been recognized in chemistry by experiments tending to prove that all so-called simple elements are only various states of vibration of one primordial element, manifesting itself in seven principal modes of action, each of which may be subdivided into seven again. The difference which exists between so-called single substances appears, therefore, to be no dif-ference of substance or matter, but only a difference of the function of matter in the ratio of its atomic vibration."* It is by changing the vibrations of cosmic ether that Mr. Keely releases this energy, and Dr. Kellner in Austria produces electricity in the same way; while it is said that a chemist in Prague produces magnetism; also Dr. Dupuy, of New York, who has been for years experimenting in this field without meeting with Keely's progressive successes.

Horace Wemyss Smith, in commenting upon the fact that, at the time of Franklin's discovery, men in France, in Belgium, in Holland, and in Germany were pursuing the same line of experiment, says that there is something worthy of observation in the progress of science and human genius, inasmuch as in countries far distant from each other men have fallen into the same tracks, and have made similar and corresponding discoveries, at the same period of time, without the least communications with each other.

Laurence Oliphant's recent works give us the clue to an explanation of this fact; and Lowe, in his <u>Fragments of Physiology</u>, condenses the answer in these words: "Man is not the governor and commander of the created world; and were it not for superhuman influence constantly flowing into created forms, the world would perish in a moment. It is this superhuman influence, felt most by those who have educated the hidden sense (with which all men are born), which inspires all discovery, all invention, all poetry, all of truth, let it take whatever form it may. This sixth sense is as much undeveloped in the mass of mankind as sight would be had we been born with our eye-lid sealed; able to distinguish nothing beyond the period of day-light from the reign of night, and remaining sealed all the years of our life upon earth. We know that some spiritually minded persons seem to possess powers unknown to those who are spoken of in Scripture as the carnal minded ; and it may be that with dim vision they are able to discern as in a glass darkly, without education of this hidden sense, truths which are hidden from others. Of such are men and women of genius. Again, there are others who possess uncertain, unreliable powers, which often lead astray those who commit themselves to the direction of these powers. What infallible medium of superhuman influence? Spiritualism represents a great truth, behind the spiritism which stands in the same relation toward it that counterfeit coin holds to sterling gold. The operations of our sixth sense are as liable to be deceptive as are the operations of our other senses; and are limited or governed by law in the same way. We cannot see in total darkness, and this hidden power, susceptible of education, can only be brought into use by an illuminated mind; a mind that has studies the laws of evolution and involution, the descent of spirit into matter, and the re-ascension of matter to spirit - laws of the life-impulse beginning in the elemental kingdom and ending in an evolution of man, far beyond the comprehension of man of the present day. Man and woman as units, continues Oliphant, are still so ignorant of the great powers which they themselves inherit that they wholly fail to see them, though they sweep like mighty seas throughout all human nature.

When mankind has become sufficiently spiritualized by the process of evolution laid down in the plan of the great Master, then shall we know ourselves and our powers as we are known to Him. True Science must first open wider the path of religion - a religion of progress, a religion suited to the wants of humanity, as well as a humane religion - the religion, taught by our Holy Master, of love for our fellow-men, of harmony with all that is good - at war only with evil; not with those who, warped by transmitted tendencies, commit evil. An eye for an eye, a tooth for a tooth, is the old Jewish law. Christ's law is the law of love, which is God's law. Do unto others as ye would have others do unto you ; and this is the law which we need to fulfil, in order to purify and regenerate mankind.

Hitherto we have been, in one respect, like the laborer in Tolstoi's Con-fession, doing the work assigned him, in the space assigned, without understanding where he was, or what the result would be, and unable to judge whether the arrangements for this work were reasonably planned by his master or not. The laborer worked the handle of a pump, he saw the water flow into numerous channels for irrigation of the soil; little by little, shrubs grew and blossomed and bore fruit,, and the laborer passed on to more important work, understanding better and better the arrangement of the establishment, and never doubting that its Lord had planned all for the best. Our race has been pumping water for generations, planting the seed, watching the growth of the plants, the shrubs, and the trees; not always satisfied, however, that the Creator of the universe had planned as well as all might have been planned, or that there was any plan, or any Creator.

There are men in various parts of the world, unknown even by name to each other, who tell us by the sign of the times that the season of harvesting is approaching; the season for gathering the fruit, which has been deferred, century after century, because mankind is yet not ready, in the opinion of many, to share the fruit with one another.

Hyndman says that capitalism has been as necessary as serfdom in the progress of the human race; and its stores will continue to be garnered and used to spread the great net-work of railways, steam navigation, telegraph and telephone lines, which have given bread to millions and millions; encouraging paid labor and bringing nearer and nearer the age of love and harmony, which, it has been predicted that the twentieth century will usher in.

Renan, the French theologian, writing of the advances to be made in science by the discovery of nature's secrets, said that, although he had ceased to look forward to anything very unexpected, he envied those who should live to see the wonders of the twentieth century. For, he added they who live then will see things of which we have no conception. Already the light of a new dawn is breaking upon the world of science. These foretold advances are heralded by the modifications of force, before alluded to. The instrument invented by Dr. Kellner collects and produces electricity directly from the ether of the atmosphere without any friction of solid corporeal substances and without any chemical agency; the invention of one of the Prague professors, which, it is said, collects and gives out magnetism, seeming to be derived from changing the vibrations of cosmic ether, as in Keely's and Kellner's experiments, and other more recent discoveries.

It has been said that when Keely's vibratory force shall have taken the place of steam-engines, the millions of working men who gain with difficulty their daily bread by the work of their hands, will find themselves without occupation. The same prediction was made in regard to steam, but instead we find the city of Boston giving work to thirty thousand men in one manufactory of boots and shoes by steam, in place of the three thousand shoemakers who were all that were occupied in this branch of labor in that city when the work was done by hand.

Dr. Kellner's colleague, Franz Hartmann, M.D., writing in reference to Keely's discovery, says: I have taken great interest in him ever since I first heard of him in 1882. As gaslight has driven away, in part, the smoky petroleum lamp, and is about to be displaced by electricity, which in the course of time may be supplanted by magnetism, and as the power of steam has caused muscular labor to disappear to a certain extent, and will itself give way before the new vibratory force of Keely, likewise the orthodox medical quackery that now prevails will be dethroned by the employment of the finer forces of nature, such as light, electricity, magnetism, *etc.*

When the time is ripe, these are of the true scientists who will come to the front to lead as Progress leads, men who know how to wait upon God, *viz.*, to work while waiting; and to such the end is, sooner or later, victory! God never hurries. He counts the centuries as we count the seconds, and the nearer we approach to the least comprehension of His underlaying purpose the more we become like Tolstoi's laborer, who knew that the fruit was ripening for him and his fellow-men, trusting implicitly in the superior wisdom of his master.

"Evermore brave feet, in all ages,
    Climb the heights that hide the coming
    day,
Evermore they cry, these seers and sages,
    From their cloud, "Our doctrines make no
    way."
All too high they stand above the nations,
    Shouting forth their trumpet-calls
    sublime,
Shouting downwards their interpretations
    Of the wondrous secrets born of time. "

No man, whose spiritual eyes have been opened to "discern the signs of the times," can doubt that we are on the eve of revelations which are to usher in the dawn of a brighter day than our race has yet known; and no prophecy of this brighter day, foretold by prophets, apostles, and inspired poets, was ever made in truer strains than in these glorious lines of Elizabeth Barrett Browning:---

"Verily many thinkers of this age,
    Aye, many Christian teachers,
        half in heaven,
Are wrong in just my sense who understood
    Our natural world too insularly, as if
No spiritual counterpart completed it,
    Consummating its meaning, rounding a
To justice and perfection, line by line,
    Form by form, nothing single nor alone;
The Great Below clenched by the Great
    Above."

MUSICAL CHART BY WHICH KEELY
CLAIMED TO HAVE DISCOVERED
HIS "ETHERIC" FORCE.

One Phase of Keely's Discovery in Its Relations to the Cure of Disease

Clara Jessup Bloomfield-Moore

"I know medicine is called a science. It is nothing like a science. It is a great humbug! Doctors are mere empirics when they are not charlatans. We are as ignorant as men can be. Who knows anything in the world about medicine? Gentlemen, you have done me the honour to come here to attend my lectures, and I must tell you now, frankly, in the beginning, that I know nothing about medicine, nor do I know anyone who does know anything about it. Nature does a great deal, imagination does a great deal, doctors do devilish little when they do not do harm. Sick people always feel they are neglected, unless they are well drugged, les imbeciles!"

Professor Magendie;
(before the students of his class in The Allopathic College of Paris)

In the year 1871, the writer was sent from Paris to Schwalbach, by Dr. Beylard, and recommended to the care of Dr. Adolph Genth. She said to the physician, I wish for your opinion and your advice, if you can give it to me without giving me any medicine. He replied, With all my heart, madam; and I wish to God there were more women like you, but we should soon lose most of our patients if we did not dose them.

This is a terrible excuse for the use of those agencies which Dr. John Good says have sent more human beings to their graves than war, pestilence and famine combined. Keely holds the opinion that Nature works under the law of Compensation and Equilibrium---the law of Harmony; and that when disease indicates the disturbance of this law Nature at once seeks to banish the disease by restoring equilibrium, He seeks to render assistance on the same plan; replacing grossly material agencies by the finer forces of nature; as has been so successfully done by Dr. Pancoast and Dr. Babbitt in America. It was the intention of Dr. Hartmann to establish a The-

osophical Sanatorium at Goritz, in Austria, this summer, where medicine would be dispensed with: but his plans have been interfered with by his visit to America, where he went last March for the purpose of ascertaining Mr. Keely's views in reference to the best manner of conducting experimental research in reference to the restoration of equilibrium in the human system; the disturbance of which occasions local disorders and all disease, according to his ideas. Paracelsus held that *Man is made out of the four elements, and is nourished and sustained by magnetic power, which is the Universal Motor of Nature.* He treated disease in two ways - Sympathetically and Antipathetically; but only a fragmentary trace of his system can now be found. Nature, says Dr. Pancoast, author of The True Science of Light, works by antagonism in all her operations: when one of her forces overdoes its work, disease, or at least a local disorder, is the immediate consequence; now, if we attack this force, and overcome it, the opposite force has a clear field and may re-assert its rights---thus equilibrium is restored, and Equilibrium is health.

The Sympathetic System, instead of attacking the stronger force, sends recruits to the weaker one, and enables it to recover its powers; or, if the disorder be the result of excessive tension of Nerves or Ganglia, a negative remedy may be employed to reduce the tension. Thus, too, equilibrium is restored.

Dr. Hartmann disclosed to me in one of his letters that he knew the most important secret involved in Mr. Keely's compound secret. But he had not in any way connected this so-called secret with Mr. Keely. In one of Dr. Hartmann's letters to me, he writes -

Mr. Keely is perfectly right in saying

Universal Laws Never Before Revealed.. Keely's Secrets

that all disease is a disturbance of the equilibrium between positive and negative forces. In my opinion, no doctor ever cured any disease. All he can possibly do is to establish conditions under which the patient (or nature) may cure himself. The universal power which Mr. Keely calls the ether, and which Dr. Kellner calls transitory element, was known to medieval philosophers as prima materia, will and thought; or, according to Schopenhauer, will and imagination are substance. I recognize only one universal and fundamental power, which I call consciousness, acting within matter by means of thought; and I have no doubt that you already know that we agree all around, although we may not all use the same terms to signify the same objects. In your most important papers, I have found my own sentiments and views reflected; and I have in my books on Magic, Paracelsus, and the Rosicrucians, attempted to explain these identical views. Why will our scientists insist on refusing to see the self-evident fact that all visible material substances, animal organs, etc., are nothing else than the ultimate products of pre-existing psychic (interior and invisible) forces? These facts were all known to the ancient philosophers; while the moderns insist on mistaking the effects for the cause. They reject the idea of God (the primordial cause of all in its highest aspect of spiritual consciousness) because they formed a misconception of that which is intellectually inconceivable; they found that God could not be that which they had imagined, and they logically(?) concluded that there could be no Divine power at all. But this subject is too grand, too sublime, and extensive to be more than alluded to in this letter, and I merely write these remarks to show you that your views, those of Mr. Keely, and my own are all identical, as they, indeed, must be with those who are capable to perceive self-evident truth; for the truth is only one, and all who know it possess that same identical knowledge. Mr. Keely's power seems to be derived by changing the vibrations of cosmic ether. The machine which my friend Dr. Kellner has invented seems to be based upon the same principle, only, while Mr. Keely transforms these vibrations into some force connected with sound, Dr. Kellner's machine transforms them into elctricity. Again, Dr. Hartmann writes: Even to the superficial observer, the fact that the world is becoming more and more spiritualized, from top to bottom, begins to be evident. The crude scientific opinions which were prevailing in the beginning of the century are disappearing before a higher knowledge in regard to the laws of nature; the materialism which flourished twenty years ago, the offspring of animalism and ignorance, has almost disappeared from view, and has to descend to the lowest strata of society to find admirers. The iron rod, with which a self-conceited and arrogant sacerdotalism ruled the people, has been broken, and its remnants exist only in those countries where priestcraft is upheld and abetted by kings and governments.

If you enter the field of therapeutics and medicine, we find a decided fermentation of new ideas; not among the fossil specimens of antediluvian quackery, but among those who are called irregulars, because they have the courage to depart from the tracks trodden out by their predecessors. The more intelligent class of physicians have long ago realized the fact that drugs and medicines are perfectly useless, excepting in cases where diseases can be traced to some mechanical obstruction, in some organ that may be reached by mechanical action. In all other cases our best physicians have become agnostics, leaving nature to have her own way, and observing the expectative method, which, in fact, is no method of cure at all, but merely consists in doing no harm to the patient. Recently, however, light, electricity, and magnetism have been employed; so that even in the medical guild the finer forces of nature are taking the place of grossly material, and therefore injurious substances. The time is probably near when these finer forces will be employed universally. Everywhere the leaven is working, and many are asking, 'What causes it to work?' The answer is 'It is spirit working in matter. But the term 'spirit' is to the majority of man-

One Phase of Keely's Discovery in Its Relations to the Cure of Disease

kind a term without any meaning, a nonentity. Nevertheless, the action of that power which is called cohesion, and which is equally invisible, but which really holds the atoms of all bodies together and prevents them from dissolving into tangible ether, is continually manifested before their eyes. Why should not the opposite form of activity, that which enters between the atoms and separates them, likewise be a reality? The scientist will answer, 'We know this activity, and we call it heat. What has heat to do with spirit?' It has been demonstrated long ago that heat is a mode of motion, and likewise every other form of energy (including spiritual activity) is nothing else but a mode of motion. Motion is that universal agent which is fundamentally and essentially only one, but whose mode of manifestation differs according to the conditions under which it manifests itself. Acting without relative consciousness, it is known as gravitation, attraction, heat, light, sound, electricity, magnetism, etc. In a higher state it is known as life, and becomes endowed with relative consciousness, acting in the highest plane of existence it becomes self-conscious and self-existent, and is called spiritual power. But there is no motion thinkable without a substance to move; we cannot imagine a force without matter, nor matter without energy. There must, therefore, be one original substance, or primordial matter, although of a kind very different from the form in which it appears to us on the externally visible plane. The existence of this primordial substance was known to the spiritual perception of the ancient Rosicrucians, and some of them have, by logical conclusions, arrived at a belief in its existence, and named it Cosmic Ether; while by the Eastern sages it was called Akasa. We therefore see that there is one primordial and universal power , which is Motion; and, likewise, one primordial and universal substance which we may call Ether, or Matter; and that all existing forms can be nothing else but various shapes of that Ether in various states of density, and existing under various conditions, while all forms of energy, from the most grossly materi-

al up to the highest spiritual seem to be merely modifications of motion in Ether, manifesting themselves in various conditions and under various circumstances, unconsciously, consciously, and with self-consciousness. Furthermore, it may be said that if there is only one God, that is to say, if all things come from only one cause of internal force acting within itself, then motion and matter must be fundamentally and essentially one and the same, and we may look upon matter as being latent force and upon force as being free matter. Finally, if the great first cause is not to remain eternally in a state of inactivity, or, in other words, if it is to manifest itself as matter and motion, and if motion is to act within matter, then there must be a cause why such an activity takes place, and this cause can be nothing else but the eternally active Great First Cause itself, because there can be only one universal cause and no other. This is a self-evident truth to all who are able to see it. There can be no special name for that cause, because it is in itself the all and cannot be specified, for it is, in itself, everything that exists. It, however, appears to us in manifold aspects, and according to the aspects under which it appears, we may give to it different names. Looked at in its aspect as an universal power, which causes action and reaction, we may call it the will, existing within all forms in an active and latent condition. Whenever it becomes active, it may act unconsciously, consciously, or with self-consciousness, according to the conditions under which it is active.

The great and universal trinity of cause, motion, matter---or, as others call it, will, thought, and manifestation---was known to the ancient Rosicrucians and adepts as prima materia. Paracelsus expressly states that each of the three is also the other two, for nothing can possibly exist without cause, matter, and energy, i.e., spirit, matter, soul, the ultimate cause of existence being that it exists. We may, therefore, look upon all forms of activity as being an action of the universal or Divine will upon the ether...It would be useless for us to speculate about the spiritual pow-

Universal Laws Never Before Revealed.. Keely's Secrets

er of the will if acting through the organism of an adept; but we may study the effects of that same will-power when it acts within a more material plane, where it is known to us as causing heat, light, sound, electricity, and magnetism. All these forms of energy may theoretically be transformed one into another, because they all manifest themselves as various rates of vibrations or undulations of the ether which is contained in everything; and if we can change the rate of these vibrations, we may transform one form of energy into another.

For a long time it has been known to modern science that one form of energy can be transformed into another, although with a certain amount of loss; and it was believed impossible that one amount of energy, if transformed into another, would cause more than the same amount to become manifest. The cause of this false conclusion rests in the still prevailing misconception that a form or substance creates or produces an energy, while, in fact, the form is only an instrument through which the universal and pre-existing motion acts....

Worlds and planets are the products of the pre-existing cosmic ether or space, and not the ether the products of the planets! The same fundamental law evidently exists in all departments of nature, manifesting itself differently according to the difference of conditions under which it acts. Universal forces are bound into forms, and the forms dissolved into forces. Every form, on giving up its ghost, renders to the universal storehouse that which has been entombed in the form, but no more; in the same sense as steam, cooled off into water and frozen into an icicle, will, if heated, produce the same amount of heat again. The universal forces exist not merely in the form, but also in the universal storehouse in nature. By means of a glass lens we may collect the heat which exists in the light of the sun's rays and set a piece of wood on fire. No heat exists in the wood; it is merely a certain motion of the ether, which has been latent, and which is rendered free by the process of burning. As in heat, so in sound. No sound exists in a fiddle; it

is the ether in the atmosphere which is transformed into vibration of sound by the instrumentality of the fiddle. No light exists in the fire; it is merely the ether which, by the process of combustion, is transformed into certain vibrations which ultimately produce the phenomenon called light. No magnetism exists in iron; but ether, in a certain state of vibration which we call magnetic, acts through the instrumentality of the iron. No life is produced through a vegetable or animal organism; but they are instruments through which the universal element may manifest itself as life. No thought is created with the brain; but the brain is an instrument through which the universal mind operates. No love, will, faith, or any other spiritual power is created by the soul; but the sole is an organism through which these eternal and self-existent powers may become manifest. There is before me a little electrical instrument, invented by a well-known Austrian inventor, which collects and produces electricity directly from the ether of the atmosphere without any friction of solid corporeal substances and without any chemical agency. Moreover, the amount of electricity produced by it is far greater than that produced by a great engine with friction; a continuous stream of electric fire proceeds from it five to seven inches in length. It clearly proves that the electricity does not reside in the substance by means of which it is produced, but in the ether contained in the atmosphere, from which it is collected by means of the instrument and rendered perceptible to our senses. It also shows that electricity(i.e., the ether in that state of atomic vibration which we call electricity; as this is Keely's definition of electricity, it should not be attributed to Hartmann;) is something substantial, for it produces an electric gush of wind similar to the vapour produced by an atomizer; or still more resembling the cold gushes known to spiritualists, and which often occur at the beginning of some so-called spiritual manifestation....If we had any means to induce certain vibrations of ether in the air, or in the ether of space, by producing them in some substance able to

One Phase of Keely's Discovery in Its Relations to the Cure of Disease

communicate them to the ether of space, we might set the whole atmosphere, or even all the ether of space, into certain vibrations, and exercise a power whose limits cannot be estimated by our present comprehension. On the material plane we can only deal with those powers which we can insulate or store up in a form. We can store up heat, light, electricity, magnetism, and motion; but we cannot store up ether in its original form, because it prevades all known substances. There is nothing which offers any resistance to it. We can, therefore, deal with ether only when it becomes manifest to us through the instrumentality of a substance or for; that is to say, we can deal with it when transformed into heat, electricity, etc. Then it has entered into a state which renders it capable to be insulated by certain substances which offer resistance to it. We must, therefore, conduct our physical experiment with ether stored up in material forms. Everybody knows that a note struck upon an instrument will produce sound in a correspondingly attuned instrument in its vicinity. If connected with a tuning fork, it will produce a corresponding sound in the latter; and if connected with a thousand tuning forks, it will make all the thousand sound, and produce a noise far greater than the original sound, without the latter becoming any weaker for it. Here, then, is an augmentation of multiplication of power, as it has been called by the ancient Rosicrucians, while modern scientists have called it the law of induction. If we had any means to transform sound again into mechanical motion, we would have a thousand-fold multiplication of mechanical motion. It would be presumptuous to say that it will not be as easy for the scientists of the future to transform sound into mechanical motion, as it is for the scientist of the present to transform heat into electricity. Perhaps Mr. Keely has already solved the problem. There is a fair prospect that in the very near future, we shall have, in his ethereal force, a power far surpassing that of steam or electricity. Nor does the idea seem to be Utopian if we remember that modern science heretofore only knew the law of the conservation of energy; while to the scientist of the future the law of the augmentation of energy will be unveiled. As the age which has passed away has been the age of steam, the coming era will be the age of induction. There will be a universal rising up of lower vibrations into higher ones, in the realm of motion, emotion, and thought. Mr. Keely will, perhaps, transform sound into mechanical motion by applying the law of augmentation and multiplication of force known to the ancient Rosicrucians; as we will apply the same law in the realm of thought, and induce people to think. Thus matter will become more subject to the action of the finer forces of nature, and the minds of men will become less gross and easier to be penetrated by the light of Divine wisdom. All this has been predicted eighty-eight years ago, at the beginning of the century.

Mr. Keely, finding in his first interview with Dr. Hartmann about ethereal force, or dynaspheric force, was so well understood by that learned gentlemen, expressed great pleasure in meeting, for the first time, one who comprehended so much more of its nature than any man whom he had ever met; and Dr. Hartmann expressed himself as equally charmed and satisfied with Mr. Keely in this interview; although he gained from him nothing in the way of information that was new to him.

Before the second meeting took place, one of Mr. Keely's papers upon disturbed equilibrium (in the brain) was given to Dr. Hartmann to read with the request that he would limit his next conversation with Mr. Keely to the proper method of re-adjusting opposing conditions in the brain --- or, in other words, ascertaining how the ruling medium could be brought to bear upon these opposing conditions, in the brain, in order to restore equilibrium. Mr. Keely's paper amply treats the cause of disturbance of equilibrium in the brain, producing insanity; and reads as follows:---

Brain Disturbance

"In considering the mental forces as associated with the physical, I find, by my past researches, that the convolutions which exist in the cerebral field are entirely governed by the sympathetic conditions that surround them.

The question arises, what are these aggregations and what do they represent, as being linked with physical impulses? They are simply vibrometric resonators, thoroughly subservient to sympathetic acoustic impulses given to them by their atomic sympathetic surrounding media, all the sympathetic impulses that so entirely govern the physical in their many and perfect impulses (we are now discussing purity of conditions) are not emanations properly inherent in their own composition. They are only media-the acoustic media-for transferring from their vibratory surroundings the conditions necessary to the pure connective link for vitalizing and bringing into action the varied impulses of the physical.

All abnormal discordant aggregations in these resonating convolutions produce differentiation to concordant transmission; and, according as these differentiations *exist in volume*, so the transmissions are discordantly transferred, producing antagonism to pure physical action.

Thus, in Motor Ataxis, a differentiation of the minor thirds of the posterior parietal lobule produces the same condition between the retractors and extensors of the leg and foot; and thus the control of the proper movements is lost through this differentiation. The same truth can be universally applied to any of the cerebral convolutions that are in a state of differential harmony to the mass of immediate cerebral surroundings. Taking the cerebral condition of the whole mass as one, it is subservient to one general head center, although as many neutrals are represented as there are convolutions.

The introductory minors are controlled by the molecular; the next progressive third by the atomic; and the high third by the Etheric. All these progressive links have their positive, negative, and neutral position. When we take into consideration the structural condition of the human brain, we ought not to be bewildered by the infinite variety of its sympathetic impulses; inasmuch as it unerringly proves the true philosophy that the mass chords of such structures are governed by vibratory etheric flows---the very material which composes them. There is no structure whatever, animal, vegetable, mineral, that is not built up from the universal cosmic ether. Certain orders of attractive vibration produce certain orders of structure; thus, the infinite variety of effects---more especially in the cerebral organs. The bar of iron or the mass of steel, have, in each, all the qualifications necessary, under certain vibratory impulses, to evolve all the conditions that govern that animal organism---the brain: and it is as possible to differentiate the molecular conditions of a mass of metal of any shape so as to produce what you may express as a crazy piece of iron or a crazy piece of steel; or, vice versa, an intelligent condition in the same.

I find in my researches, as to the condition of molecules under vibration, that discordance cannot exist in the molecule proper; and that it is the highest and most perfect structural condition that exists; providing that all the progressive orders are the same. Discordance in any mass is the result of differentiated groups, induced by antagonistic chords, and the flight or motions of such, when intensified by sound, are very tortuous and zig-zag; but when free of this differentiation are in straight lines. Tortuous lines denote discord, or pain; straight lines denote harmony, or pleasure. Any differentiated mass can be brought to a condition of harmony, or equation, by proper media, and an equated sympathy produced.

There is good reason for believing that insanity is simply a condition of differentiation in the mass chords of the cerebral convolutions, which creates an antagonistic molecular bombardment towards the neutral or attractive centers of such convolutions; which, in turn, produce a morbid irritation in the cortical sensory centers in the substance of idea-

One Phase of Keely's Discovery in Its Relations to the Cure of Disease

tion; accompanied, as a general thing, by sensory hallucinations, ushered in by subjective sensations; such as flashes of light and colour, or confused sounds and disagreeable odours, etc., etc.

There is no condition of the human brain that ought not to be sympathetically coincident to that order of atomic flow to which its position, in the cerebral field, is fitted. Any differentiation in that special organ, or, more plainly, any discordant grouping tends to produce a discordant bombardment---an antagonistic conflict; which means the same disturbance transferred to the physical, producing inharmonic disaster to that portion of the physical field which is controlled by that especial convolution. This unstable aggregation may be compared to a knot on a violin string. As long as this knot remains it is impossible to elicit, from its sympathetic surroundings, the condition which transfers pure concordance to its resonating body. Discordant conditions, i.e., differentiation of mass, produce negatization to coincident action.

The question now arises. What condition is it necessary to bring about in order to bring back normality, or to produce stable equilibrium in the sympathetic centers?

The normal brain is like a harp of many strings strung to perfect harmony. The transmitting conditions being perfect, are ready, at any impulse, to induce pure sympathetic assimilation. The different strings represent the different ventricles and convolutions. The differentiations of any one from its true setting is fatal, to a certain degree, to the harmony of the whole combination.

If the sympathetic condition of any physical organism carries a positive flow of 80 per cent on its whole combination, and a negative one of 20 per cent, it is the medium of perfect assimilation to one of the same ratio, if it is distributed under the same conditions to the mass of the other. If two masses of metal, of any shape whatever, are brought under perfect assimilation, to one another, their unition, when brought into contact, will be instant. If we live in a sympathetic field we become sympathetic, and a tendency from the abnormal to the normal

presents itself by an evolution of a purely sympathetic flow towards its attractive centers. It is only under these conditions that differentiation can be broken up, and a pure equation established. The only condition under which equation can never be established is when a differential disaster has taken place, of 66 2/3 against the 100 pure, taking the full volume as one. If this 66 2/3 or even 100 exists in one organ alone, and the surrounding ones are normal, then a condition can be easily brought about to establish the concordant harmony or equation to that organ. It is as rare to find a negative condition of 66 2/3 against the volume of the whole mass, as it is to find a coincident between differentiation; or, more plainly, between two individuals under a state of negative influence. Under this new system, it is as possible to induce negations alike as it is to induce positives alike.

Pure sympathetic concordants are as antagonistic to negative discordants as the negative is to the positive; but the vast volume the sympathetic holds over the non-sympathetic, in ethereal space, makes it at once the ruling medium and re-adjuster of all opposing conditions if properly brought to bear upon them."

(signed) Keely

Until Keely's Theoretical Expose is given to science, there are few who will fathom the full meaning of these views. So little did Dr. Hartmann comprehend the principle involved that he ignored them altogether, and in the more than one hour's conversation with Mr. Keely which followed, instead of keeping to this subject matter as requested, he made no illusion to it whatever, and confined his investigations to the mechanical work of Mr. Keely in its application to machinery. In leaving, Mr. Keely again expressed his great delight in meeting one who knew so much of the hidden working of some of nature's laws; whereas, after his departure, Dr. Hartmann announced it as his opinion that, although Mr. Keely had made the greatest discovery of this or of any other age, he would never be able to utilize the force in mechanics, and that his mission would be to spiritualize the world instead of advancing its material progress.

Some days later, when Mr. Keely was asked why it was that Dr. Hartmann no longer believed in the mechanical success of Mr. Keely's inventions, the reply was made that Dr. Hartmann, in disclosing his own views and theories and philosophy, had prevented Mr. Keely from any attempt to point out the errors in these views and theories: feeling, as Mr. Keely did feel, that he would be wanting in humility to dispute with one so learned as Dr. Hartmann, and preferring to wait until the court had removed the injunction placed upon him (Keely), when he would be at liberty to demonstrate to Dr. Hartmann the nature of his errors by the operation of his inventions. However, this delay was not necessary, inasmuch as upon the occasion of Dr. Hartmann's first visit to the workshop, where he saw the old generator, the old Liberator and other machinery, his knowledge that, by means of the vibrations of Ether called Sound, the molecular structure of bodies may be changed, even though these vibrations are not audible to the human ear, caused Dr. Hartmann to confess his error, and to assert that his confidence in Mr. Keely's mechanical success was reestablished and stronger than it had ever been before. Those scientists who, because they could not hear the vibrations of sound, in Mr. Keely's Liberator, denied its operation, saying that one could not make something out of nothing, seem to forget that there are inaudible vibrations of sound as there are invisible rays of light.

Dr. Hartmann knows that everything in nature has its own appropriate 'sound', 'color', and 'number', and can be acted upon as soon as we are in possession of its 'key-note'. This knowledge enabled him to grasp the principle of Mr. Keely's inventions, as soon as the action of the mechanism was explained to him. Although Dr. Hartmann then and there expressed his intention of sacrificing some of his property in order. to invest in the new company, in process of organization, it was from no sordid motive that he was so intensely interested in the practical part of Mr.

Keely's work; but, having seen such marvelous effects produced in occult experiments, while residing in India, he was inclined to attribute to Mr. Keely natural occult powers which could never be made available in mechanics. Mr. Keely's financial success depends upon the prolongation of his life until his work of evolution is completed. Therefore, the writer of this paper has never advised anyone to invest on such an uncertainty and she requested Dr. Hartmann not to do so.

Mr. Keely's discovery embraces the manner or way of obtaining the keynote, or chord of mass, of mineral, vegetable, and animal substances; therefore, the construction of instruments, or machines, by which this law can be utilized in mechanics, in arts, and in restoration of equilibrium in disease, is only the question of the full understanding of the operation of this law. Herein lies Mr. Keely's work of evolution.

The principal point of difference existing between Mr. Keely and Dr. Hartmann, in their views respecting force, lies in the former attributing the so-called forces of nature to various modes of vibration, as to the length and direction of the vibrations; while the latter attributes all forces to various modes of vibration, as to the number of vibrations in a second. Electricity Mr. Keely defines as a certain form of atomic vibration.

Keely estimates that, after the introductory impulse is given on the harmonic thirds, molecular vibration is increased from 20,000 per second to 100,000,000. On the enharmonic sixths, that the vibration of the inter-molecule is increased to 300,000,000.

On the diatonic ninths, that atomic vibration reaches 900,000,000; on the dominant etheric sixths, 8,100,000,000; and on the inter-etheric ninths, 24,300,000,000; all of which can be demonstrated by sound colours.

In such fields of research, Mr. Keely finds little leisure. Those who accuse him of dilly-dallying, of idleness, of always gong to do and never doing, of visionary plans, etc., etc., know nothing of the infinite patience, the persistent energy, which for a quarter of a century

One Phase of Keely's Discovery in Its Relations to the Cure of Disease

has upheld him in his struggle to attain this end. Still less, if possible, is he understood by those who think he is seeking self-aggrandizement, fame, fortune, or glory.

The time is approaching when all who have sought to defame this discoverer and inventor, all who have stabbed him with unmerited accusations, all who have denounced him as a bogus inventor, a fraud, an impostor, a charlatan, a modern Cagliostro, will be forced to acknowledge that he has done a giant's work for true science, even though he should not live to attain commercial success. But history will not forget that, in the nineteenth century, the story of Prometheus has been repeated, and that the greatest mind of the age, seeking to scale the heavens to bring down the light of truth for mankind, met with Prometheus's reward.

Mrs. Clara F. Bloomfield-Moore
July 1, 1888

NOTE.---Dr. Hartmann, in a report, or condensed statement, in reference to Keely's discovery, writes as follows: He will never invent a machine by which the equilibrium of the living forces in a disordered brain can be restored.

As such a statement would lead the reader of the report to fancy that Keely expected to invent such an instrument, it is better to correct the error that Dr. Hartmann has fallen into. Keely has never dreamed of inventing such an instrument. He hopes, however, to perfect one that he is now at work upon, which will enable the operator to localize the seat of disturbance in the brain in mental disorders. If he succeeds, this will greatly simplify the work of re-adjusting opposing conditions; and will also enable the physician to decide whether the differential disaster has taken place which prevents the possibility of establishing the equation that is necessary to a cure.

According to Keely's theories it is that form of energy known as magnetism - not electricity - which is to be the curative agent of the future, thus reviving a mode of treatment handed down from the time of the earliest records, and made known to the Royal Society of London more than fifty years since by Professor Keil, of Jena, who demonstrated the susceptibility of the nervous system to the influence of the natural magnet, and its efficacy in the cure of certain infirmities, as thousands can testify in our day who are indebted to Parke's Compound Magnets for relief; trying them as the last resort after having suffered much at the hands of many physicians, as St. Paul said. A grandson of Goethe, after calling upon Robert Browning many years since, returned to inquire if he had dropped the magnet there which he was wearing, as he has missed it after leaving the house. The effect of the magnet is one of the effects of the law of sympathetic association, which Keely demonstrates as the governing medium of the universe throughout animate and inanimate nature.

As Cheston Morris, M.D., has well said in his paper on Vital Molecular Vibrations, We are entering upon a new field in biology, pathology, and of course, therapeutics, whose limiits are at present far beyond our ken.

The adaptability of drugs, says Dr. Henry Wood, to heal disease is becoming a matter of doubt, even among many who have not yet studied deeper causation. Materia Medica lacks the exact elements of a science. The just preponderance, for good or ill, of any drug upon the human system is an unsolved prolem, and will so remain ... After centuries of professional research, in order to perfect the art of healing, diseases have steadily grown more subtle and more numerous ... Only when internal, divine forces come to be relied upon, rather than outside reinforcement, will deterioration cease. Said Plato, 'You ought not to attempt to cure the body without the soul.'

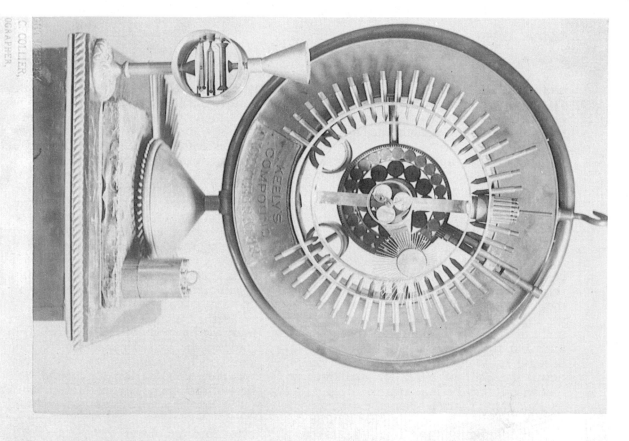

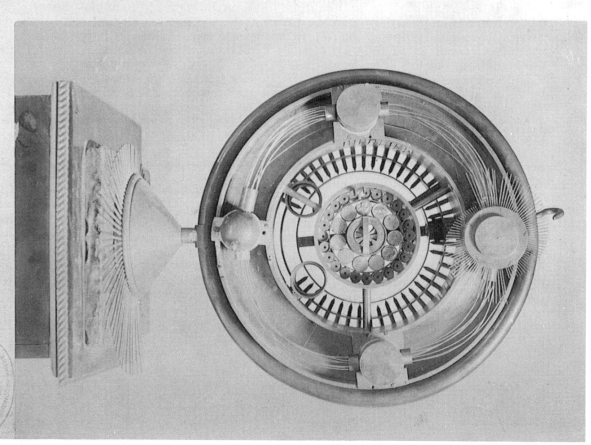

Keely's Compound Disintegrator.

38

On Dynaspheric Force

by Laurence Oliphant, 1888

Recent scientific research has proved conclusively that all force is atomic. That electricity consists of files of particles, and that the interstellar spaces contain substance, whether it be called ether, or astral fluid, or by any other name, which is composed of atoms, because it is not possible to dissever force from its transmitting medium. The universe, therefore, and all that it contains, consists of matter in motion, and is animated by a vital principle which we call God. Science has further discovered that these atoms are severally encompassed by an ethereal substance which prevents their touching each other, and to this circumambient interatomic element they have given the name dynasphere--- but inasmuch as it has further been found that in these dynaspheres there resides a tremendous potency, it is evident that they also must contain atoms, and that these atoms must in their turn be surrounded by dynaspheres, which again contain atoms, and so on ad infinitum. Matter thus becomes infinite and indestructible, and the force which pervades it, persistent and everlasting.

This dynaspheric force, which is also called etheric, is conditioned as to its nature on the quality of the atoms which form its transmitting media, and which are infinite both in variety and in their combinations and permutations. They may, however, be broadly divided into two categories, the sentient and the non-sentient atoms.

Dynaspheric force, composed of non-sentient atoms, is the force that has been already mechanically applied by Mr. Keely to his motor, and which will probably ere long supersede the agencies now used for locomotives, projectiles and other purposes; when the laws which govern it come to be understood, it will produce materially a great commercial and industrial revolution. There is no hard-and-fast line between the sentient and non-sentient atoms; just as zoophytes are a connecting link between the animal and vegetable creation, so there is a graduated scale of atoms between those which, although animated by the divine life, are not sentient, and those which are as highly developed relatively to them as man is to a cabbage. For the highest class of sentient atoms through which divine force is transmitted are in the perfect human form. They are infinitesimal bisexual innocences male and female, two in one. The tradition of fairies is the lingering consciousness, come down from a remote past, of this fact.

Owing to the unhappily debased condition of our planet, this force is not now operant upon it, except to a very limited and imperfect degree - it is struggling, however, to penetrate into the human organism through the channel provided for it, and this channel must, of necessity, partake of the nature of the forces operant within it---in other words, it must be a bi-sexual channel. It was this bi-sexual channel which Christ came to restore by his mission to earth; and thus inaugurate a process by which man should regain his lost bi-une condition. That process has now partially achieved its consummation in the advent of the complementary half of man whom we call the sympneuma. It is only through the sympneuma that the dynaspheric force, consisting of bi-sexual atoms, can be projected into nature. It comes for the healing of the nations, and is all the more necessary now because the conditions of nature have of late years undergone such a change as to render possible the invasion of the human organism by forces

Universal Laws Never Before Revealed.. Keely's Secrets

similar in character, with this one difference, that the atoms of which they are composed are not bi-sexual. These forces exhibit themselves in the phenomena of hypnotism, thought-reading, telepathy, mesmeric healing, spiritualistic manifestations, and in divers other ways, and depend for their quality on the source of their projection in the invisible and the human medium through whom they are transmitted---where both are bad, the atoms are in the form of infusoria, or predatory animalculae, who prey upon each other, and work moral and physical malady. Where both are relatively good, they are in the form of separate uni-sexual beings, depending for their quality upon the medium, and partaking of what moral taint his nature may possess. It must be said that the same remark applies to the bi-sexual atoms of the sympneumatic force; but, although imperfect, there is this guarantee for their superior quality, that it is not possible for a human being to enter upon sympneumatic conditions, excepting after a long and arduous discipline and self-sacrifice for his neighbor, and of great sufferings.

The sympneuma visits none who have not been thus prepared, and who do not live exclusively for the service of humanity, to the extinction of private affections, personal ambitions, or worldly considerations of any kind.

A false sympneuma may, however, visit those who are wholly engrossed by self; such are the succabi and incubi---well-known by the Church---and the force acting through them is the most fatal which can operate upon earth.

There are methods, however, not necessary to enter upon here, by which the true can be distinguished from the false with absolute certainty. All human emotion is atomic, and it has never been possible that it should be otherwise. The peculiarity of the atomic force of the present day is, that it has received an immense accession of energy, through changes which have operated in the invisible.

It is these changes which render will-force, and magnetic influence so much more powerful now than they were formerly; and hence it becomes of such transcendent importance that persons who find themselves in possession of this reinforced energy, and able to operate upon others hypnotically or for curative purposes, should realize the character of the agency they are dealing with---for it is quite impossible for them to project this will-force, or magnetic influence, into the organism of another, without projecting the atoms with it. Now, these atoms vary in quality from the predatory animalculae to the human form through an infinite variety of types; none of them pure and good, though some are far purer and better, relatively, than the others---still no magnetiser is so perfect that his magnetism does not convey to his patients the atoms of the vices and defects peculiar to his own nature, of which they may have been comparatively free.

It may thus happen that a magnetiser, while healing the body of a patient, may work irreparable moral injury to his soul, and this while animated with the best intentions, and quite unconsciously to himself. It often happens, moreover, that the progress of the soul can only be achieved by an attenuation of the external structural atoms, thus producing physical disease; to heal a person thus under going moral treatment, directed from the unseen world, by a sudden and premature exercise of will-force in this one, applied to his surface organism, is to render him a fatal service. Again, it may be that the welfare of a person's soul is dependent upon its removal from the body at a certain juncture; here, again, human interference, by the operation of the human will being free, and yet under specific law, that free operation cannot be arbitrarily hindered in defiance of the law under which it acts.

The reason why material remedies of all kinds may be employed with safety and propriety, is because the curative forces they contain are not composed of sentient atoms, and can be controlled from the unseen in quite a different manner from those which are---which may, to a certain extent, be influenced by them, but cannot be controlled. When a person has reached the point, which may be attained after a long sympneumatic training, and a life passed under the influence of that training, of having no will but that of God operating freely in him, as his own, he may, under a pressure, which he will recognize as a divine impulse, put forth a healing power, but he will have no personal desire connected with it; the healing force will be put through him irrespective of any conscious will he used; the energy he projects will convey bisexual atoms, which may prove a seed sown as a preparation for a sympneumatic descent.

At such moments the operator will hold himself exclusively open to Christ, for it cannot be too earnestly insisted upon, that Christ is the one source and channel of sympneumatic life, and the healing which comes through it, when a person's moral condition renders such physical healing desirable.

In the presence of the rapid development which dynaspheric force is acquiring, and of the great interest which it is attracting, especially among good and earnest truth seekers, who are only in-

vestigating it with the object of turning it to account for the benefit of humanity, it has seemed to me necessary to make these remarks. I have done so in the hope that they might serve as a warning and an encouragement---as a warning of the dangers that beset the unwary explorers into these little known and almost untrodden regions; and as an encouragement as indicating the immense potentialities now descending upon the world for its succor in the hour of its approaching need.

If I seem to have written with the certainty of conviction, it is with no desire to impose my authority arbitrarily upon my readers, but in all humility to give them the facts as they have been revealed to me, after an arduous struggle and investigation into the methods of operation of these forces, which has lasted nearly twenty-five years.

Dualism or Polarity

The ancient symbol of Yin-Yang symbolizes the two opposites of male/female, positive/negative which are really two sides of the same thing.

They are ONE and work as one when the whole is united.

Black is usually taken to be the negative or female while white is usually understood to be the positive or male polarity.

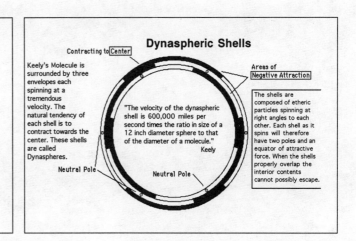

Dynaspheric Shells

Contracting to Center

Keely's Molecule is surrounded by three envelopes each spinning at a tremendous velocity. The natural tendency of each shell is to contract towards the center. These shells are called Dynaspheres.

"The velocity of the dynaspheric shell is 600,000 miles per second times the ratio in size of a 12 inch diameter sphere to that of the diameter of a molecule."
Keely

Neutral Pole

Neutral Pole

Areas of Negative Attraction

The shells are composed of etheric particles spinning at right angles to each other. Each shell as it spins will therefore have two poles and an equator of attractive force. When the shells properly overlap the interior contents cannot possibly escape.

Universal Laws Never Before Revealed.. Keely's Secrets

What Is Matter And What Is Force

(from The Theosophist, September, 1888)

[The continual discoveries with which modern science astonishes and bewilders the world create a presumption in the many minds that an article dealing with scientific subjects becomes unreliable when it is a few years old, because most probably superseded by new facts or theories, discovered or formulated in the meantime by the heirophants of the laboratory or the lecture hall, but not yet generally known. Some of these discoveries would in legal phraseology be termed retroactive - they upset theories hitherto upheld as axioms of science or laws of nature; and science that has become out of date is quite as much to be avoided as last year's fashions. This, of course, is a danger which necessarily threatens anyone who, not being in the inner circle of scientists, quotes from even the latest editions of scientific works, and the uncertainty thereby created does much to keep up the unquestioning faith which so many persons feel in the dicta of modern science, paradoxical as that may sound. The reason is plain enough. Men of science stand to the vulgar in the position of revelators. It does not so much matter if they are mistaken today, since they will most likely correct their mistakes tomorrow; and this uncertainty does for the men of science what the constant promise of a new revelation did for Joe Smith and Brigham Young - it creates expectant attention and happy anticipation. This uncertainty of science tends also to discourage undue curiosity and criticism on the part of the public, and to favor the autocratic assumptions of scientific authorities; for naturally there does not seem to be much use for outsiders to spend their time in learning abstruse things that may be discovered, in a few months or years, to have after all been altogether falsely conceived and wrongly explained. In the case of the following article, however, most of the scientific theories and data quoted are still standing, although the article is over five years old; and the occult views of nature it puts forth are true for all time. For this reason it has been thought well to republish it without delay, before the scientific views it deals with have any more time to turn sour or explode. The article, it should be mentioned, was written in answer to some objections raised by a correspondent in a previous number of The Theosophist, as to the designation of electricity as a form of matter; and the writer does not imagine that the question which forms its title is fully answered in the text. There remain several aspects of force almost wholly unnoticed, and it would, of course, be ridiculous to suppose that the subject of Force has been exhausted by dealing with some of its manifestations. Had it been the intention of the article to settle the questions at issue, the writer would not have taken for a title the query, What is Matter and What is Force? but would probably have adopted the usual style of teachers of science, and headed the article, What Matter and Force are. Enough is said in the article, however, to answer its original purpose, namely, of showing that the all-important questions, What is matter? and What is Force? have received no satisfactory answer from modern science, and of proving that no one has any right, in the present state of scientific knowledge, to assert, in the face of the occultists, that electricity is not a form of matter, more especially so since Helmholtz has declared it to be as atomic as ponderable matter itself.]

It is a question of science, which, as such, has to be strictly kept within the boundaries of modern materialistic science. All discussion on the subject, however desirable, would prove, on the whole, unprofitable. Firstly, because science confines herself only to the physical aspect of the conservation of energy or correlation of forces; and, secondly, because, notwithstanding her own frank admission of helpless ignorance as to the ultimate causes of things, judging by the tone of our critic's article, I doubt whether he would be willing to admit the utter inaptness of some of the scientific terms as approved by the Dwija, the twice-born of the Royal Socie-

Universal Laws Never Before Revealed.. Keely's Secrets

ty, and obediently accepted by their admirers. The fact that modern science has been pleased to divide and subdivide the atmosphere into a whole host of elements, and to call them so for her own convenience, is no authoritative reason why Occultists should accept that terminology. Science has never yet succeeded in decomposing a single one of the many simple bodies miscalled elementary substances, for which failure, probably, the latter have been named by their elementary. And whether she may yet, or never may, succeed in that direction in time, and thus recognize her error, in the meanwhile, we Occultists permit ourselves maintain that the alleged primordial atoms would be better classified under any other name but that one. With all respect due to the men of science, the terms element and elementary applied to the ultimate atoms and molecules of matter of which they know nothing do not seem in the least justified. It is as though the Royal Society agreed to call every star a Kosmos, because each star was supposed to be a world like our own planet; and then would begin taunting the ancients universe. So far, however, science admits herself that the words element and elementary, unless applied to primordial principles or self-existing essences, out of which the universe was evolved, are unfortunate terms, and remarks there upon that experimental science deals only with legitimate deductions from the facts of observation, and has nothing to do with any kind of essences except those which it can see, smell, or taste. Professor J.P. Crooke tells us that science leaves all others to the metaphysicians (New Chemistry, 1887). This stern pronunciamento, which shows the men of science refusing to take anything on faith, is immediately followed by a very curious admission made by the same author, Our theory, I grant, may be all wrong, he adds, and there may be no such thing as molecules...The new chemistry assumes as its fundamental postulate that the magnitudes we call molecules are realities, but this is only a postulate. We are thus made suspect that the exact science of chemistry needs to take as well as transcendental metaphysics something on blind faith. Grant her the postulate - and her deductions make of her an exact science; deny it - and exact science falls to pieces! Thus, in this respect, physical science does not stand higher than psychological science, and the Occultists need fear but very little of the thunderbolts of their exact rivals. Both are, to say the least, on a par. The chemist, though carrying his subdivision of molecules further than the physicist, can no more than he experiment on individual molecules. One may even remind both that neither of them has ever seen an individual molecule. Nevertheless, and while priding themselves upon taking nothing on faith, they admit that they cannot often follow the sub-division of molecules with the eye, but can discern it with the intellect. What more, then, do they do than the Occultists, the alchemists, the adepts? While they discern with the intellect, the adept, as he maintains, can as easily discern the sub-division ad infinitum of that which his rival of the exact methods pleases to call an elementary body, and he follows it - with the spiritual in addition to the physical intellect...We must pass to the more important question now, and see how far science is justified in regarding electricity as a force and . . . Eastern Occultists in maintaining that it is still matter. Before we open the discussion I must be allowed to remark that, since a Theosophist wants to be scientifically accurate, he ought to remember that science does not call electricity a force, but only one of the manifestations of the same; a mode of action or motion. Her list of the various kinds of energy which occur in nature is long, and many are the names which she uses to distinguish them. With all that, one of her most eminent adepts, Professor Balfour Stewart - one of the authorities he quotes against our President - warns his readers (see The Forces and Energies of Nature) that their enumeration has nothing absolute or complete about it, representing, as it does, not so much the present state of our knowledge as our want of knowledge, or rather profound ignorance, of the ultimate constitution of matter. So great is that ignorance, indeed, that, treating upon heat, a mode of motion which is supposed to be better understood than electricity, that scientist confess that if heat be not a species of motion, it must necessarily be a species of matter, and adds that the men of science have preferred to consider heat as a species of motion to the alternative of supposing the creation of a peculiar kind of matter. And, if so, what is there to warrant us that science will not yet find out her mistake some day, and recognize and call electricity, in argument with the Occultists, a species of a peculiar kind of matter. Thus, before the dogmatic admirers of modern science take the occultists to task for viewing electricity under one of its aspects - and for maintaining that its basic principle is - matter, they ought first to demonstrate that science errs when she herself, through the mouthpiece of her recognized high priests, confesses her ignorance as to what is properly force and what is matter. For instance, the same Professor of Natural Philosophy, Mr. Balfour Stewart, LL.D., F.R.S., in his lectures on the Conservation of Energy, tells us as follows: - We know nothing or next to nothing of the ultimate structure or properties of matter, whether organic or inorganic, and . . . it is in truth only a convenient classification and nothing more.

Furthermore, one and all, the men of science admit that though they possess a definite knowledge of the general laws, yet they have no knowledge of the individuals in the domains of physical science. For example, they suspect a large number of our diseases to be caused by organic germs; but they have to avow that their ignorance about these germs is complete. And in the chapter What is Energy? the same great naturalist staggers the too-confiding profane by the following admission: - If our knowledge of the nature and habits of organized molecules be so small, our knowledge of the ultimate molecules of inorganic matter is, if possible, still smaller. It thus appears that we know little or nothing about the shape or size of molecules, or about the forces which actuate them. The very largest masses of the universe sharing with the very

smallest this property of being beyond the scrutiny of the human senses. Of physical human senses he must mean, since he knows little, if anything, of any other senses. But let us take note of some further admissions, this time by Professor Leconte, in his lecture on the distinction between force and energy is very imperfectly, if not at all, defined in the higher forms of force, and especially in the domain of life. . . Our language cannot be more precise until our ideas in this department are far clearer than now.

Even as regards the familiar liquid - water - science is at a loss to decide whether the oxygen or hydrogen exist as such in water, or whether they are produced by some unknown and unconceived transformation of its substance. It is a question, says Mr. J.P. Crooke, Professor of Chemistry, about which we may speculate, but in regard to which we have no knowledge. Between the qualities of water and the quality of these gases there is not the most distant resemblance. All they know is that water can be decomposed by an electrical current; but why is it so decomposed and then again recombined, or what is the nature of that they call electricity, *etc.*, they do not know. Hydrogen, moreover, was still very lately one of the very few substances which was known only in its aeriform condition. It is the lightest form of matter known.

There is not an atom in nature but contains latent or potential electricity which manifests under known conditions. Science knows that matter generates* what it calls force, the latter manifesting itself under various forms of energy - such as heat, electricity, magnetism, gravitation, *etc.*, - yet that same science has hitherto been unable as we find from her own admissions, as given above, to determine where it is that matter ends and force (or spirit, as some erroneously call it) begins. Sci-

---

*Using the term generated in the lesser sense of calling forth into manifestation. Force or energy is known to be eternal, and cannot of course be 'generated' in the same sense of being created.

Universal Laws Never Before Revealed.. Keely's Secrets

ence, while rejecting metaphysics and relegating it through her mouthpiece, Professor Tyndall, to the domain of poetry and fiction, unbridles as often as many metaphysicians her wild fancy, and allows mere hypotheses to run riot on the field of unproved speculation. All this she does, as in the case of the molecular theory, with no better authority for it than the paradoxical necessity for the philosophy of every science to arbitrarily select and assume imaginary fundamental principles; the only proof offered in the way of demonstrating the actual existence of the latter being a certain harmony of these principles with the observed facts. Thus, when men of science imagine themselves subdividing a grain of sand to the ultimate molecule they call oxide of silicon, they have no real but only an imaginary and purely hypothetical right to suppose that, if they went on dividing it further (which, of course, they cannot), the molecule, separating itself into the chemical constituents of silicon and oxygen, would finally yield that which has to be regarded as two elementary bodies - since the authorities so regard them. Neither an atom of silicon nor an atom of oxygen is capable of any further subdivision into something else, they say. But the only good reason we can find for such a strange belief is because they have tried the experiment and - failed. But how can they tell that a new discovery, some new invention of still finer and more perfect apparatuses and instruments, may not show their error some day? How do they know that those very bodies or molecules, which, when analyzed with still greater minuteness, may show containing in themselves the real primordial elementary globules, the gross encasement of the still finer atom-spark, the spark of life, the source of electricity - matter still! Truly has Henry Kunrath, the greatest of the alchemists and Rosicrucians of the middle ages, shown spirit in man, as in every atom - as a bright flame enclosed within a more or less transparent globule - which he calls soul. And since the men of science confessedly know nothing of (a) the origin of either matter or energy; (b) nor of electricity or life; and (c) that

their knowledge of the ultimate molecules of inorganic matter amounts to a cipher. Why, I ask, should any student of Occultism, whose great masters may know, perchance, of essences which the professors of the modern materialistic school can neither see, smell, or taste - why should he be expected to take their definitions as to what is Matter and what is Force as the last word of unerring, infallible science?. . .The term imponderable agents is now regarded as a scientific absurdity. The latest conclusions at which modern chemistry has arrived, it seems, have brought it to reject the word imponderable, and to make away with those text books of premodern science which refer the phenomena of heat and electricity to attenuated forms of matter. Nothing, they hold, can be added to or subtracted from bodies without altering their weight. This was said and written in 1876, by one of the greatest chemists in America. With all that, have they become any wiser for it? Have they been able to replace by a more scientific theory the old and tabooed phlogiston theory of the science of Stahl, Priestley, Scheele, and others? Or, because they have proved, to their own satisfaction, that it is highly unscientific to refer the phenomena of heat and electricity to attenuated forms of matter, have they succeeded at the same time in proving what are really Force, Matter, Energy, Fire, Electricity, Life? The phlogiston of Stahl - a theory of combustion taught by Aristotle and the Greek philosophers - as elaborated by Scheele, the poor Swedish apothecary, a secret student of Occultism, who, as Professor Crooke says of him, added more knowledge to the stock of chemical science in a single year than did Lavoisier in his lifetime, was not a mere fanciful speculation, though Lavoisier was permitted to taboo and upset it. But, indeed, were the high priests of modern science to attach more weight to the essence of things than to mere generalizations, then, perhaps, they would be in a better position to tell the world more of the ultimate structure of matter than they now are. Lavoisier, it is well known, did not add any new fact of prime importance by upsetting the phlogiston theory, but only added grand generalization. The Occultists are perfectly aware, it need hardly be said, of modern theories of combustion, and fully recognize the part which oxygen plays therein. They prefer, however, to hold to the fundamental theories of ancient sciences, knowing well that a very large balance of real knowledge lies on that side, when the ancient and the modern are compared. No more than the authors of the old theory do they attach to phlogiston - which has its specific name as one of the attributes of Akasa - the idea of weight which the uninitiated generally associate with all matter. And though to us it is a principle, a well defined essence, yet no more than we did they view it as matter in the sense it has for the present men of science. As one of their modern professors put it - Translate the phlogiston by energy, and in Stahl's work on Chemistry and Physics, of 1731, put energy where he wrote phlogiston, and you have . . . our great modern doctrine of conservation of energy. Verily so it is the great modern doctrine, only plus something else, let me add. Hardly a year after these words had been pronounced, the discovery by Professor Crookes of radiant matter - of which farther on - has nigh upset again all their previous theories.

Force, energy, physical agent, are simply different words to express the same idea, observes our critic. I believe he errs. To this day the men of science are unable to agree in giving to electricity a name which would convey a clear and comprehensive definition of this very mysterious agent, as Professor Balfour Stewart calls it. While the latter states that electricity or electrical attraction may probably be regarded as peculiarly allied to that force which we call chemical affinity; and Professor Tyndall calls it only a mode of motion; Professor A. Bain regards electricity as one of the five chief powers or forces of nature:--- One mechanical or molar, the momentum of moving matter, the others molecular, or embodied in the molecules, also supposed(?) in motion - these are heat, light, chemical force, electricity. (The Correlations of Nervous

and Mental Forces.) Now, these three definitions would not gain, I am afraid, by being strictly analyzed . . . Light was never regarded as a force. It is, says science, a manifestation of energy, a mode of motion produced by a rapid vibration of the molecules and transmitted by the undulations of ether. The same for heat and sound, the transmission of the latter depending, in addition to the vibrations of ether, on the undulations of an intervening atmosphere. Professor Crookes thought at one time that he had discovered light to be a force, but found out his mistake very soon. The explanation of Thomas Young of the undulatory theory of light, holds now as good as ever in the theories of modern science at least, and according to this explanation that which we call light is simply an impression produced on the retina of the eye by the wave-like motion of the particles of matter. Light, then, like heat - of which it is the crown - is simply the ghost, the shadow of matter in motion! . . The men of science have just found out a fourth state of matter, whereas the Occultists have penetrated years ago beyond the sixth, and, therefore, do not infer, but know of the existence of the seventh, the last. Professor Balfour Stewart, in seeking to show light to be an energy or force, quotes Aristotle, and remarks that the Greek philosopher seems to have entertained the idea that light is not a body, or the emanation of any body (for that, Aristotle says, would be a kind of body), and, that, therefore, light is an energy or act. To this I respectfully demur, and answer that if we cannot conceive of motion without force, we can conceive still less of an energy or act existing in boundless space from the eternity, or even manifesting without some kind of body. Moreover, the conceptions about body and matter of Aristotle and Plato, the founders of the two great rival schools of antiquity, opposed as they were in many things to each other, are nevertheless still more at variance with the conceptions about body and matter of our modern men of science. The Theosophists, old and modern, the Alchemists, and Rosicrucians have ever maintained that there were no such things

Universal Laws Never Before Revealed.. Keely's Secrets

per se as light, heat, sound, electricity, least of all could there be a vacuum in nature. And now the results of old and modern investigation fully corroborate what they had always affirmed, namely, that in reality there is no such thing as a chemical ray, a light ray, or a heat ray. As far as can be ascertained by those whose observations and experiments are confined to the material plane, there is nothing but radiant energy; or, as a man of science expresses it in the Scientific American, radiant energy, motion of some kind, causing vibrations across space of something between us and the sun; something which, without understanding fully (verily so!), we call 'ether,' and which exists everywhere, even in the vacuum of a radiometer. The sentence, for being confused, is, none the less for it, the last word of science. Again: We have always one and the same cause, radiant energy, and we give this one thing different names - 'actinism,' 'light,' or 'heat.' And we are told also that the miscalled chemical or actinic rays, as well as those which the eye sees as blue, or green, or red, and those which the thermometer feels, are all one thing, the effects of motion in ether. (The Sun's Radiant Energy, by Professor Langley.)

Now, the sun and ether being beyond dispute material bodies, necessarily every one of their effects - light, heat, electricity, *etc.* - must be, agreeably to the definitions of Aristotle (as accepted, though slightly misconceived, by Professor Balfour Stewart), also a kind of body, ergo - matter.

Now what is in reality matter? We have seen that it is hardly possible to call electricity a force, and yet we are forbidden to call it matter under the penalty of being called unscientific. Electricity has no weight - ergo, it cannot be matter. Well, there is much to be said on both sides. Mallet's experiment, which corroborated that of Pirani (1878), showed that electricity is under the influence of gravitation, and must have, therefore, some weight. A straight copper wire, with its ends bent downwards, suspended at the middle to one of the arms of a delicate balance, while the bent ends dip in mercury. When the

current of a strong battery is passed through the wire by the intervention of the mercury, the arm to which the wire is attached, although accurately balanced by a counterpoise, sensibly tends downwards, notwithstanding the resistance produced by the buoyancy of the mercury. Mallet's opponents, who tried at the time to show that gravitation had nothing to do with the fact of the arm of the balance tending downward, but that it was due to the law of attraction of electric currents, and who brought forward to that effect Barlow's theory of electric currents, and Ampere's discovery that electric currents, running in opposite directions, repel one another, and are sometimes driven upwards, only proved that men of science will rarely agree, and that the question is far an open one. This, however, raises a side issue as to what is the law of gravitation. The scientists of the present day assume that gravitation and attraction are quite distinct from one another. But the day may not be far distant when the theory of the Occultists that the law of gravitation is nothing more or less than the law of attraction and repulsion will be proved scientifically correct.

Science may, of course, if it so pleases her, call electricity a force. Only by grouping it together with light and heat, to which the name of force is decidedly refused, she has either to plead guilty of inconsistency, or to tacitly admit that it is a species of matter. But whether electricity has weight or not, no true scientist is prepared to show that there is no matter so light as to be beyond weighing with our present instruments. And this brings us directly to the latest discovery, one of the grandest in science; I mean Mr. Crookes' radiant matter, or, as it is now called, the fourth state of matter. That the three states of matter, the solid, the liquid, and the gaseous, are but so many stages in an unbroken chain of physical continuity, and that the three correlate or are transformed one into the other by insensible gradations, needs no further demonstration, we believe. But what is of far greater importance to us Occultists is the admission made by several great men of science in various articles upon the discovery of that fourth state of matter. Says one of them in Scientific American:--- 'There is nothing any more improbable in the supposition that these three states of matter do not exhaust the possibilities of material condition than in supposing the possibilities of sound to extend to aerial undulations to which our organs of hearing are insensible, or the possibilities of vision to ethereal undulations too rapid or too slow to affect our eyes as light.

And as Professor Crookes has now succeeded in refining gases to a condition so ethereal as to reach a state of matter fairly describable as ultra-gaseous, and exhibiting an entirely novel set of properties, why should the Occultists be taken to task for affirming that there lie beyond that ultra-gaseous state still other states of matter; state so ultra-refined, even in their grosser manifestations - such as electricity under all its forms - as to have fairly deluded the scientific senses, and let the happy possessors thereof call electricity - a force! They tell us that it is obvious that if the tenuity of some gas is very greatly increased, as in the most perfect vacua attainable, the number of molecules may be so diminished that their collisions under favourable conditions may become so few in comparison with the number of masses that they will cease to have a determining effect upon the physical character of the matter under observation. In other words, they say: The free-flying molecules, if left to obey the laws of kinetic force without mutual interference, will cease to exhibit the properties characteristic of the gaseous state, and take on an entirely new set of properties. This is radiant matter. And still beyond lies the source of electricity - still matter. . . Speaking of his discovery, Professor Crookes justly remarks that the phenomena he has investigated in his exhausted tubes reveal to physical science a new field for explanation, a new world, a world wherein matter exists in a fourth state, where the corpuscular theory of light holds good, and where light does not always move in a straight line, but where we can never enter, and in which we must be content to observe and experiment from with-

out. To this the Occultist might answer: If we can never enter it with the help of our physical senses, we have long since entered and even gone beyond it, carried thither by our spiritual faculties and in our spirit bodies.

And now I will close this too lengthy article with the following reflection. The ancients never invented their myths. One acquainted with the science of occult symbology can always detect a scientific fact under the mask of grotesque fancy. Thus one who would go to the trouble of studying the fable of Electra - one of the seven Atlantides - in the light of occult science, would soon discover the real nature of Electricity, and learn that it signifies little whether we call it force or matter, since it is both, and so far, in the sense given it by modern science, both terms may be regarded as misnomers. Electra, we know, is the wife and daughter of Atlas the Titan, and the son of Asia and of Pleione, the daughter of the Ocean. . . As Professor Leconte well remarks, there are many of the best scientists who ridicule the use of the term vital force or vitality as a remnant of superstition, and yet the same men use the words gravity, magnetic force, physical force, electrical force, *etc.*, and are unable withal to explain what is life, or even electricity; nor are they able to assign any good reason for the well-known fact that when an animal body is killed by lightning, after death the blood does no coagulate. Chemistry, which shows to us every atom, whether organic or inorganic, in nature susceptible to polarization, whether in its atomic mass or as a unit, and inert matter allied with gravity, light with heat, etc., hence as containing latent electricity, that chemistry still persists in making a difference between between organic and inorganic matter though both are due to the same mysterious energy, ever at work by her own occult processes in Nature's laboratory, in the mineral no less than in the vegetable kingdom. Therefore do the Occultists maintain that the philosophical conception of spirit, like the conception of matter, must rest on one and the same basis of phenomena, adding that force and matter, spirit and matter, or viewed as opposite poles in their respective manifestations, yet they are in essence and in truth but one, and that life is present as much in a dead as in a living body, in inorganic as in organic matter. This is why, while science is searching still, and may go on searching for ever, to solve the problem What is life? the Occultist can afford to refuse taking the trouble, since he claims, with as much good reason as any given to the contrary, that life, whether in its latent or dynamical form, is everywhere, that it is as infinite and indestructible as matter itself, since neither can exist without the other, and that electricity is the very essence and origin of life itself. Purush is non-existent without Prakriti; nor can Prakriti, or plastic matter, have being or exist without Purush, or spirit, vital energy, life. Purush and Prakriti are, in short, the two poles of the one

eternal element, and are synonymous and convertible terms. Our bodies as organized tissues are indeed an unstable arrangement of chemical forces, plus a molecular force - as Professor Bain calls electricity - raging in it dynamically during life, tearing asunder its particles at death, to transform itself into a chemical force after the process, and thence again to resurrect as an electrical force or life in every individual atom. Therefore, whether it is called Force or Matter, it will ever remain the omnipresent Proteus of the universe, the one element, Life, Spirit or Force at its negative, Matter at its positive pole; the former the Materio-Spiritual, the latter the Materio-Physical Universe, Nature, Swabhavat or Indestructible Matter.

Unsigned

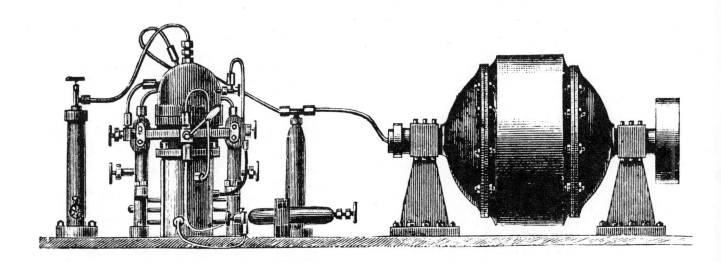

The Astral Light

by Louise A. Off

The Astral Light, as the source of all world phenomena, is a theme of no little importance to the student of occultism. The root of the word Astral is to be found in the Assyrian Istar, signifying star, and was applied to this element by the Kabbalists and later mystics, because they considered the heavenly bodies as the concrete crystallizations of the Astral Light. Some Theosophic writers have confounded the nature of this element with that of Akasa, while in fact the latter comprehends infinitely more both in quality and quantity. Literally the Sanscrit term Akasa means the sky, but occultly the impalpable Ether or the Soul within the Ether. Our most logical authority, The Secret Doctrine, defines it as the immortal spirit, the progenitor of Cosmic life and universal intelligence whose characteristic property is Buddhi. Akasa is the sphere of the pure undifferentiated Monad, the essence of wisdom, while the Astra Light at its opposite pole is the abstract atom of matter, the plane of generation, and the great womb out of which issues all planetary life. Ether, which is the highest vibration of the Astral Light, is but as a vehicle for Akasa, a gross body in comparison. The functions of the Astral Light are as manifold as the expressed universe. Its nature is dual - the highest Ether forming its positive, and the concrete, or differentiated elements, its negative pole. Its cause reaches back to the root of all causes, and its effects involve all our physical and psychical experiences. We deal with its familiar phenomena in every breath and every motion, while the rare and abnormal phases are as strictly subject to its laws. It is not substantially identical with any one of the material elements of Cosmic matter, but is one degree superior to Prakriti (Nature as apprehended by the senses), and it impenetrates and vitalizes each atom. It is itself the one underlying element in which all other known elements have their source and supply. In its physical aspects it includes the Ether of modern scientists, but in the metaphysical sense they scarcely touch its borderland. For while it is the reservoir of Heat, Light, Magnetism, and Electricity - the field of all degrees of vibration - it is also the sphere of all intellectual life, and the ruling agent in the alchemical process which frees the cerebral atom and converts it into thought. Its vibratory rate determines individual mental tendencies, and also establishes our intimate relations in body with the stars. Paracelsus maintains that, as fire passes through an iron stove, so do the stars pass through man with all their properties, and go into him as the rain into the earth, which gives fruit out of that same rain. While the modern spectroscope reveals the identity in substance of infinitesimal man, and the greatest luminiferous body that glides in vast revolutions through space, no instrument has, as yet, been discovered so sensitive as to register the subtle and evanescent fluid which, by its uniform nature, makes astronomical research and thought-transference possible. Keely's Motor has, however, already foreshadowed such a discovery.

The Astral Light is the great record-book upon whose pages every thought and act of differentiated consciousness is engraven, there to be read by the individual who has learnt the secret of exalting his vibrations until they become synchronous with the waves of this finer element. The definition of Memory which has ever been the enigma of science, a function with an inapprehensible cause, is relegated to the domain of

Universal Laws Never Before Revealed.. Keely's Secrets

the occultist, who may briefly define it as the correlative vibration of the cerebral center with the Astral Light. Within this correlation reside all the possibilities of consciousness from the horizon of Maya (illusion) to the zenith of pure Ether of transcendental life. Madame Blavatsky sweepingly states: The psychic forces, the 'ideomotor' and 'electro-biological powers,' latent thought' and even 'unconscious cerebration' theories can be condensed into two words, the Kabbalistic 'Astral Light.' Quesnes treated of it as a universally diffused fluid permeating all things, and differing in action only according to the mobility of the organism by which it is confined.

The differentiated will to live accompanying each primary monad is the sculptor of the astral images which constitute individual experience. An intense power of concentration makes these images subjective, in which case they are realities only to the operator, but under still more acute and intelligent development, these images may assume a concrete objective form with power of duration proportioned to the original impulse or determined purpose of the projector. Determined will, says a fire-philosopher, is a beginning of all magical operations, and the great magician, Abbe Constant, states: To acquire magical power, two things are necessary: to disengage the will from all servitude and to exercise it in control. He alone can become a Master whose physical and psychical organization is attuned to the Astral Key-note - whose self-consciousness has outgrown the limits of personal slavery, and whose will is so cultivated as to act without fear and without desire - intelligent, determined, self-possessed and confident. While the majority of mankind is occupied in mere negative registration of sense-impressions the occultist classifies these, and admits only those most useful to his purpose. Colonel Olcott refers to the manipulation of the Astral Light in his statement, that the efficacy of all words used as charms and spells lies in what the Aryans call the vach, a certain latent power resident in Akasa. Physically we may describe it as the power to set up certain measured vibrations, not in the grosser atmospheric particles whose undulations beget light, sound, heat and electricity, but in the latent spiritual principle or force - about the nature of which modern science knows almost nothing. As an illustration of this we have the word Aum, which, as all students know, has an equilibrating effect which resists the inroad of passion.

The symbol used to express the astral realm by the mystics of all ages is the serpent, or the fiery dragon. It is stated that long before our globe or even our universe became egg-shaped, a long trail of Cosmic dust (or fine mist) moved and writhed like a serpent in space, This was the beginning of our Eternity, exoterically expressed by a serpent with its tail in its mouth, or in the act of incubating the Mundane Egg with its fiery breathe. The Chaldean Oracles refer to the Astral Light as winding in form, which qualification refers to the vibratory motion that characterizes it. The intense rate of its pulsation may be faintly realized in the rapidity with which successive images are recorded in the dreaming or hypnotized state. An illustration is recounted of a student who was making scientific experiments in this psychological field with a friend. While a drop of water was descending down upon his forehead, he closed his eyes and dreamed that he started out from a harbor upon the wide main, soon passing several beautiful islands full of villages, cities, verdant fields and mountains. The sun was beaming generously, but little by little the sky grew darker and heavier, and drifts of black clouds swept upon the scene. A great gal arose. Consternation and horror pervaded the crew. The waves began to rise higher and higher, until finally the heavens and the sea were blended into one dense chaos.

The crises was at hand. The dreamer suddenly felt as though the whole sea had burst asunder and drawn him in - he awoke just as the drop of water touched his skin, fallen from the hand of his friend and held but a few inches above his head. He had registered the full episode of dramatic changes during the instant in which the sensor nerve flashed its irritation to the brain. Far more remarkable than this are illustrations on record which cover an extent of years and are recorded in an instant of time, experimentally proven to be less than the period required for transmitting a nervous current. The wondrous rapidity with which feeling and thinking may be condensed has also been frequently analyzed in the experience of persons nearly drowned, and as Helmholtz has demonstrated that the period in which a nerve-current may be conducted is a definite one, we have no alternative but to assume that a far subtler element or vehicle is employed in the registering psychic experiences. By the astral current throughout the ayras, around the nerve-centers and nerve-tubes, mind contacts mind, thoughts are flashed in upon us and emotions conveyed. It radiates from the individual man as an impalpable but intelligent aura - the medium of his psychic and intuitional life, by means of which he evinces sympathy and understanding; while in its higher aspect it is the sensitive plane that records Cosmic ideation, and conveys impressions of truth and of universal law to the human mind.

Experiment with trained sensitives has proven that when an intellectual concept is formed, the astral aura photographs it instantaneously, while, when an emotion is evinced, the aura changes in intensity of color, and, on volition becoming manifest, there is a positive increase of vibration. We, therefore, carry with us all we have ever thought and felt - and self is the ever-refining essence of this thought and feeling. From this point of view responsibility assumes enormous proportions, and we perceive why the great Teachers of the world have ever agreed that Man is his own heaven and his own hell.

The great mesmerizer, Du Potet, declares that the faculty of directing this fluid is inherent in certain organizations, that it passes through all bodies, and that everything can be used as a conductor - no chemical or physical forces are able to destroy it. Treating thus with the merest initial of this latent power, who can say where its further unfoldment will lead the collective consciousness of Humanity?

In the present age, our science informs us, we perceive in the main only the lowest vibrations and inferior qualities of the Astral Light, because we are in the lower arc of our present cycle, and the energy of the life-wave is at its ebb. Mme. Blavatsky says of Plato's method of expression that he divides the intellectual progress of the universe during every cycle into fertile and barren periods . . . When those circulations, which Eliphas Levi calls 'currents of the Astral Light' in the universal Ether, . . take place in harmony with the divine spirit, our earth and everything pertaining to it enjoys a fertile period. The occult powers of plants, animals, and minerals magically sympathize with its superior natures, and the divine soul of man is in perfect intelligence with these inferior ones. But during the barren periods the latter lose all their magic sympathy, and the spiritual sight of the majority of mankind is so blinded as to lose every notion of the superior power of its own divine spirit. We are in a barren period. Ignoring our latent inherent forces, we drift in negative submission to the lower laws of Nature, suffer deprivation, want of thought, emotion, and volition, while the precious fluid, in mute anticipation, haunts our dreamless sleep, and awaits the dawning of a higher Consciousness.

Keely's Secrets

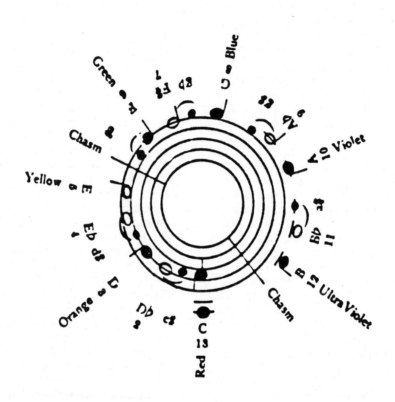

Mr. Plum's Visit to Keely's Laboratory

(sometime in late 1893)
from Dashed Against the Rock

"I have seen a spectacle I would have pronounced impossible according to all accepted theories of physics with which I am familiar. Without apparent exhibition of heat, electricity, or any other form of energy hitherto operated by man, I have seen a strong metallic wheel, weighing seventy-two pounds, in swift and steady revolution by the hour, and absolutely without cost. It is but a subsidiary engine, made and used simply to help equip with similar mysterious capacity of movement the large commercial engine by its side. And that is a most strange and complex mechanism, which perhaps no one but the inventor can even understand at present, and which, but for too frequent previous unauthorized fixing of dates, might be said to give promise of being itself in motion very soon. What is 'very soon' in such an undertaking? Another thirty years of patient, lonely plodding on this labyrinth path would be nothing, if then this explorer could reach his goal. How long after Franklin's kite did the world wait, and how many hundred great experimenters, before a dynamo engine kindled our lamps and whirred our wheels? Yet this solitary pioneer, grown half blind by groping in these dim intricacies so long, again and again hurled aside, broken and almost dieing by the terrific force with which he is seeking to cope, is met with the sneer, 'Why don't you do something?' He has done much, of ignorant, senseless, and cruel abuse. His immortality, however, is sure. For the world at length honors an honorable purpose, persistently pursued in a high undertaking. And he has already so enlarged the domain of human knowledge, he has lifted man into such a new world of facts, the truths his experiments unveil are so novel, suggestive, and inspiring, that whether all this is ever turned to practical account or not, his name will never die. But if he should turn out to be a prophet, if he is a seer, and does really discern a promised land of lightened toil into which mankind will eventually enter, even though he may not live to lead them in, then the world will gratefully build his tomb.

But the world asks, who is the witness that testifies so boldly to these surprising things? Is he competent and worthy of trust? The witness is not a capitalist, and he has no relations with investors, and is free to say that if Keely were to die tomorrow, it might be a hundred years before another mind would arise able to complete his work; if indeed, it is capable of being completed at all, which no one at present knows. Impelled by a life-long interest in the wonders of natural science, and honored by the personal friendship of Keely and a few of his advisers, I have followed the course of this investigator for years with the intensest interest and sincerest admiration. I spent more of my vacation this season in the Philadelphia laboratory, and saw greater wonders there, than in the Chicago Fair.

In whose judgement greater? Is a layman in physical science competent to judge in such matters? Confessedly not, on some questions. To most men the learned physicists speak an unknown tongue. Too profound for the common apprehension are the mathematical formulas, even, with which their works abound, though their theories and arguments are full of interest. And many would confess also that they can no more understand the ground of Keely's assertions concerning the number of millions of oscillations taking place in a given substance each second, nor his fluent discourse upon clustered thirds and introductory ninths, upon nodal transmit-

Universal Laws Never Before Revealed.. Keely's Secrets

ters and neutral centers, and upon streams and waves of polar and depolar influence. On these declarations this witness has no testimony to offer. In electrical science the world gladly accepts the terminology and the philosophy by which the specialists creditably seek to gain some practical apprehension of the elusive mystery with which they deal; elusive, for through all their technical terms and fine-spun theories, the futility of their endeavor to gain any exhaustive comprehension of it plainly appears. Experts have their field, but as Mr. Gladstone says of the Hebraist and the scientist in reference to the higher criticism and the scriptural cosmogony, 'their title to speak with authority is confined to their special province, nor are they inerrable there; and if we allow them to go beyond it, and still to claim their authority, when they are what is called at school "out of bounds," we are much to blame, and may suffer for our carelessness.' 'My contention is,' he says, 'that there is a ground which the specialist is not entitled to occupy in his character as a specialist, and on which he has no warrant for entering, except in so far as he is a just observer and reasoner in a much wider field.'

It is into this wider field of fact, where any can go whose general training fits him to be in any wise 'a just observer and reasoner,' that this witness deems it not improper to enter, especially as he follows in the wake of not a few who rank high as experts in mechanical engineering, in chemistry, in electricity, and other departments of superior culture. For, not only has Keely's legal counsellor, Charles B. Collier, an experienced patent lawyer, acute, cultured, and discerning, given him from the first his sincere and hearty support, but numbers of other men of honorable character and position, many of them eminent for scientific attainments, have given their unqualified testimony that Keely is an original and able investigator in an interesting and promising, though wholly novel, field - a wonder-worker, whose work seems to overturn certain accepted theories, and has puzzled and baffled their learned advocates. Yet, partly, perhaps, because Keely is not in the fraternity of

college bred men, but has educated himself (though his writings show familiarity with scholarly works), partly because his claims are so astonishing and his methods so incomprehensible, and partly because of premature predictions of a practical issue of his labors, and because also of unfortunate differences reported in respect to the business side of his enterprise, there are comparatively few men of public prominence who seem to be willing to be known as believers in the importance of his investigations, or even in the integrity of the man. At any rate, ridicule and contempt continue to be thrown at him and at the faithful friends who have long and nobly stood by him. Only lately a prominent journal intimated that 'an interruption of Keely's personal freedom' ought to result from what it calls his 'gigantic jugglery.' It is these unworthy flings, together with a sense of the public importance of the whole matter, which have prompted my voluntary and unsolicited testimony in the interest of truth.

For though scores of assemblies, comprising learned scientists, skillful engineers, and men of large success in the practical conduct of affairs, have witnessed various experiments by Keely during the past dozen years, and although their clear and positive statements of the interest and value of his researches have been repeatedly published in leading newspapers, with the names and professional titles of the witnesses given, yet the general public appears either to overlook or forget all these testimonies, and to be rudely impatient of every undertaking that does not immediately issue in commercial success. Seldom does any public journal refer to Keely in terms of appreciation and respect. As his labors have now reached some new results which only a few persons have witnessed, this further testimony is offered as information upon a matter of scientific interest, certainly, and with a possible bearing upon industrial advance.

What, then, is the testimony that the present witness has to give? After some ten years of acquaintance with Keely, and after personally seeing many of his experiments, 'witness deposeth and of one of the most beneficent revolutions in the history of human progress; a man of wonderful insight and truly amazing fertility of inventive genius in overcoming obstacles and in contriving appliances for attaining his mechanical ends; that he is dealing with and trying to employ in practical mechanics a force absolutely new among all the forces hitherto handled by man, although its presence in nature is affirmed by the theories of scientists, and demonstrated by various observed phenomena; a force of mysterious and awful energy, boundless in extent, and literally costless as the air. Electricity is subtle and powerful and illimitable in supply, but it requires constant and costly expenditure of energy to call it into exercise and keep it at work. This new force, beyond the curious and complicated mechanism which this wonderful wizard has contrived for it to employ, the harness he has fashioned for it to wear, seems to require but a few slight musical sounds, the sonorous vibrations of certain metallic appliances, to set it in motion, and then it will keep in motion - for all that at present appears, in steady, noiseless, and almost resistless motion - till the solid metals of which it is composed wear out.

What! one and all exclaim, is the absurdity of perpetual motion to be revived again? But the physicists tell us there is perpetual motion all around us in nature, intense and all-prevading, and always has been, since the hour 'when the morning stars sang together, and all the sons of God shouted for joy.' Here we touch the robe of the Infinite One, who 'upholdeth all things by the word of his power.' Of him the Un-erring One declared, 'My Father worketh hitherto and I work.' Aye, works unceasingly now, in the incessant and intense molecular vibration all the time going on in all matter; in the solid table by which we sit, in the firm granite of the building which encloses us. Action, motion in everything, by everything, everywhere, all the time, and swift, more nimble-footed sometimes than thought almost, but with such a soft and easy pace that no footfall is heard, no movement discerned save as we take observation by the distant heavenly orbs among which we all here on the earth are

traveling, hurled along our pathway over a thousand miles a minute. Movement of everything from here to there, and movement in everything while here or there. And so harmonious is the movement, on such delicate anti-friction cushions do the bearings rest, that it is all inaudible, save to that One alone whose ear discerns the music of the spheres - the spheres immensely great and infinitesimally small -

'Forever singing as they shine,
The hand that made us is divine.'

And only now, after thousands of years of unheard song, this great magician arises and strikes the chord of sympathy to which this vibrating force responds, and lo! it comes forth from its secret chambers like the mighty Genius unloosed by the Arabian fishermen from the copper flask, and waits on man to do his bidding, bending its tough sinews and plying its facile fingers to perform his humblest tasks.

And what proof can there be that this dream of poetry and fancy of story is in any degree an accomplished fact? Look and see. Here is a wooden table, sometimes covered by a heavy slab of glass. Standing on the glass or on the wood, and capable of being moved freely upon it, is a metal standard say a foot high, bearing a copper globe about a foot in diameter. Around the base of the standard project horizontally numbers of small metal rods a few inches long, of different sizes and lengths, vibrating like tuning forks when twanged by the fingers. In the hollow globe is a Chladni plate and various metal tubes, the relation which can be altered by turning a projection like a door-knob, on the outside of the globe, at the outer end of a small shaft, round and round to the right or left. This construction is called a 'sympathetic transmitter.' Some two or three feet distant on the table stands a movable metallic cylindrical case, some six inches by eight in size, composed of certain metal resonating tubes, and certain other metal fixtures. You take it all apart and see there is no magnet there. You place on top of this cylinder a small pocket compass, a brass cup of two inches in diameter with its glass face. The

Universal Laws Never Before Revealed.. Keely's Secrets

six inches by eight in size, composed of certain metal resonating tubes, and certain other metal fixtures. You take it all apart and see there is no magnet there. You place on top of this cylinder a small pocket compass, a brass cup of two inches in diameter with its glass face. The needle points north. From the periphery of the globe of the 'sympathetic transmitter' extends a wire of the size of a common knitting-needle, made of gold and silver and of platinum. The free end of this wire is now attached to the cylinder. The needle is still true to the pole. Then the vibrating rods are twanged, the knob is turned, and on a rude harmonicon trumpet for a moment or two certain sounds are made, when lo! the needle is invisible, it is whirling on its pivots fast. The operator talks of the variant length of waves and of a continuous stream, and in some instances it is half a minute, sometimes three minutes, before the needle comes to rest, and it has kept in swift revolution for many hours; but when it pauses it points no longer to the north, but to a particular part of the mechanism. You leave it there, and are busy with other wonders for an hour or so. Returning, you find the needle still points to its new master. You lift the compass off, and at once it resumes its normal position. You slowly lower it towards the silent cylinder, and when within an inch or two it obeys the new impulse again, and points as before. So also it veers from the north when you carry it near the knob of the copper globe. As Gladstone says, 'Our hands can lay hold of truths that our arms cannot embrace,' and though it takes a physicist to comprehend this miracle, any careful observer can apprehend it, and, after seeing it repeated many times, if he is measurably well read, is competent to testify that here is a new, subtle, silent, continuous influence, and that it is called into exercise in connection with certain brief musical sounds.

Look again. On this rude harmonicon trumpet this magician blows through a small window into the next room towards a common zither some ten feet distant, held upright on a table by a small standard composed of a group of metal tubes. The two musical instruments have been carefully attuned to each other. Attached to the back of the zither is a common silk thread loosely hanging and extending some eight feet away, where it is tied to a movable framework of half-inch iron rods, supporting and bracing in position, on an isolated table of glass, a metal globe, fifteen inches in diameter, capable of turning freely in either direction, on its axis, which bears inside the globe certain resonant tubes and plates, the table standing at an angle of 45 degrees from the face of the zither. Louder sounds the horn, till in a minute or two the metal globe begins to revolve. The horn stops, the globe stops. Again the horn resounds, again the globe turns, and the stronger and more continuous the blast, the more swiftly whirls the globe. You snip the thread apart with your scissors, and the ear of the globe has grown dull; no sound can awake it to motion again. Does a man need to be an expert in physics after he has seen that marvel repeated a few times, and has moved all that apparatus freely hither and thither, to testify that the rapid revolution of that metal globe was not caused by compressed air, coming in concealed tubes from a hidden reservoir, or that a silk thread is not the highway usually cast up for electricity to travel?

But these are philosophical toys. What about an engine with power to help human toil?

I have in my study a paper weight - a disc, said to be composed of an alloy of three metals. It looks like steel, measures two and a half inches by three-quarters of an inch, weighs about a pound, is enclosed in a brass ring, and exhibits no magnetic power. I am told that shut up in a glass chamber and connected with the wire which seemed to affect the compass, it absorbed some seven pints of hydrogen gas. The story runs that it was also rapidly whirled by a steam engine a certain number of hours, still in connection with the apparatus from which seemed to flow that subtle influence which the needle of the compass obeyed. Whatever may be thought of this, it is a fact that the disc thus 'vitalized in its atomic or molecular constitution' adheres to the under side of a certain metallic resonant structure as if held there by magnetic attraction, and also supports a weight hung to itself of over two hundred and thirty pounds. Dissociated from the peculiar vibrating apparatus, it falls like any other heavy body, and though that apparatus attracts the disc, even with the attached weights, it is incapable of attracting anything else; it will not support the smallest iron filing. Here then is a strong pulling power in exercise in certain circumstance when two bodies are in contact. Can it pull bodies together which are not in contact?

I see before me on a table a glass jar, ten inches in diameter and forty-eight inches high, filled with water. At the bottom lie three metal balls like the one I hold in my hand, which weighs about two pounds. The jar has a metal cap to which is attached the gold and platinum wire reaching from the copper globe. I am told each ball, like every mass of matter, has its peculiar musical chord. I am reminded of well-known facts of sympathetic vibration; *e.g.*, a large mill trembling in response to the note of a neighboring waterfall, and only quieted and rendered safe by building on an addition, changing its musical chord. And now again the rods are twanged, the knob is turned, the trumpet sounds and keeps sounding till, in a moment or two, I see one ball begin to sway from right to left, then slowly leave the bottom of the jar and rise through the water till with a bump it strikes the metal cap, rebounds a few inches and comes to rest in contact with it on the surface of the water. Still the horn blows, and by this time the second ball responds in like manner, and then the third. Then the music ceases, and we turn to other experiments, but as long as I stayed in the shop that day something made that metal swim. My companion said he had often seen the weights brought slowly down, or held midway, as shown by photographs, by sounding other chords. On the top of the jar lay certain pieces of metal. Keely said, 'Do not remove those. I once did that, and crash went the balls through the bottom of my jar.' Now here was a pulling power acting at a distance of four feet, not capable of lifting the weights

through the air, but before all eyes lifting them through water. Can this pulling power turn a wheel?

Here is a wheel of stout metal weighting, as stated, seventy-two pounds, free to move either way on its stationary axis. Its hub is a cylinder containing certain resonant tubes parallel to the axis. It has eight spokes, each carrying one of the 'vitalized discs' at its outer end, the face of the disc at right angles with the spoke. There is no rim to the wheel, but there is a stationary metal rim some six inches wide and thirty-two inches in diameter, within which the wheel turns without touching it. This rim carries on its inner surface nine similar discs, and on the outside, attached to each disc, a resonating cylinder. The requisite amount of the metallic volume of this cylinder is obtained by enclosing in its tubes a few cambric needles, more or less as required, and curiously enough, some of these needles at length become magnetic. Attached to this engine is a gold and platinum wire, some ten feet in length, running through the small window to the copper globe in the other room, where sits the man who has fashioned all this. He twangs the rods of the sympathetic transmitter on the table at his side, he turns its knob, the musical instruments sound for a moment, and peering through the window along the line of the wire his face lights up with a smile of triumph. He settles back in his chair, and all is still. That wheel at the end of the wire is in rapid revolution before your eyes. You turn and look with amazement upon Orpheus returned to earth again and outdoing his fabled exploits of old. For by the enchantment of the subtle harmonies he evokes, too fine for human ear to catch, you see the untamed forces of nature obey his behest; that most constant of all things, the magnetic needle, you see charmed into fickleness by his magic spell; you see balls of iron swim; you see insensate matter - as you thought it, but sensitive now to his call - leap forward into instant rotation, continuous and swift. Long we stand around that flying wheel. The friend who photographed it at rest again levels his camera upon it. In vain; its spokes can-

Universal Laws Never Before Revealed.. Keely's Secrets

not tarry long enough to be caught by his snare. It is still as death, and almost as mysterious. We listen to long dissertations upon the reason for the relative position of the eight discs on the wheel and the nine on the stationary rim, and how the adjustment can be so altered that, instead of a revolution, there will be a violent oscillation back and forth. We are shown the corresponding wheel and the rim of the large engine close by, which is to bear the discs not singly, but in groups, the steel resonating drums with their circles of tubes inside, and thirty-five inch Chladni plate underneath the 'sympathetic transmitter' on top; the extra wheel bearing on its spokes cylindrical cases, each filled solid with a hundred thin-carved plates of steel, to get the utmost superficial area, we are told, and it is all so utterly beyond comprehension, that we can see no reason why it should have been made as it is, or how any one can be sure it will ever run. But we turn around and look again on that noiseless wheel, still running rapidly all alone, and confess we should have said the same thing about that. And we are inclined then to trust the word of the inventor when he says the running of the smaller insures the running of the larger; that the wheel you see spinning so fast cannot be stopped by any force except one that would tear it into fragments, unless with thumb and finger you loosen that golden wire along which 'the stream of sympathetic vibration' is said to flow, and that there is no reason why the wheel should not keep in motion till the bearings wear out.

I say nothing now of the wonders of which other witnesses can speak, and which are said to have appeared in the slow progress this incomprehensible man has been making all these years; of a pressure obtained from the disintegration of water by vibration of twenty thousand pounds to the square inch; of a slowly revolving drum which went no slower when winding tightly upon itself a stout inch and a half rope fastened to a beam, and no faster when the rope parted under the strain; of the disintegration of rock into impalpable powder; of raising heavy weights by aid of a 'vibratory lift,' recalling the 'negative gravi-ty' of our modern story-teller.

The engine you have been looking upon requires as part of itself for some mysterious purpose certain heavy tubular copper rings. Skillful artisans failed in various endeavors, by electrical deposit and otherwise, to make them right. The inventor contrived machinery for bending into semicircles sections of copper tube, one and a half inch bore, three-eights of an inch thick, forcing a steel ball through them to keep the tube in shape. To make a ring, he placed two of those half-circles together and joined the ends in some way (without heat), by what he calls sympathetic attraction, so the resonant properties of the ring are satisfactory, and though you see the line of union, the two parts cannot be severed. You see one of these rings, some fifteen inches in diameter, hanging by block and tackle from the ceiling, and lashed to the lower half swings a big iron ball weighing five hundred and fifty pounds, and there it has swung for weeks. Has the man who has done simply that, and done it merely to furnish a subsidiary adjunct to his main contrivance, won no place among the great artificers? Is it worthy business to revile him as a swindling charlatan? The end is not yet. We shall see what we shall see, or some one will. One thing, however, we see clearly now, and that is that John Worrell Keely deserves the esteem and admiration of his fellow-men. Who does not hope that he has solid grounds for the persistent belief which has been his star of hope these many years; that a merciful Providence is about to confer a new boon upon the suffering industries of mankind; that the time at length has come when man is wise enough to fashion and strong enough to handle the beneficent gift of a costless motor to ease the burdens of human toil?

Wise enough and strong enough, perhaps, some may say, but is man trusty? For the question has arisen whether a force of such fearful energy as some of these experiments disclose can safely be entrusted to such a being as man, who can destroy as well as build. But why should man have been set to discover and harness it? 'I take great comfort in God,' said James Russell

Lowell, in one of his recently published letters, 'I think. ... He would not let us get at the match-box as carelessly as he does unless he knew that the frame of his universe was fireproof.'

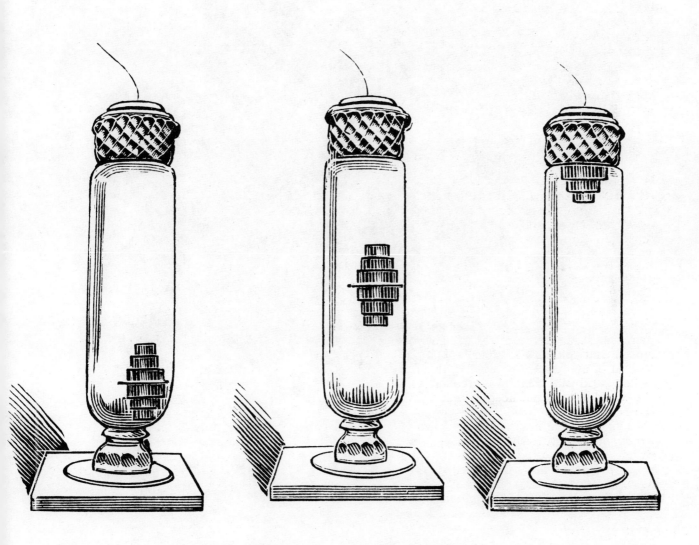

GRAVITY OVERCOME

EXPERIMENTAL MODELS FOR RESEARCHING.

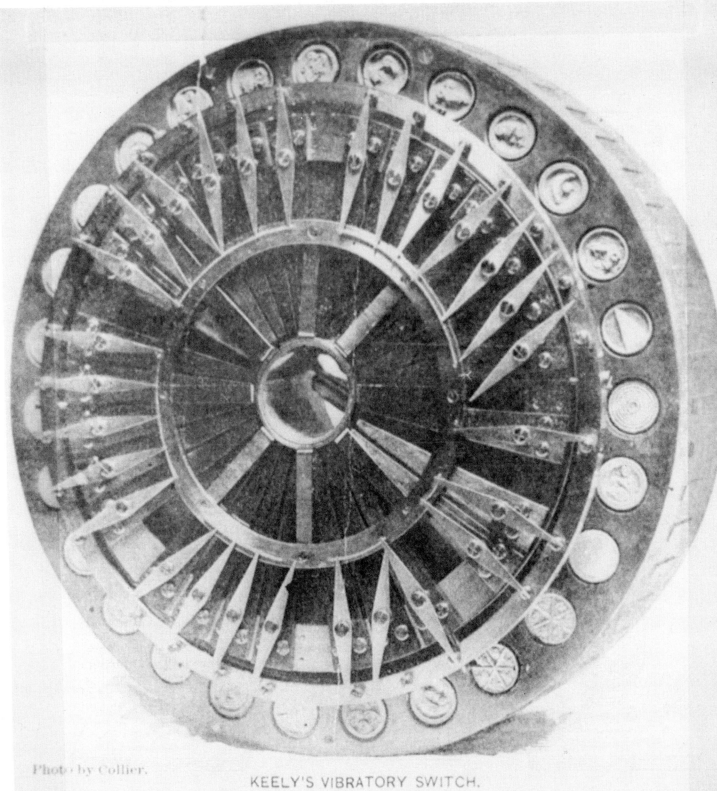

KEELY'S VIBRATORY SWITCH.

No one understands it but himself.

Pyramids, Telescopes and Light

John Ernst Worrell Keely
from Dashed Against the Rock

A building, pyramidal in shape, two hundred feet high, one hundred feet at the base, and having at the apex a disc with a minute aperture in its center, and a triple combination of reflectors, which must concentrate upon one center which must be focalized upon the minute aperture in the disc, - the image being received at the base of the pyramid upon a white surface prepared to receive it, - would yield results beyond the dreams of the most sanguine astronomer of the present day. The distinctness of the image taken would be the most wonderful part of the phenomenon, and the size of the magnification would be limited only to the diameter of the base of the pyramid. This probably explains the great Egyptian pyramid, with its circular opening through its center and cavity at the bottom. The apparatus from its summit has probably been destroyed during some of the many ravages to which the land of strange vicissitudes has so frequently been subjected. The Great Pyramid proves that, among the ancient Egyptians, the knowledge of astronomy was amazingly great, although they need not necessarily have known of the modern telescope to have obtained it. The almost impossible labor of making lenses is done away with in this system, which embraces also a microscope on a similar principle without lenses, far superior to anything now in use.

Vibrations necessary to the production of colors are very high, reaching to millions of vibrations per second. The true relation between the vibration and the color can only be a harmonic one, as colors commence in the millions and end not lower than in trillions of vibrations per second. The conditions essential of this class of phenomena are, first, a condition relating to the structure in which they take place, free from all ex-traneous vibrations; *the experimenter's presence even influences to a great extent the motions of the molecules* used in the experiments. A bath is employed, arranged so that light rays can be projected upon it at certain angles, and from that upon a screen. The bath must have what are termed centers of association and concentration, and suspended across its surface in such a manner that the centers approach very near the surface of the liquid, which is preferably water, whose surface must be free from all films. Upon this is dropped a single drop of naptha dissolved in ether, which constantly spreads over the surface and gradually evolves most beautiful variations of color. The vibrations are transmitted from an instrument capable of producing vibrations of varying intensity and pitch, across the line of resonating centers, nine in number. The first center shows a *light* straw color, condensing about the center; the second shows a *very dark* straw color; the third exhibits an orange red; the fourth, a bluish red; the fifth is largely green. The entire gamut ranges from a very light yellow to a dark blue. The theory is that the vibrations produced gather certain numbers of the molecules together about the centers, which represent different ranges of motion, and which by the color evolved affords a demonstration of a certain connection between that vibration and the colors it educes. Under different conditions, using films suspended in the air, and light passing through these films under polarization, (polarized light) the vibrations influence the molecules in the film, producing again exhibitions of varying colors when projected upon a screen. Experiments of this kind are most difficult, on account of the unstable conditions found everywhere.

Keely's Secrets

DIAGRAM 1.

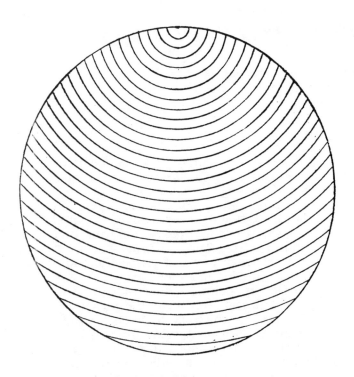

External View of Atom.

DIAGRAM 3.

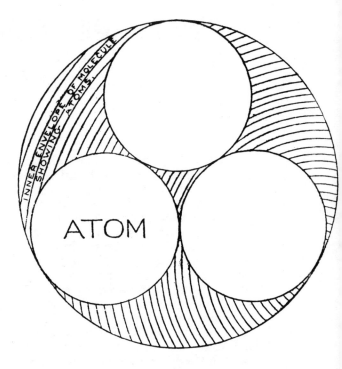

Showing Positions of Atoms in Inner Envelope.

DIAGRAM 2.

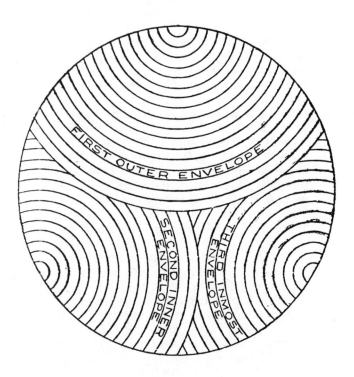

Showing Sections of the Three Envelopes.

DIAGRAM 4.

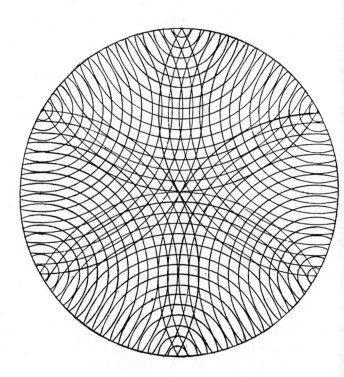

Showing Lines of Interference of Triple Envelope.

Levitation

John Ernst Worrell Keely
from Dashed Against the Rock

A small instrument, having three gyroscopes as a principal part of its construction, is used to demonstrate the facts of aerial navigation. These gyroscopes are attached to a heavy, inert mass of metal, weighing about one ton. The other part of the apparatus consists of tubes, enclosed in as small a space as possible, being clustered in a circle. These tubes, represent certain chords, which were coincident to the streams of force acting upon the planet, focalizing and defocalizing upon its neutral center. The action upon the molecular structure of the mass lifted was based upon the fact that each molecule in the mass possessed a north and south pole, - more strictly speaking, a positive and negative pole, - situated through the center, formed by the three atoms which compose it. No matter which way the mass of metal is turned, the poles of the molecule point undeviatingly to the polar center of the earth, acting almost exactly as the dipneedle when uninfluenced by extraneous conditions, electrical and otherwise. The rotation of the discs of the gyroscopes produces an action upon the molecules of the mass to be lifted, reversing their poles, causing repulsion from the earth in the same way as like poles of a magnet repel each other. This repulsion can be diminished and increased according as the mechanical conditions are operated. By operating the three discs, starting them at full speed, then touching two of them, so as to bring them, according to the tone they represented by their rotation, to a certain vibratory ratio, the weight then slowly sways from side to side leaves the floor, rising several feet in the air, remaining in that position, and as the discs gradually decrease their speed of rotation the weight sinks to the floor, settling down as lightly as thistle-down. Where one molecule can be lifted, there need be no limit as to the number in a structure that may be operated upon as easily as one. The vessel in contemplation, the aerial navigator, will be over two hundred feet long, over sixty feet in diameter, tapering at both ends to a point, made of polished steel, and will be capable of being driven under the power of depolar repulsion, at the rate of three hundred miles an hour. It can be far more easily controlled than any instrument now in use for any phase of transit. Another very remarkable feature connected with this system of aerial navigation, is that the vessel is not buoyed up or floated in the air through the medium of the air, so that if there were no atmosphere it would float just as readily; hence, under mechanical conditions most certainly capable of production, involving massive strength of resistance to interstellar vacuity this can be made capable of navigating even the remote depth of space, positions between planets where polarity changes being controlled by other adjuncts of concentration for that purpose.

Safely enclosed within this structure, a man possessing the chemical knowledge these new laws give, with sufficient supply of material from which to make oxygen, by the enormously increased rate of speed attained by such navigator where atmospheric friction is avoided, the time occupied in traveling from one planet to another would be amazingly brief, and one can travel to other planets in this system of worlds as easily as the same ship could navigate the depths of the ocean.

The great obstacle hitherto preventing the solution of this problem has been the strength of structure needed under conditions above presented. With this knowledge of matter, the size of structure is unimportant; the heaviest can be as easily controlled as the lightest.

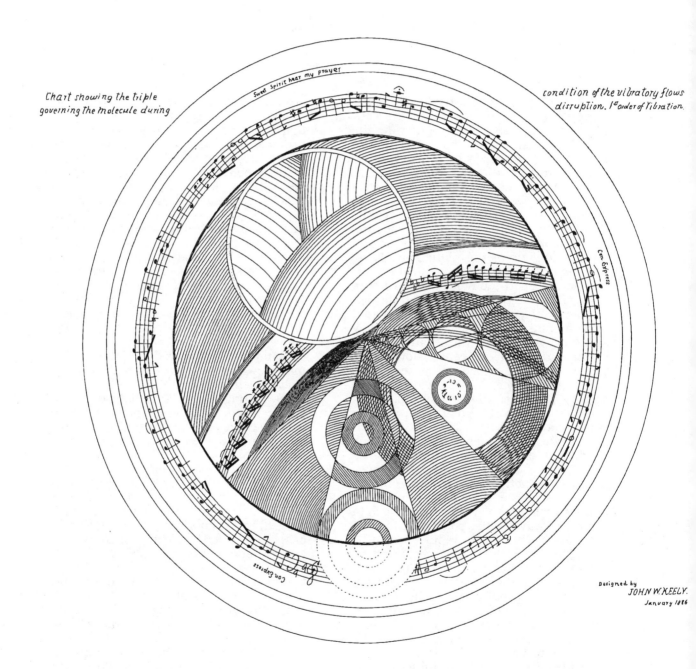

Chart showing the triple governing the molecule during

condition of the vibratory flows disruption. 1st order of vibration.

Sweet Spirit hear my prayer

Con Express

Con Express

Designed by
JOHN W. KEELY.
January 1886

Amplitude of Force

John Ernst Worrell Keely
from Dashed Against the Rock

The amplitude of vibrations is directly increased or diminished by increasing or diminishing the size or number of creative aggregates.

The human EGO, subject to the forces of love or hate, kindness or cruelty, forgiveness or revenge, is according to circumstances ruled or dominated by these forces in proportion to their intensity.

The intensity of a force is precisely proportionate to the number of units vibrating at that particular pitch. For instance, let fear assail one man, and according to its intensity will be the effect; but let a crowd of men experience fear, see the result in the augmentation of fear, though its source be relatively insignificant. A curtain in a theater, for example, takes fire; one or two persons, cowardly at heart, become afraid through the dominance of the purely animal instinct of bodily preservation; there is actually no real danger, but these two or three persons are sufficient to arouse the unreasoning dread which lies latent in every breast, with perhaps a very few remarkable exceptions. The fire burns nobody; but blind fear, which is extremely contagious among people mutually sympathetic, by reason of the rapidity with which etheric waves transmit all feeling, occasions a terrible panic, during which many severe accidents and many instances of fierce cruelty occur, all because of this sympathetic transfer of feeling starting from one or two augmented or intensified fear-centers, each person being a center emanating the feeling of fear. Were there no counteracting centers of influence in an audience, radiating contrary feelings, the result of a panic would be the total bodily extinction of a very large percentage of the assembled multitude.

Thus the human race is immersed in forces whose intensity is vast in proportion to the number of EGOS adding each its quota to the already intense vibration, tending either to love or hate, kindness or cruelty, timidity or bravery. Those who intensify the force of cruelty in the place where they reside, may be strengthening a murder's hand to strike the deadly blow in a distant land. This result is brought about through the agency of etheric waves, which transmit forces with undiminished intensity even to uncalculated distances. This phenomenon may be termed *transympathetic*.

They who feel that force called *love*, which on higher planes is known as *sympathy*, thrill with waves of force which are already strong, augmenting them or increasing their intensity. They who indulge such sentiments and encourage such forces may stop the falling hand on evil sped.

In order to protect ourselves effectually from becoming the dispensers or propagators of deadly force, we must consciously and deliberately relate ourselves by resolute determination, to awaken within us such centers only as are concordantly sympathetic with all force radiating in the interest of universal goodwill, thereby aiding the establishment of universal brotherhood.

All ye who feel a longing for a better life or nobler existence draw to yourselves streams of force which they alone feel who have attuned their bodies to the higher harmonies. For a moment you feel as they who dwell perpetually in communion with higher harmonies, living immersed in that higher force; they are the true heirophants, and you, O neophytes, struggling to attain the goal which they have reached, do not despair though at present you find yourselves unable to maintain this high altitude for long together. Though you fall many times, be not discouraged, for as yet your organisms and all their centers of resonation are not yet concordant to the focalized vibrations of the higher harmonies; being still related to the mass, you are drawn again and again into the whirlpool of the vibrations which affect the mass, for these you cannot resist. But know that you can change all this rapidly or slowly as your purpose is steadily intense or vacillating.

With the cessation of your lower desires comes the cessation of the action upon you of the lower forces; the resonating centers which formerly distributed this force, no longer active, become latent and are absorbed back to an embryonic condition.

Let him realize fully the transient character of his own personality and contrast therewith his eager longing to know the immortal.

Every man contains, developed or embryonic, all conditions of the Infinite; therefore no height is too great to reach. Impossibility is a meaningless word to the man who apprehends the fathomless contents of his own nature. Thou comest here, O man, with the instrument thou hast graduated in thy many past existences; how few of thy chord-settings, if thou art numbered with the many, respond to the higher harmonies! Universal unity or fraternity has been absorbed to almost embryonic conditions by the prevalence of material self-regard. Charity has been rendered almost latent, that beautiful chord-setting found even in the lowest forms of creation - LOVE, the dominant chord of the cycles. Love has an amplitude of action in the brute which may well make the selfish man ashamed, but until the crust of selfishness is broken through, the beauty of love is obscured, and though it exists all about him, the poor blind egotist has no eye to discern it. The centers of love, brotherhood, charity, voice their music loud and clear, yet the masses will not listen. I do not mean the immortal EGO when I say man will not listen; I refer to the personality which is the resultant of

all the ages of action in this, now rapidly closing, cycle.

You who exist to-day, to-morrow would exist no longer in your present personalities did you but dare to yield to these higher harmonies. I say YIELD because it is a *yielding* process for this personality. In a moment your outer life would end, and you, the warrior, would enter peace.

The immortal EGO is an entity of which man can become thoroughly conscious while here on earth, but to arrive at this consciousness necessitates the entire abandonment of all the petty considerations involved in the transient and subordinate EGO, which is the only self of which the unenlightened man is conscious. Let him who desires to reach this inner consciousness enter his inner sanctuary, wherever that sanctuary may be; it matters not whether it be his own chamber, the open field, the mountain top, the seashore, the stately cathedral, or the humble village chapel. Let him realize fully the transient character of his own personality and contrast therewith his eager longing to know the immortal. Let him concentrate his whole consciousness upon his personality, fully arousing all his personal conditions as a distinct individual; then with all the aspiration of which this personality is capable, let him beseech of the immortal EGO - which is eternal and does not incarnate, but overshadows all incarnations, waiting until one is formed capable of illumination, to whom it may reveal itself - to consider him worthy of illumination, and according to his preparedness to receive illumination will it then be granted. He who asks this, knows not what he asks; for were the prayer answered, life henceforth for such an one would be a weary round, as Hamlet says: "to-morrow and to-morrow and to-morrow brings in this weary round of life"; for, having seen the glory of this immortal EGO, all else seems so base, so commonplace and mean, so inglorious, that oftentimes the personality has utterly collapsed when thrown back from the radiant vision of this glorious immortal entity possessed by all alike, though scarcely dreamed of by any save the very few who, discontented with the ignorance and emptiness of terrene existence, aspire to know the great reality of the supernal. As the incarnations of every entity, passing through certain orders of experience through numerous lives, inevitably culminate in this moment of conscious realization of the immortal entity; the Buddha says: "All shall reach the sunlit snows."

You who through your daily life move on unthinking, not caring, inactive, you shall hear when your supplications reach this high entity, *"Lo! thou didst not even try, knowing that even thy failures were acceptable to me."*

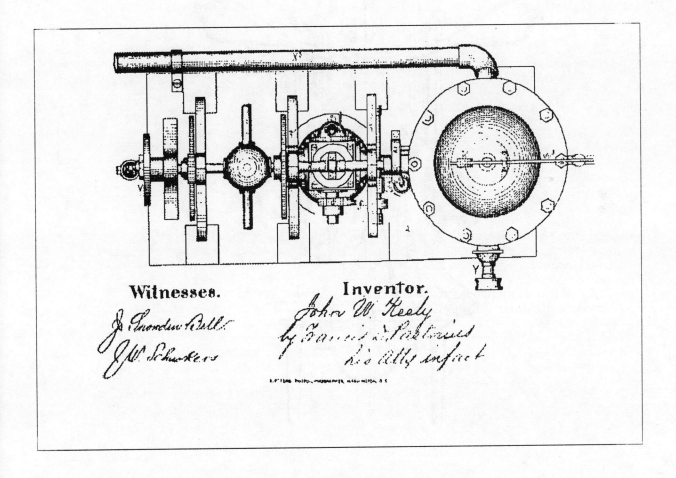

Top view looking down on the original Keely motor.
Scanned image from original patent drawings.

Front view looking straight on the original Keely motor.
Scanned image from original patent drawings.

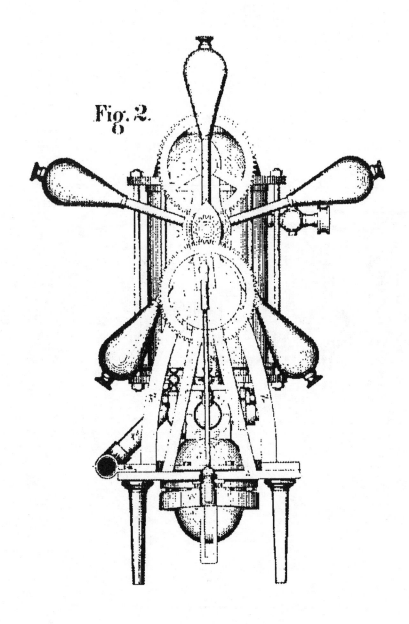

Fig. 2.

The Chord Settings of Life

John Ernst Worrell Keely
from Dashed Against the Rock

Question: "By what term shall we define that force which, when differentiated, expresses itself on the lower planes of manifestation as charity, self-forgetfulness, compassion, and the tendency of all illuminated ones to association in universal brotherhood?"

Keely's reply: "I hold that ONE SUPREME FORCE, which we may term the incomprehensible, holds within itself all these sublime qualities, as an octave embraces its many tones. This force expressed in the human organism, has what may be termed CONCORDANT CHORDSETTINGS dominated by one or other of the above-named differentiations of this supreme force.

Now let us ask what makes human beings differ the one from the other. The reason we give for this striking natural phenomenon is that in one individual these chord-settings are allowed full amplitude in action, while in others they are suppressed, and by suppression rendered latent. To illustrate: we will picture a beggar asking alms of a richly dressed gentleman, who passes by entirely oblivious of the suppliant's needs; but here the wonderful law of sympathetic action intercedes, making the wealthy individual comprehend the necessitous condition of the pauper.

At this point the *ego* enters the chamber of the ordeal; here, in commonplace life, in everyday surroundings, man is tried; this is *initiation*.

The well-to-do man goes on his way, not caring to stop, hurried perchance by the urgency of worldly affairs; the chord-setting representing that differentiation of infinite force called by us *compassion*, acting upon its concordant chord-setting, loudly proclaims to the *ego* what is right action, and the opportunity passing when it should be seized, powerfully exerts its force against the will of the personality that would suppress its action.   Here is where the battle is fought; simple though the illustration may appear, it forcibly sets forth the actual conflict continually waging between divine wisdom and mortal error, carelessness, and ignorance.

The man of wealth and position goes on, perhaps, for some distance, the battle all the while continuing; finally, he stops and turns back, he yields to the dominating influence of that chord-setting; he gives the beggar alms and goes on his way with the skies bright above him; he has won a battle he will not have to fight again. Understand that victory is won, *not by the giving of alms*, but by *yielding to that divine force-differentiation.* If this chord-setting had not retained its dominance, it would only require a few instances of the above type to render it latent, and when latent the person is no longer amenable to influences calculated to arouse compassion. In like manner, other centers may be rendered latent by repeated suppression, until we find a person so dead to all appeals from the various chord-settings that his whole course in life is represented by the sum-total of the antagonisms internally produced;   results proving this are seen everyday.

You ask why do people commit such blunders and perform such acts as they do, all the while seemingly unable to help themselves.   The reason is that they have rendered latent these centers which otherwise would have given them the power to rightly control their deeds instead of being, as they now are, dominated exclusively by the forces of aggregated matter which we usually call the self-will of the outer personality, as distinquished from the distinctly humane individuality which always responds to

70

Universal Laws Never Before Revealed.. Keely's Secrets

a divine appeal.

It can be readily seen from this example that a man can mould himself practically as he chooses; though he may have to encounter many obstacles erected by himself in past periods of earthly existence, as he comes to earth anew with these chord-settings latent, or developed to the extent they were so, at the conclusion of his earth-embodiment; a man has therefore only to carefully examine the condition of these settings to learn whether they are latent or developed; if latent, he knows well that if he yields to the dominance of the chord-settings of the supreme force - and he needs no monitor other than these to instruct him, their voice being loud-toned, full, strong, deep, and high - to carry him on to the consummation of his highest ideal, their suppression leading him to the lowest condition in which we behold that section of humanity which is dominated by the action of the blind forces inherent in aggregated matter, - forces which are at all times powerfully and intimately associated with everyone who possess a material body.

The work of arousing to activity the latent chord-settings is sometimes equivalent to giving birth to an entirely new condition in the person, the intellect and the imagination having to actively cooperate in the endeavor to produce even the minutest degree of activity.

In such persons their hardest experiences may be the greatest benefit to them, if rightly taken; for it is through certain orders of experience - not unattended with suffering - that these centers are powerfully acted upon. The foregoing illustrations of the merchant and the beggar introduces one in whom the action of the centers is to a certain degree active.

In experiences where the emotions are *intensely* aroused their action is far greater, and we may see the result of the conflict, in the event of a person of hitherto unnoticeable traits being developed either into a person of crabbed, irritable disposition or into one of considerable moral beauty and attractiveness, and all because a center hitherto dormant has been powerfully aroused or more completely suppressed.

Who knows but that all the varieties of disposition we see expressed every hour in the persons of those about us is due to HABIT; in the case of the sweet and lovable, to the habit of constant yielding to the dominance of what we may term super-celestial force, while on the other hand, the sour and morose are but the suffering victims of their own habitual suppression of these same divine centers of radiation, which are continually dispersing the divine energy focalized upon them throughout the eternal ages of unwasting life.

Concerning *circumstance* let it be most emphatically stated that they never need be permitted to suppress the upward tendencies of our nature; that they have, like *all* experiences, and opportunity contained within them, to act either for the more perfect dominance of the celestial or the terrestrial, none need deny; but it rests with every individual to *embrace* or *reject* opportunities as he will, to accept the honors of initiation or undergo the regrets consequent upon failure.

Only the keen, sensitive soul can understand when these opportunities come and go, for only such have won this right by successive victories gained through yielding to these celestial streams of force, and the conqueror over himself is the victor *always*, though he may seem sometimes to yield obedience to a force greater than himself. Let the supreme desire of each one of us ever be that these resonating centers, permanent throughout measureless cycles of time, graduated by the all-wise builders of the universe to perfect concordance with the Divine Force which is in essence incomprehensible, - shall vibrate to fullest amplitude of action; so shall we each escape from the pains, sorrows, and disappointments associated with their suppression and *inevitably* resulting from it."

71

The Dynamics of Mind

Henry Wood
reprinted from ARENA, #LXIII February, 1895

In the light of recent psychical demonstrations, it has been said that thoughts are things, perhaps a more exact statement would be that they are forces.

In physical science, the present trend of teaching is distinctly from the former accepted atomic basis, which included the solidity and potency of matter, towards a hypothesis in which energy is regarded as the underlying principle of all phenomena. Thus the atom, which has never been discovered, and is not likely to be, is no longer recognized as the real unit in the physical economy, energy being now accepted as the primal starting point.

Manifestations to our senses, which we call light, heat and sound, are only differentiated modes of vibratory forces. Primal energy, unitary in its essence, and always conserved in the aggregate, takes on, to us, one of several qualitative appearances, according to the form of its waves, or rather, perhaps, the rapidity of its vibrations. Under certain circumstances and through the action of laws yet imperfectly understood, these various modes of manifestation are interchangeably transformed in constant repetition.

Modern science has accepted the conclusion that vibration is a universal law, and the recognition of this fact is the key which is unlocking mysteries and solving phenomena hitherto unexplainable. It has furnished an all-comprehensive working hypothesis. Beginning with an inter-molecular rhythm of inconceivable rapidity in all bodies, even those that appear to be solid and at rest, its domain of wave movements extends through all space, and its impulses are coursing in every conceivable direction. They are ceaseless and endless. The cosmos may truly be said to be "all of a quiver."

The basic medium of these enumerable wavy motions is undoubtedly the universal ether, the nature of which can only be dimly conjectured through its multiform manifestations. Who can say that this is not the boundless common meeting ground between the spiritual and the material? Unaccountably enough, the myriads of vibrations of different kinds and velocities that are sweeping through space do not appear to disturb or neutralize each other in the least. There is a clear path for all.

These late developments in physical science, which have only been hinted at in the most general of terms, carry with them necessary inferences and correlations, the scope of which can yet hardly be imagined. The dematerialization, or perhaps what may even be called the *spiritualization of physics*, as a science, is one of the marked logical tendencies. There is also a growing demonstration and conviction of the deceptive and utterly unreliable nature of sensuous appearances. Science, before finally accepting any proposition as proven, has always insisted upon material and mathematical demonstration. This is well in its place but it is not all, in fact it is only the lower and cruder side.

Matter, as formerly regarded, seems to be consciously melting into mind or spirit. It is no longer inert or dead, but instinct with life. Its transformations are ceaseless and mysterious. Can any one explain just how and why a visible solid can take the form of an invisible gas and *vice versa*?

The theoretical boundary line between the immaterial and the material is getting very faint if not actually disappearing. Let us drop our crude, childish materialism and rise easily and reasonably to the grand conception that differ-

72

entiated forces are being traced back, even through the methods of the physicist to the *One Primal Energy* - INFINITE MIND. The veils which in our infantile development we have hung around external nature are growing so attenuated that we can almost discern with unaided vision the active operation of Supreme Intelligence, Goodness and Beneficence.

All profound discernment and analogy lead back to the grand fundamental premise, that behind all manifestations, energy is One, that it is an Intelligent Energy, and is therefore Omni-present Mind. Monisn, or the inherent unity of all things, is the growing inspiration of science. It is thereby confirming the impressions already received through the delicate vision of the unfolded interior faculties. Paul's immortal aphorism, that "in Him we live and move and have our being" has waited long for scientific endorsement, but it is apparently soon to be realized. We behold the universe as soulful and not mechanical. This is no ancient superstitious pantheism resurrected. Rather the Deity is infinitely honored as compared with any and all past human concepts.

If all energy, in its last analysis, be Intelligent Mind, and vibration the universal method, we may reasonably infer that human mind or volition, being in, and a part of the whole, should form no exception in the working plan of its orderly activities. If essential, potential and ideal man be the "offspring," "image" and manifestor of God, nothing unlike it could be normal. As the former ideals of a Deity, localized, personified, changeable and in every way unconsciously limited, are slowly replaced by the transcendent ideal of the unconditioned "All in All," the interrelation of all things, to and in God, is being grasped. When man refines, enlarges and elevates his consciousness of Divinity, he does the same for his own deeper and generic spiritual nature, which though temporarily obscured, is in reality, himself. If God be spirit, man, His reflection and likeness, must also be spirit and not dust. By a traditional and distorted self consciousness he has thought himself to be a poor, sinful, *material* being, and the formative power of his mental specification has

externally actualized his model. He *is* mind or spirit, but his physical expression, which should be of ideal quality, outpictures his perverted estimate of himself. Not recognizing his true being, he has drawn a mistaken outline and then naturally filled it out. He has thus unwittingly hidden his own potential and divine forces, though they are still within. The mirror of false consciousness has reflected a doleful image which he has seriously taken for himself.

The purer and higher trend of science is characterized by a gradual refinement and immateriality. The laboratory should become a sanctuary, for in it are gained glimpses of the Eternal. Man himself is being more truly interpreted as the highest expression of divinity. He is a concrete manifestation of the One Mind, finite, but with unlimited possibilities. He is inconceivably great, though ignorantly unaware of it. But a significant indication of his growing consciousness of the possession of supernal power is found in the recent discovery of the dynamic and formative potency of his thought. The Infinite Uncreate is the primal and universal energy, but man is its embodier and manifestor. His mental forces cannot create *de novo*, but they can mould, utilize and express. The unfolded soul having developed a self-consciousness of its transcendent power, intelligently sends out its own vibrations from its own center. Conforming to the divine plan and chord, it becomes a reflection, or secondary radiator of rhythms which are concordant with the Original.

We are logically led to the conclusion that the recent recognition of the potency and utility of the projective vibration of thought, is an unprecedented and immense step in scientific achievement, human unfoldment and spiritual evolution. Man is finding his rightful dominant place in nature, in the arcana of soul force and expression, and in his relation to the Infinite.

Before considering specifically the dynamic relations between mind and mind, it may be well to note briefly these relations as they exist between a human mind and its physical counterpart, Man is mind, and this statement implies that the physical organism is not man, but only his visible index or expression. To attempt to prove this is like demonstrating an axiom, but yet mankind at large indicate by their action that they do not practically believe it. Nine-tenths of the care, labor, and attention of the world is bestowed upon the body and its gratification, or upon those subordinate mental powers, the product of which will command the greatest commercial value. Most of the prevailing systems of education, so called, have the same end more or less directly in view. The trained intellect, including not only technical and professional attainment, but also the powers of literary, poetic and dramatic ability, eloquence and wit, are largely rated and valued on an economic and material basis. To train, control and uplift the mind, and develop its higher faculties for its own sake, and that of others, is not common. The world is still endeavoring to "live by bread alone."

Prevailing systems of philosophy, science, theology, therapeutics, sociology and charity, including Darwinian evolution, all proceed upon the general hypothesis that man is intrinsically a *material* being. He has an attenuated quality called a soul, dependent upon fleshly brain cells.

The "fall," not historic but continuous, is from the ideal, potential and in mostly actual, into the external of appearances, and this comprises the Adamic consciousness. Men cling to the sensuous Eden until they are started and driven from it by the loud calling of the divine voice within. The beneficent expulsion from that Eden, and the succeeding necessary restlessness, furnish the true and only impetus for voluntary moral and spiritual evolution. The world is still largely peopled with Adams who practically believe that they are made of red earth or dust.

Is man to grasp, mould and rule that little portion of dust that he has temporarily taken on, and which before has often been used to express and embody other qualities of life, or must he believe himself in bondage to it? Shall the shadow, even though real as a shadow, dominate the substance? Not forever, even in what is called this life. So soon

as man recognizes the fact that he is a mental and spiritual dynamo he will no longer remain a vassal in his own legitimate kingdom. But the more specific treatment of the relations of mind to body must be reserved for a subsequent paper.

A dominant vibration in the thought-atmosphere is able to arouse a nation, or a continent. Great minds, as well as those of less development, are submerged and swept along by it. Crusades, reformations, revolutions, and reforms, furnish numberless illustrations of psychic upheaval and contagion. *Through sympathetic vibration a vast number of responsive mental strings are stirred into action.* As the rhythmical step of a regiment will powerfully shake a strong bridge, so the concerted energy of mind will generate tidal waves of tremendous import. The result is not merely from a contemporaneous logical process, carried on respectively by many individuals, but from a great immaterial gulf stream, deep and mighty, though silent and unconscious.

Mind, as a *force*, is no more unintelligible or unthinkable than other vibrations of unseen energy. And there lies the tremendous significance of the new psychology or recognition of soul force. Till recently conventional science, as taught in all accepted textbooks, recognized no extension of the dynamics of thought beyond the confines of the physical organism. The mind, with feeble domination, through nerve channels, could transmit its orders to different parts of its visible counterpart, but it was not believed that it could go one inch beyond that limit. Any suggestion that telepathy, or thought transference, could take place at a distance of a thousand miles, or even one mile, would have been pronounced impossible.

We shall waste no time in the mere attempt to prove the fact that thought is, and can be, projected through space, both consciously and unconsciously. No well-informed individual who has given any adequate attention to the subject now questions it. Scores of pages might be filled with examples, now on record, which are entirely beyond collusion or coincidence. Every one of thousands of

Universal Laws Never Before Revealed.. Keely's Secrets

hypnotic experiences proves it, and every case of healing through mental treatment attests it. There is no fact in physical science better assured.

And how has the world received this transcendent truth which is transforming in its potency, all-inclusive in its sequences, and divine in its possibilities? Very much as it would a new *curio* or an ingenious toy. The institutional psychologist fondles it, turns it over, weighs and measures its properties in his laboratory, speculates *about* it, and makes a profession of it. But the last thing to be thought of, is to make it useful to mankind. That would be unprofessional. To harness and utilize this force of all forces for the good of humanity would lower it from the select and charmed circle of professional theory and speculation to the broad plane of practical and beneficent agencies.

The average psychical researcher shows much of the same indifference as to any utilization of his favorite principles of pursuits. He is engaged in a never-ending pursuit of phenomena. He will strain his investigative powers, and burn midnight oil in testing, comparing and recording curious manifestations, and in interpreting their methods and laws, but as to their practical application in ethical culture, therapeutic potency or spiritual unfoldment he is as innocent as a child. It has not occurred to him. These reflections are made in no impatient spirit as applied to individuals, but rather to show the negative character of systems of thought into which we have allowed ourselves to become crystallized. How much freedom, originality and progress would at once be manifest if the fear of being called unprofessional and unconventional, which now holds men in bondage, could be eliminated!

Besides the classes already noted there are many excellent people, lovely in character and pure in motive, whose temperamental fondness for the mystical leads them to seek visions, dream dreams, and to cultivate an order of phenomena more dramatic than profitable. Abstract truth and vivid demonstration are well, but the world is hungering for their application to its woes.

If we gained some knowledge of the laws which govern a force inconceivably grander and higher than electricity, may we not dismiss undue sensitiveness as to deviations from traditional scholasticism, and for the sake of humanity, step out of the ruts which have been grooved by the schoolmen of the darker and narrower past? All great advances in their earlier aspects have been irrational innovations.

Regarding the fundamental basis of psycho-dynamics, not only as admitted but overwhelming proven, let us now concisely sum up a few of the results which logically should be realized. They are of stupendous significance, but surrounded as we are by the blank walls of our self-imposed and traditional limitations we can hardly picture them even to the imagination.

Thoughts being forces, every mind is a creative center from which rhythms of qualitative energy are going out in all directions. By their impact upon corresponding chords in other minds, these are also swept into active vibration. Throw a pebble into a lake and the placid surface at once becomes vibrant with a series of ever-widening circles which go out to its utmost boundary. They are never quite lost, or neutralized, though we may be unable to trace them to their final destination. So every soul is the seat of a great centrifugal current, which is generated and set free in the simple process of thinking. This is true - though less in degree - of desultory or aimless thought, as well as of that which is concentrated and projected with definite intent. *Every thinker is a battery of positive forces even though he utter never a word.*

The soul - which is the man - is a resonant instrument with innumerable tremulous strings of the most delicate quality. The water in the lake responds to the pebble, but the medium through which thought-waves pass is infinitely more subtle and elastic.

What volumes of potential energy are wasted and far worse, in negative and discordant mental activities! We are not thinking for ourselves but for the world. With the shuttle of thought in the loom of the mind, we are weaving the multi-colored fabric of conditions, and these not merely immaterial but to be outwardly actualized and manifested. If one in his own soul strikes the discordant notes of anger, envy, avarice, selfishness or even those seemingly more harmless ones of simple fear, weakness, grief, pessimism or depression, he is creating and vibrating those conditions far and near, thereby stirring the corresponding chords in other souls into sympathetic activity. The sphere of outward action is limited, while that of thought is boundless. Mere doing makes ephemeral reputation, while quality of thinking determines, or rather *is*, vital character.

Every one's thought-images are being constantly impressed both upon himself and others. His mind is a busy factory where conditions are positively manufactured. He weaves their quality, consciously or unconsciously, into every nerve, muscle and tissue of his own body. His materialistic thought tethers him in a little circle of limitation, while boundless green fields lie beyond waiting for occupation. His mental pictures of evil, disorder and disease, photograph themselves not only upon his own mind and body but upon those of his fellows.

One cannot afford to think much about evil, even for the well-intentioned purpose of its suppression. The true remedy is its displacement. Thought-space given to it confers realism, familiarity and finally dominion. To silence discordant strings in ourselves or others we must vibrate their opposites. To truly sympathize with a friend who is quivering with trouble or sorrow, is not to drop into his rhythm and intensifying it - as is usual - but to lift his consciousness by striking a higher chord in unison. The road to mental and physical invigoration lies through the dynamics of formative thought. Our way to elevate other lives is also through their creative mental energies.

When the art of projecting thought vibrations on a high plane is systematically cultivated, and the concentrative habit developed, potency for good is increased a hundredfold. Force is no longer squandered in worse than useless discordant negations, but intelligently conserved in positive vigor and exuberance. *Purposeful thought ministration, spiritual and pure in quality, accurately and scientifically projected, like an arrow towards a target, will be the great harmonizing and uplifting agency that will transform the world.* Vibrations of love, peace, spirituality, health, sanity and harmony, will be radiated in ever widening circles, striking responsive unisons that are only waiting for a well-directed concordant impulse.

The dynamics of mind, when generally utilized, will be the sovereign balm that with scientific accuracy will heal all the infelicities of society. It will usher in not only reform but regeneration. In its copious fulness it will overflow from the altitude of spiritual development, until the subordinate plains of intellectuality, ethics, therapeutics, sociology, economics and physics are swept purified and uplifted. The highest includes everything below. With the kingdom of heaven - which is subjective harmony - first sought, "all these things" will be added.

(*from left to right*) - Sympathetic Negative Transmitter; Triple Column for Measuring Specific Gravity of Gases; Dominat Scale and Resonator; Hydrogen Generator

The Neutral Center

John Ernst Worrell Keely

"A center of introductory action is necessary in all operations of Nature."

All structures require a foundation. This neutral center is the foundation.

"Every molecule, every mass, every moving body in space, every solar system, every stellar system, EVERY ROTATORY SYSTEM, is built about a NEUTRAL CENTER. It is the indestructible unit around which all that we recognize as matter is built. Immovable itself, it moves all things. Indestructible itself throughout infinity of time, it creates all things. It produced and preserves the incalculable energy of motion of the entire Universe. It bears the unthinkable burden of the mass of the Universe. It is the most wonderful thing Man has discovered in the Universe since he discovered fire.

"If we should take a planet of say 20,000 miles diameter and should displace a portion of the interior so as to have a crust of say 5,000 miles thickness, and at the center of the planet, place a billiard ball, that small mass, immeasurably smaller than the bulk of the earth, would bear the entire burden of the mass of the crust 5,000 miles thick and would keep it equidistant from itself. No power, however great, could possibly displace this central mass so as to bring it into contact with the crust. Furthermore, to move this central mass in any direction, would require a force sufficient to move the entire mass of the planet, and in propagating or continuing any such motion the neutral center, this billiard ball, will at all time periods remain still in the exact center, bearing the same equidistant relation to its hollow shell. The mind staggers in contemplating the burden borne by this neutral center, where weight ceases." No less wonderful are other properties of the neutral center.

"It is the cause of the physical Universe. Its attraction condensed that which we recognize as substance. Matter was evolved from the affinity of this neutral center for sympathetic streams and since it is immovable, it caused, through negative attraction the formation of nodes in these streams, where the vibrations thereafter continued to meet in a center of sympathetic coincidence causing the permanence of form and matter. Every nebula, an embryonic world, is acted upon, created and preserved by this neutral center, and at the termination of its cycle, it is ultimately also destroyed by it, causing its absorption into the Unknown from whence it came.

"The actual neutral center of the earth is, in fact, even infinitely smaller than the billiard ball referred to above. It consists of a compound interetheric point in space, so small that were we to magnify a pin head to the size of the sun, and from that substance take a particle of matter the same size, again magnifying it to the size of the sun, the neutral center would still be invisible, even though the structure of this last substance was examined through the highest powered microscope ever created, or to be created. For the neutral center is INDIVISIBLE. Its attributes do not belong to matter, and pertain in no way to matter, which is but its exterior manifestation.

"Every aggregate mass consists of molecules, each of which has its neutral center where the three modes of vibration, dominant, harmonic, and enharmonic, meet in a center of sympathetic coincidence and are equated without cancellation of their energy."

"The fixed neutral center of the earth

Universal Laws Never Before Revealed.. Keely's Secrets

is the concentration or totalized power of all the several molecular neutral centers in the earth's mass. This neutral center, which is absolutely WITHOUT WEIGHT, an interetheric point in space, communicates direct by means of its outflow of sympathy, with every planetary mass in the Universe. Through its inflow of sympathy, through the solar intermediate, the sun, it receives the life flow from the SUPREME NEUTRAL CENTER that enables it to perpetuate its existence. Thus through the outflow from this Supreme Neutral Center that pivoting point of the Universe controls the existence and motion of not only every stellar, solar and planetary mass in space, but also the rotatory vibration, in every individual molecule, intermolecule, etc. through all the subdivisions of matter, thereby sustaining their existence and motion with the life flow.

"All foundations must be sufficient to bear their burden. Conceive then the Universe centered upon and resting the burden of is incalculable mass and kinetic energy on a vacuous interetheric point in space, so minute that it is actually INDIVISIBLE. This conception can only be fully comprehended by an infinite mind. Independent of time, because indestructible in its unity, independent in space, because through its properties space itself exists and without it would not exist, independent of matter because its properties in an external direction created all that we know as matter and gave it seeming permanence, the neutral center is that protean, uncreated, indestructible, forever-existing FIRST CAUSE. Without hands, without tools, without thought, without emotion, without love, without form, without substance, it, of itself, created all these. All that we see or can see in the objective Universe exists because of and by means of the properties and powers of the NEUTRAL CENTER.

"No machine heretofore constructed has been made with a neutral center. This conception of mechanics has never before dawned on man's thought field. Had this been done, perpetual motion would have become a demonstrated fact. Were a machine so constructed as to use its properties, an introductory impulse would suffice to run it for centuries. However, this would not be a useful mechanical contrivance for no more energy could be obtained from it than was originally given, and its only value would be as a timekeeper." Keely did not seek to invent, nor did he claim to have invented, perpetual motion.

"The neutral center is only established when rotation exceeds 100 revolutions per minute, which is sufficient, with the vibratory circuit running at 100,000 per second, to neutralize the influence of gravity on the volume of the neutral third of the sphere." The neutral center controls its sphere of operation, whether that mass controlled by it be homogeneous or complex. All differential mass antagonism is equated on the induction of certain orders of vibration. The structural conditions can be entirely adverse, even of unlike states --- gases with liquids, liquids with solids, solids with gases, its control will be as complete in one case as in the other.

"The condition of unstable equilibrium was born in each neutral center, that by means of this arrangement, the neutral center might become the connective link or controlling tendency, holding these two properties in balance and assuming either phase at will. Between the dispersing positive and the attractive negative it stands, the deciding factor, the Universal Will. "The action that induces this property I call the connective link is sympathetic planetary oscillation."

Theory And Formula Of Aqueous Disintegration

by John Keely

The peculiar conditions as associated with the gaseous elements of which water is composed, as regards the differential volume and gravity of its gases, make it a ready and fit subject of vibratory research. In submitting water to the influence of vibratory transmission, even on simple thirds, the high action induced on the hydrogen as contrasted with the one on the oxygen (under the same vibratory stream) causes the antagonism between these elements that induces dissociation. The differential antagonistic range of motion, so favoring the antagonistic thirds as to become thoroughly repellant. The gaseous element thus induced and registered, shows thousands of times much greater force as regards tenuity and volume than that induced by the chemical disintegration of heat, on the same medium. In all molecular dissociation or disintegration of both simple and compound elements, whether gaseous or solid, a stream of vibratory antagonistic thirds, sixths, or ninths, on their chord mass will compel progressive subdivisions. In the disintegration of water the instrument is set on thirds, sixths, and ninths, to get the best effects. These triple conditions are focalized on the neutral center of said instrument so as to induce perfect harmony or concordance to the chord note of the mass chord of the instruments full combination, after which the diatonic and the enharmonic scale located at the top of the instrument, or ring, is thoroughly harmonized with the scale of ninths which is placed at the base of the vibratory transmitter with the telephone head. The next step is to disturb the harmony on the concentrative thirds, between the transmitter and the disintegrator. This is done by rotating the siren so as to induce a sympathetic communication along the nodal transmitter, or wire, that associates the two instruments. When the note of the siren becomes concordant to the neutral center of the disintegrator, the highest order of sympathetic communication is established. It is now necessary to operate the transferable vibratory negatizer or negative accelerator, which is seated in the center of the diatonic and enharmonic ring, at the top of the disintegrator, and complete disintegration will follow (from the antagonisms induced on the concordants by said adjunct) in triple progression, thus: First thirds: Molecular dissociation resolving the water into a gaseous compound of hydrogen and oxygen. Second: sixths, resolving the hydrogen and oxygen into a new element by second order of dissociation, producing what I call low atomic ether. Third: ninths, the low atomic ether resolved into a new element, which I denominate high or second atomic harmonic. All these transmissions being simultaneous on the disturbance of sympathetic equilibrium by said negative accelerator.

EXAMPLE:

Taking the chord mass of the disintegrator B flat, or any chord mass that may be represented by the combined association of all the mechanical parts of its structure (no two structures being alike in their chord masses) taking B flat, the resonators of said structure are set at B flat first octave, B flat third octave and B flat ninth octave by drawing out the caps of resonators until the harmony of thirds, sixths, and ninths are reached; which is simple movement of the fingers on the diatonic scale, at the head, will determine by the tremulous action which is highly sensible to the touch, on said caps. The caps are then rigidly fixed in their different positions by set screws. The focalization to the neutral center is then established by dampening the steel rods, on the back of the scale, representing the thirds, sixths and ninths, drawing a piece of small gum tube over them, which establishes harmony to the chord mass of the instrument. Concordance is thus effected between the disintegrator and the ninths of the scale at base of transmitters with telephonic head.

This scale has a permanent sympathetic one, set on the ninth of any mass chord that may be represented, on any and all the multiple variations of mechanical combinations. In fact, permanently set for universal accommodations.

The next step is to establish pure harmony between the transmitter and the disintegrator, which is done by spinning the siren disk, then waiting until the sympathetic note is reached, as the siren chord, decreasing in velocity, descends the scale. At this juncture, the negative accelerator must be immediately and rapidly rotated, inducing high disturbance of equilibrium between the transmitter and the disintegrator by triple negative evolution, with the result that a force from five to ten, fifteen, twenty, and thirty thousand pounds to the square inch is evolved by the focalization of this triple negative stream on the disintegrating cell, or chamber, whether there be one, two, three, five, or ten drops of water enclosed within it."

"When moist air is subdivided by atomic vibration, the hydrogen is dissociated or separated from the oxygen but neither of them pass from the intermolecular state. Not until the intermolecular structure of hydrogen is subdivided by interatomic vibrations can it assimilate with the introductory etheric element."

"The latent force from liquids and gases differs from that liberated in metals in that it results from the breaking up of their rotating etheric envelopes, increasing simultaneously the range of their corpuscular action giving under confinement forces of almost infinite variety of pressures. When liberated from the tube it is confined in it seeks its medium of corresponding tenuity with a velocity exceeding that of light."

"The sympathetic neutral flow (from the molecular neutral centers to the mass neutral center) is the latent power liberated in the disintegration of water. In water this power is dispersive, liberating latent elastic energy, while in metals the latent force manifests itself only in negative attraction and when these vibrations are applied to minerals, there is evolved the primal ether which is dissipated, leaving behind only an impalpable intermolecular dust, in which is contained in virgin form an metals originally in the mineral mass."

A non-intermittent flow of sympathy must flow along the Trexar, consisting of harmoniously adjusted thirds. Differential molecular weight is required, that is, the gas must contain heavy atoms and light atoms. This condition is satisfied by water, which consists of two light atoms of hydrogen and one heavy atom of oxygen. The oxygen atom weighs sixteen times as much as the hydrogen.

It is absolutely necessary to release the molecular ether by reducing the water to the interatomic state, before the atoms within the intermolecules can be released. Also the etheric capsules of the atomic and interatomic must be ruptured before the interatomic force can be produced. The ether from one subdivision is essential to subdividing the next higher.

Keely systemized the proper vibratory chords progressively, from the introductory molecular to the interetheric, embracing seven distinct orders of triple subdivision. He proved to his own satisfaction that progressive subdivision evolves new and distinct elements "too multiple to enumerate."

Water is a ready and fit subject for vibratory research on account of its "differential volume" and gravity of its gases. Even on simple thirds the differential action between hydrogen and oxygen causes antagonism and dissociation. The differential of mass is such that the hydrogen and oxygen become thoroughly repellant and thereby exhibit thousands of times more force than could be induced by heat on the same amount of water. Vibration of antagonistic thirds, sixths and ninths on the mass chord will compel progressive subdivisions and to get the best effect on water, the instrument is set on all of these. First, the focalizing chord of sixths induces perfect harmony to the mass chord. Then the diatonic scale and enharmonic scale at the top of the instrument (or ring) is harmonized with the scale of the ninths at the base of his Trexar with the telephone transmitter. His next procedure was to disturb the harmony between the transmitter and disintegrator on the concentrative thirds or sixths, by rotating a siren. This he used to induce sympathetic communication along the Trexnonar between the vibrator and disintegrator. When the siren concorded to the neutral center it established the highest order of sympathy. He then operated the "transferable vibratory negatizer" or "vibratory accelerator" in the center of the "diatonic and enharmonic ring" at the top of the disintegrator and complete disintegration followed. The thirds first resolved the water molecules into hydrogen and oxygen, then the sixths resolved the hydrogen and oxygen into new elements by dissociation, producing "low atomic ether." Then the ninths resolved the low atomic ether into a new element or "high or second atomic harmonic." All these transmissions were simultaneous on the sympathetic equilibrium being disturbed by the negative accelerator.

Keely's first efforts toward disintegration of the elements of water were successful because of the differential weight of the respective atoms composing its molecules. Subsequently, he discovered that this same method, disintegration by differential mass, may be carried out with any gas, in other words, it must contain heavy atoms and light atoms. The heavy atom or oxygen in water weighs just sixteen times as much as either of the hydrogen atoms to which it is joined by chemical affinity.

"In the dissociation of water, molecular and intermolecular dissociation produces the first order of ozone, which is refreshing and vitalizing to breathe. Atomic and interatomic dissociation produces the second order of ozone, which is too pure to breathe, for it produces insensibility." The third order of ozone, produced by etheric and interetheric dissociation, Keely used in his "carbon

Theory and Formula of Aqueous Disintegration

register" to produce a high vibratory circuit to break up cohesion, which he recognized as molecular magnetism. It is possible that this "dissociation" in the "carbon register" depolarized the iron molecules by allowing the corpuscular outreach to return within the molecular embrace. The acceleration of vibration producing these different orders is governed by the introductory impulse and the subsequent chords, as arranged in his Liberator, by which he dissociated water. In molecular dissociation he used one fork of 620, setting chords on the first octave. In atomic separation, he used two forks, one of 620 and one of 630, setting chords on the second octave. In etheric separation he used three forks, one of 620, one of 630 and one of 12,000, setting the chords on the third octave.

"Not until the intermolecular structure of hydrogen is subdivided by interatomic vibrations, can it assimilate with the introductory etheric element."

Certain differential, dual, triple or quadruple chords act as an introductory impulse exciting action on molecular masses (liquid or gaseous) decreasing molecular oscillation. They are then in a receptive state for vibratory disintegration. The diatonic-enharmonic is sounded, increasing molecular oscillation. Molecular subdivision takes place when oscillation exceeds 50% of their diameters. (Molecular or intermolecular?) The gas is now molecularly subdivided and assumes a high velocity of rotation in any confining container, be it sphere or tube and becomes the medium or prepared subject for further disintegration. At this particular time Keely sought to further excite this preparatory medium by the use of an "illuminated revolving prism" a condenser (concave mirror or convex lens) and colored lenses, thereby giving the vibratory frequencies of their respective colors. In his disintegrator a glass tube of sufficient strength to withstand a pressure of 1000 lbs. per square inch was arranged leading to the neutral center and the Trexar was attached to the external end of this glass tube. His use of this tube was probably also to convince the skeptics that the production of his power was genuine and possibly also was used to transmit color vibrations of such frequencies as to release the energy in the neutral center of the sphere.

When the triple introductory impulse or chords in three octaves, are transmitted to the disintegrator it SUBSERVES OR RENDERS NON-OPERATIVE THE MOLECULAR CONCORDANT THIRDS AND ANTAGONIZES WITH DISCORDANT THIRDS, extending their range of oscillation and thereby inducing the highest degree of repellant antagonism or repulsion toward the neutral center of the sphere volume.

The etheric dominant or celestial current induces aqueous disintegration and thermal concentration which two prime conductors display a coincident chord of sympathy with the celestial current. These two prime conductors link the terrestrial to the celestial, without which electricity and magnetism would tend to become static or stable, all life and motion are governed by a dual power disturbance of equilibrium and sympathetic equation, both of which are in turn moved and regulated by electricity and magnetism.

Progressive molecular and intermolecular dissociation reproduces on a small scale Nature's system of light production and also invariably results in vortex motion. All corpuscular action in Nature is vortex motion. The vortex action between the terrestrial and celestial streams, terrestrial condensation against solar tensions, shows conditions analogous to those displayed in the dissociation of water into hydrogen and oxygen, that is, vortex motion of the highest order, but peripheral only.

EXAMPLE OF DISINTEGRATION

If the mass chord of the disintegrator is B flat, the resonators of that structure are set at B flat first octave, B flat third octave and B flat ninth octave, by drawing out the resonator caps and clamping the set screws. A simple movement of the fingers on the diatonic scale at the head will determine by the tremulous action of the caps when exactly resonant. Neutral focalization is then established by dampening the steel rods on the back of the scale representing thirds, sixths, and ninths, by drawing a piece of small gum tube over them, which establishes harmony to the mass chord of the instrument. This effects concordance between the disintegrator and the ninths of the scale at base of transmitter with telephone head.

This instrument had a universal accommodator for all ninths in all multiple variations. This was possibly his sphere resonator.

Concordant harmony must now be established between the transmitter and the disintegrator by spinning the siren disk and waiting for the sympathetic note as its velocity decreases. As soon as this note sounds, the negative accelerator must be rapidly rotated inducing high disturbance of equilibrium between the disintegrator and the transmitter by triple negative evolution resulting in enormous pressure. By triple negative evolution he doubtless means disintegration to the etheric stage.

"In the beginning was the word"

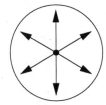

The neutral negative center

Sensitized - reaching out

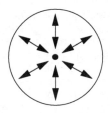

Establishing range of outreach

Positive Propulsive
Establishing Resonance

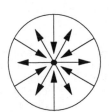

Equilibrium or
Harmony

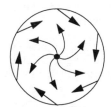

Introductory Impulse
Giving Vortex Motion

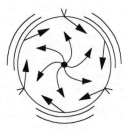

Vibration into
Thirds at Nodes

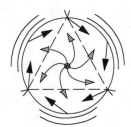

Nodes forming
Tensorial Lines of
Negative Force

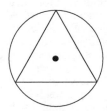

Completed Unit
of Duality

solid matter
in 3 dimensions

Keely's Motor Secret Revealed at Long Last

by Dale Pond

For over 120 years the secret concerning the function and operation of the Keely Hydro-Pneumo-Pulsating-Vacuo motor has baffled all the scientists and engineers who saw it. This mystery of mysteries has been solved.

I had developed a theory of operation over the past several years regarding its secret of operation. What was needed was to rebuild and run the motor to prove the theory.

During the second week of August, Vic Hansen and I resolved to recondition the original Keely motor in his possession. Extraordinary care was taken not to damage any part and all gaskets were replaced and all leaks fixed. We succeeded in recuperating only one of the two pistons as a valve in the second piston was frozen and we loathed to dismember the motor that this second piston would function. We were able to reestablish the functionality in only one piston. This proved to be sufficient for the test. Running on only one cylinder was not sufficient for the motor to run on its own power so we ran water through it in reverse. This was sufficient to prove the principle as we could clearly hear the "pop" of the one live cylinder coinciding with the timing and function of principles. As the piston "popped" the crank and connections responded to the momentary decrease in pressure. Yes, I said decrease in pressure.

This function of this motor represents the female or nightside forces at work. The force is one of implosion or centralization of vibratory forces. It is exactly opposite in function to every known type and manner used to today to derive motive power. This explains, in part, why it has remained a mystery all these years. Because they were looking for expansive force or the male, propulsive type forces,

they remained baffled because no such force exists in its function. Two other notable things can be said about its function: one, it uses a lot of water to run, second, there is no heat whatsoever as it operates. The need for so much water can be resolved with better engineering - this should be simple feat as we know Keely eventually generated thousands of psi using but a few drops of water as he improved the design of the motor. The coldness of operation is a boon just the way it is. This means new models can be built of PVC or other plastics.

The importance of this discovery cannot be over stated: 1) It proves Keely wasn't a fraud as some allege. 2) It gives mankind a whole new energy source that is clean, powerful and simple. 3) It uses a plentiful and costless fuel - water. 4) It gets us into the doorway to reach for his greater and more wonderful discoveries based on his etheric vapor. This motor, as simple as it is, led Keely to the discovery and development of his etheric vapor and etheric force. By understanding its prime principle of function, we too, can make this giant step into the far reaches of applied physics.

So, how does it work? Where does the energy come from to propel itself? From cavitation of water. You are no doubt familiar with the phenomenon of water hammer. This is cavitation and is the very same source of energy in the Keely Motor. Water hammer is the development of a negative pressure cell in a flowing stream of water by cutting off its supply quite suddenly. The resulting partial vacuum collapses (implodes) with a force that can reach several thousand pounds per square inch instantly. In his motor this pressure was controlled to around 50 psi which was sufficient to run this little model.

Those of you working with implosion forces will be glad to see this practical application of the phenomenon of cavitation and the resulting implosive force.

Thus, the engineers investigating Keely's Motor were all looking for a male or explosive force and found none. During the collapse of the cavitation bubble formed in the piston chamber the piston was sucked down and not pushed up as in our "modern" engineering concepts.

The design of Keely's motor is so simple and basic that anyone with a modicum of talent can replicate and even improve on his design. He built his machine over 120 years ago and was hindered by not having the convenience we have of modern valves, ready made materials and 120 years of hydraulic engineering as support. Since the motor runs cold and with ordinary water the parts to build a unit can be had at your nearest hardware store. I suggest looking into PVC pipe and automatic valves such as are used in building sprinkler systems. Two valves, one for intake and one for exhaust coupled to a PVC cylinder should be all that is needed.

To go about building your own working model of his motor you should first acquire a copy of the book *Cavitation* by F. Ronald Young, MacMillan and Co. This book is now out of print. This book is the first and hence only book detailing cavitation. The different kinds of cavitation and their technical parameters are explored very thoroughly. The resulting effects of cavitation such as sonoluminescence and sonochemistry are all explored. The book further gives hundreds of references for source materials or previous research and lab work on this most fascinating of subjects. There is also a very good technical description of water hammer on page 249.

How the motor works

Water hammer is caused by a stream of water being shut off quickly. The trailing edge of the water stream (next to the shutoff valve) becomes rarefied (partial vacuum) and forms into a negative pressure area filled with a *sensitized* vapor composed of water, air and any gases that may have been present in the water. This vapor is the first stage or the basic form of Keely's etheric vapor. The negative pressure cell collapses when the water stream bounces back against the shutoff valve. The physics of these actions and reactions is fascinating and promises so much for development that we will all be very busy developing them for years to come.

In the Keely Motor the water is first drawn into the central pulsating vacuum chamber by a light vacuum formed when the pistons pull water into the system. This vacuum chamber maintains a steady negative pressure on the water from this point on. Between the vacuum chamber and the pistons are two valves. The first is a one-way check valve which serves to maintain the vacuum in the central pulsating vacuum chamber yet allows the pistons to pull water into itself as it is needed. The second valve is quite ingenious and simple. Its function is: 1) to allow water into the piston, 2) close for implosion and then 3) to allow drainage of the spent water.

The water then passes directly into the piston during its up (suction) stroke. The valve rotates shutting off the water stream just as the piston reaches its apex and cavitates which brings the piston down again. Instantly the valve rotates a little more opening two exhaust ports and the water is pushed and drained out through the bottom. This is all there is to the Keely motor. It is simple, elegant and functional. Rules of thumb are: 1) the more vacuum the better the cavitation, 2) the greater the velocity of the water the better the cavitation. The book "Cavitation" has more ideas on improving cavitation than we have space here to list.

Editor's Note (June, 1994): Since this article was written much more has been learned about this motor. Please refer to booklet *The Keely Motor* available from Delta Spectrum Research P. O. Box 316 Valentine, Nebraska 69201 (402) 376-1523.

Sympathetic Vibratory Physics

The Science and Technology of John Ernst Worrell Keely

Lecture given by Dale Pond before the
Swiss Association of Free Energy,
October 28, 1989, Einseideln, Switzerland

Mankind has placed himself in a grave situation. He has divorced himself from Nature with his current attitudes towards Science and Religion. The study of Nature is really a study of Science and Religion. Science is man's effort to know about Nature. Religion is man's effort to reconnect with that Nature. Hence through the arts of science and religion Mankind is attempting to know what Nature is in its truest sense and by way of this ever-expanding understanding to establish his kinship with Nature. These two subjects are bound together as a two sided unit. Science on the one side is ever expanding understanding and Religion is the assimilation of himself into this ever growing awareness of all that is around him. This concept is of course the ideal situation. Mankind has rarely attained this ideal state.

In actuality Mankind has separated himself from Nature with his ever increasing materialistic views embodied in both Science and Religion. His Science admits no connection between himself and his experiments. Atheistic attitudes separates him from Nature and natural processes. This is in error and has lead ultimately to the abysmal situation we find on earth today. Pollution is rampant and uncontrolled. Hunger, pain and suffering, and a lack of the basic material necessities plagues people in all countries. In fact, this century has been the bloodiest time in all of Mankind's history with nearly 100 million souls destroyed in all parts of the globe.

It would seem, at first glance, that with all the modernizations and increases in human science and technology, that we are living in the greatest age of history. But this is not so. To those who have perished and those who now suffer this is a terrible time in history. The question remains "why is this so?"

It is an easy thing to point one's finger at the "bad guys" and lay blame at someone else's feet. It is easy to say one political group is evil and one's own political group is innocent. The truth of the matter is these problems were not created by any one or several groups of politically oriented peoples. These problems were created and perpetuated by ignorance. This ignorance is a lack of awareness that all of Mankind is a part of Nature. This materialistic ignorance does not recognize that we are all part of a single natural scheme closely bound together in our actions and circumstances. A concept of Oneness, an idea that Mankind is a valuable part of Nature, has long been held and preserved through the centuries most conspicuously by the religious and metaphysical organizations. Materialistic science has cut off these tried and true ideas at the knees and left man bereft of his common foundation. Materialistic science has left mankind with nowhere to go except along the paths he has established in this century. These paths have lead to more bloodshed, pain and suffering than all previous paths he has ever choosen.

Free energy will not liberate Mankind from these evils. Neither will faster and more powerful machines free him of these self imposed burdens. Certainly more money, more people and more bureaucracies will not help either. We already have cheaper energy, more people, more bureaucracies and have spend vast amounts of human effort towards the solution of these problems and the net result has been an increase of the same problems. Mankind is on the wrong path.

What is needed is a comprehensive awareness that binds Mankind together within a wholistic knowledge that he is a part, an important part, in the natural processes of Nature in which he finds himself. What one man does has an effect on his neighbor and the natural processes surrounding them both. This dual view of nature is fundamental to science, religion and common sense. It is called the Law of Cause and Effect by science and karma by certain religions. This is an almost impossible law for most science or most religions to accept because it implies responsibility to one's self. It also implies that the perpetrator be charitable. He must concede that his neighbor have as much importance to him as himself. Another false premise of materialistic science is that of insufficiency. The establishment of monopolistic and totalitarian organizations is based on this false idea of there not being enough energy or materialistic substances to go around. With a broader paradigm that concedes the Universal Forces of Nature are limitless mankind can then be charitable. But to even concede this much many are hesitant because it implies their knowledge and power structures are based erroneously on false premises. These ideas of endless abundance implies sharing and most refuse to share because they believe in limited materialities as opposed to limitless potentialities. -- Hence, the exercise of charity has not been one of Mankind's greatest achievements.

My message to you today is that there is a paradigm of both Science and Religion that encompasses the highest of virtues expressible by Man. There is a field of science so powerful that it can build a new and better future for Mankind. There is a philosophy and science so all-encompassing that it can bring Mankind to a realization of his Oneness with his neighbors and with all of Nature. This paradigm has latent within itself, because of its breadth and scope, more than enough material and spiritu-

al benefits for everyone because it recognizes and uses the very foundation principles of Nature itself. Because of its recognition and acceptance of its role in life it does not trample human rights or the rights of Nature and assumes full responsibility for itself within its own scope of possibilities. More than all this, it recognizes the valuable parts of all sciences and religions and merges them into a comprehensive and usable paradigm that has within itself seeds for unlimited growth and expansion. This paradigm of science is called Sympathetic Vibratory Physics.

What is Sympathetic Vibratory Physics? It is the science of Harmony, of Oneness. It holds the concept that all comes from One Source, One Force. It maintains that the fantastic array of things and activities throughout the universe are related in a simple manner. This simple basis of relativity is called vibration. It has been long recognized that everything in the universe vibrates. Thus, a study of vibrations is the study of the very foundation of Nature. For once we grasp the inner functioning of the vibratory Universal Creative Forces as they operate throughout the universe, then, and only then, can we correlate them into a comprehensive paradigm and bring them into practical modes of usefulness for the benefit of mankind. Unlike dogmatic, cold science, Sympathetic Vibratory Physics does not isolate one phenomena from another but accepts and shows the inter-connectivity between all things and forces. This interconnection between all things is vibration and related vibratory phenomena. To understand vibration we must develop a comprehensive organized science of vibration governed by laws and principles. Fortunately a great deal of this development work has already been done. We have a well developed science of music. Music is an organized art and science of vibrations found within the audible range of the infinite Electromagnetic Scale. A major segment of Sympathetic Vibratory Physics is therefore a study of music, its arithmetical and philosophical basis of development and how these may be

Sympathetic Vibratory Physics

applied to procedures for inventing new and useful devices and processes.

The scientific implications of this science are no greater than the social implications. In fact, one person suggested to Keely that he cease his scientific work and proceed with the spiritualization of civilization. This is to say that Sympathetic Vibratory Physics is as important to mankind's spiritual and moral growth as it is to his material benefit. It has been often said that this science can not be fully mastered without first having mastered self - a very metaphysical principle to be sure. The greatest pursuit of any man is to know himself and his connection to all that is around him. This self-knowledge then brings an awareness of Oneness and defeats the ideas of separateness As a consequence it brings an awareness of responsibility to the individual himself and to those around him.

Should we dare to place in man's hands such fantastic instruments as this science appears capable of delivering without the requisite moral and spiritual understanding such that man might not misuse this knowledge to his own detriment? Technology is a double edge sword - its products can be used for man's benefit or his destruction. How wonderful it is that this technology, which promises so much in the form of new discoveries and controls over natural forces, also contains within itself that which may guide man in the correct usage of them. Stories abound of Keely's accomplishments in this regard and point to a new method of engineering and building machines - a method that binds the purposes of the mind of man to mechanical function.

Rudolph Steiner said in 1913: The "West people" of the English-speaking countries, Great Britain and North America, will develop the new mechanical faculty. They will be able to create machines and mechanical devices which work with hardly any human effort; which work with help of the "Laws of Sympathetic Vibrations." These machines will do about 90% of the labor,

and all social and material trouble as we know it will cease to exist." Steiner went on to say: "The famous technology of our days will come to its end soon; because she will in a certain way wind up herself. The following phenomenon will then appear: Man will achieve the faculty to employ the fine vibrations of his ethereal body to impulsate mechanical devices. The individual will be able to transmit his own vibrations onto the machine, and only he will be able to set the machine in motion, by the vibrations generated by himself. The men who are now practical technicians will soon discover that they are standing before a complete change as to what one calls practical, when man will be involved with his will in the objective feeling of the world."

In 1918 Steiner brought the matter up again from another direction: "All searching in solid matter is nonsensical. One will at a certain time abandon it -- and mankind will do this before the year 4000 -- that searching in solid matter as underlying nature. Mankind will discover something totally different; he will discover rhythms everywhere in nature, rhythmic arrangements. And when this knowledge about nature's rhythms is carried on, one will come to certain employments of these rhythms in technology. That is the goal set for the future technology of Sympathetic Vibrations, vibrations generated on a small scale, and then continued on a large scale, so that by this simple sympathizing, harmonizing, an incredible lot of work can be done." As some of you know, this is exactly what Keely did over 100 years ago.

John Ernst Worrell Keely worked incessantly for over 30 years to dis-cover the simple laws governing naturally occurring or artificially derived vibratory forces. The result of his work was the rediscovery of 40 laws that govern all vibration and vibratory phenomena. These laws have been and are being published in The Journal of Sympathetic Vibratory Physics. Much work has gone into the interpretation and application of these laws as they apply to modern physics and technology. Modern science is using some of these laws unbeknownst to itself. The laser, microwave, quantum physics (chip design), musical and audio component manufacturers are all using some of these laws in the design and construction of their products. Because of the differences in paradigms however, it will be many years before these laws become recognized for their true worth. Modern science is based in the concepts of mass vs energy begun by Newton and furthered by Einstein. Sympathetic Vibratory Physics is based on the actions and interactions of polar and depolar vibrations and the resultant sympathetic associations. It appears that these actions are the causes of mass and energy. It is believed that a study of causes advances science to greater accomplishments with more surety and speed than the study of the results or symptoms of these causes.

Sympathetic Vibratory Physics focuses on the inner nature of vibratory phenomena. It is well known that vibratory activity contains within itself many differing characteristics and phenomena. These include: amplitude, velocity, mode, sympathy, number and periodicity. Each of these characteristics can be regarded as independent factors as they are generally considered in conventional solutions. However in order to have validity within an integral synapsis they must be considered as parts of a whole. In a wholistic paradigm each of these characteristics or components must be considered as being relative one to the others. This viewpoint is generally referred to as the Law of Relativity. No thing can be considered of and by itself as no thing in the Universe is isolated from interactions upon or by something else. The isolation of one phenomenon from all others is science's greatest mistake. Until this error in thinking and practice is corrected we will continue to experience deleterious effects of our scientific endeavors. Sympathetic Vibratory Physics gives us a broad field in which all things can be studied as relative parts of a comprehensive whole. Through the study of

music and music development we have this relativistic paradigm. The fundamental principle of music is relativity. A simple frequency is nothing of and by itself. But relate that frequency to another and we instantly have two separate entities locked together by a fixed interval between them. This relationship is always expressed as a ratio or the relative values rigidly fixed in a given relationship known as an interval.

These actions are held to be in certain and specific relations one to another. It is fundamental to grasp the significance of this concept of relativity. In an analysis of a simple hair comb which part, the teeth or the space between the teeth, is more important? The teeth of the comb are the active parts - the part that does the work but without the spaces between the teeth the teeth would have no value whatsoever. Just so with frequencies of vibration. The frequency of a vibration is the active component within an environment but the importance of this frequency can only be derived from its action and interaction with other frequencies in that same environment. This interaction with other frequencies is the embodiment of known natural laws of forces: every force has or creates a reaction (Law of Polarity or Opposites), two forces summed or differenced result in a third force or reaction (Law of Three).

A study of synthesized wave forms best explains the relationship between music and quantum physics as used by John Keely. Among his legacy to us are a number of charts showing musical notations arranged according to his paradigm. It has been discovered that these musical notes are placed so as to be synthesized into more complex wave forms. Modern engineering recognizes the value of and uses harmonics of frequencies. This is a doubling or halving of a given frequency as part of an analysis of vibratory phenomena (Keely's Law of Harmonic Vibrations)3. Keely teaches us that there are many more relationships in vibrations than just the fundamental and its harmonics. There are also Sixths, Thirds, Fourths and Sevenths as well as many others (Keely's Law of Harmonic Pitch4). It is an established fact that several frequencies synthesized together form a complex wave form. If concordant frequencies are merged we have one kind of vibratory force having specific characteristics. If enharmonic frequencies are merged we have a different vibratory character. These differences in character can be readily seen or heard in the differences between a trumpet's middle C and middle C sounded on a piano. The fundamental is the same yet the chordal tone produced is altogether different. The auditory and physiological impact on the human organism is altogether different also. It is this difference that can be understood and applied to mechanical devices. The vibratory tones of a string are more harmonious than the chord components of a brass instrument. One can calm or bring quietude and the other can bring discord or activity. Activated atomic particles can thus be created and used as a power source in a device once this association of frequencies is more fully understood. When considering compositions of molecules it is assumed they all have the same component parts, i.e., electrons, photons, etc. The basic differences are the number of these particles making up the aggregate and their individual orbit characteristics. Since each one of these particles has a chord of composite frequencies it must therefore be safe to assume that the apparent differences between aggregates is the sum total or summed difference of their composite frequencies.

Within these 40 Laws of Harmony are the defined relationships between electricity, magnetism and gravity. Keely demonstrated this relationship to be as thirds or 33 1/3, 66 2/3 and 100. This relationship of forces he eventually applied to his inventions such that they operated without any apparent energy input. By establishing the proper relationships of these three forces his equipment developed unheard of power and force. Since these laws govern the very vibrations from which all material substances are built up they also therefore govern all material things. Through their use Keely was able to liberate incredible forces of the atom in such a way that harmful and deleterious nuclear forces such as radioactivity were not evident or experienced. All atomic and nuclear forces are measured in terms of frequency and these frequencies can be manipulated to either liberate forces or they can be modified to absorb or form into new products - transmutation, in other words. This process does not require hugh energies as are found in common accelerator configurations or nuclear piles. Nature is subtle and subtle means are required to awaken her energies. This science demonstrates that all things are related and that the resultant effects of a relationship are a consequence of the characteristics of that relationship. Thus no thing or function can exist in and by itself. There must be an active force, a receptive force and a neutral zone or zones of communication between these two forces.

Herein lies the hidden power of Sympathetic Vibratory Physics as developed by John Keely. A concordant waveform, composed of harmonic frequencies, tends to pull subatomic particles together. On the other hand discordant waveforms will tend to split or explode the particle or aggregate. A simple analogy is that of dynamite, a harmonious substance when at rest, one which is held together by the molecular and atomic component frequencies. The introduction of a strong introductory impulse from a dynamite cap destroys it's homogeneous integrity and the component subatomic particles are liberated from their bonds. Keely explained the relationship between matter and force thusly:

"There is no dividing of matter and force into two distinct terms, as they both are ONE.
FORCE is liberated matter.
MATTER is force in bondage."

Keely, 1893

This quote is a demonstration of an understanding of nuclear and atomic forces well before our much heralded and over-thought-of "Nuclear Age." In our age we have begun to decipher the true relationships between matter and force. We have a long way to go yet.

There is far too much knowledge to cover in this short paper. We have yet to cover Keely's work with: acoustic levitation, water and mineral disintegration, cold steam, colors from sounds, telescope and microscope developments and his incredible work with healing mental illness with acoustical resonators. It would take years of study and application to unravel the many mysteries of Keely's scientific discoveries. So much of our current scientific thought is based on false premises that it will be years before the accepted paradigms are evolved sufficiently for a continuous and unhindered growth. But even more difficult is the evolution of Man's spiritual and philosophical ideas. If man's actions during this century are any indication - it may be that Steiner and Blavatsky were correct by saying it would be centuries before man could assume his true birthrights.

In America there are many individuals and companies working in some way with this new view of science. It will not be long before we have practical functioning machines. New techniques and new devices are constantly being developed that will allow even more work to be done with less work or energy. It is now possible to acquire quite easily components and processes that employ the principles Keely demonstrated for us over 100 years ago. These materials range from simple auditory devices to powerful and expensive instruments for testing and measuring vibratory phenomena. They are becoming quite plentiful which leads me to assume it won't be long before many new and wondrous things are made manifest in the affairs of man. These new devices and processes won't reflect all that will be done eventually - but will provide further foundations upon which we can build towards this new technology now open

to us. As part of my paper I am including Keely's forty Laws of Sympathetic Vibratory Physics as he left them to us. Keely left these laws to mankind in the hope that one day man may create a better and more bountiful life for himself. The Journal of Sympathetic Vibratory Physics has been publishing these laws and attempting to decipher them that they might be applied in the work of others.

All of you in this room are in some way working to develop this and other areas of science. It is sincerely hoped that as you develop your particular field you will give thought to the imperative development of the philosophical, moral and spiritual growth of yourself and those around you. Failure to create the proper individuals to handle these new forces you are about to release on mankind may prove to be our own undoing.

Keely's Definitions of His Own Terms

ATOMOLES are elementary units of matter uniform in size and weight, and exist in solid, liquid, gaseous, and isolated forms.

ATOMS are multiple combinations of atomoles, and they also exist in solid, liquid, gaseous, and isolated forms.

SIMPLE MOLECULES are formed by the union of two atoms of the same kind.

COMPOUND MOLECULES are unions of two atoms of dissimilar kind.

COMPLEX MOLECULES are unions of molecules with other molecules or atoms.

PITCH is the relative frequency of vibration.

VIBRATION is the rhythmical motion of a body within itself.

OSCILLATION is a rhythmically recurring translatory movement.

TRANSMISSIVE ENERGY is rhythmical motion of condensation and rarefaction produced by the vibrating or oscillating body in the medium in which it is immersed.

ATTRACTION is the mutual approach of aggregates caused by concentrated waves of harmonic energy, tending to move in line of least resistance, by becoming the center of one series of concentric waves instead of two or more series.

HARMONY is the simultaneous vibration of two or more bodies whose harmonics do not produce discords, and whose fundamental pitches are harmonics of the lowest pitch, or are a unison with the resultant notes or overtones, or undertones, of any two or more of them.

ETHER is an atomolic liquid 986,000 times the density of steel.

ELECTRICITY is the oscillation of the atomoles of an atom.

INDUCTION is the transmissive force of the electric vibration in ether.

MAGNETISM is the mutual attraction of juxtaposed bodies vibrating at unison or harmonic electric pitches.

GRAVITY is the mutual attraction of atomoles.

GRAVISM is the transmissive form through a medium of atomoles in the fourth state, or a medium composed of atomolini.

ATOMOLINI are ultimate units of atomoles, and when in a liquid state are the media for the transmission of gravism. The illimitable divisibility and aggregation of matter is a logical sequence.

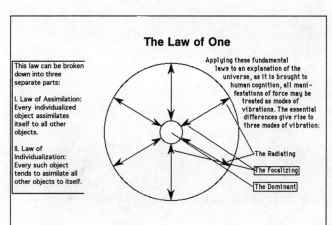

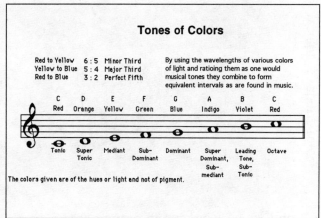

Disintegrator for eliminating vaporic force under vibration. Lever for weighing vaporic force.

The Basis of a New Science

"The newly discovered forces, and laws governing all forces, make possible the processes herein described. Scientific investigations no longer consist in a blind groping after facts; an untried chemical combination can now be planned and its results predicted. Synthetical operations covering the entire domain of organic chemistry can be worked according to simple rules and methods deducible from these newly discovered laws and by the aid of these, to us, new forces. With a knowledge of these facts it is possible for man to work a wondrous change in his methods of manipulating matter.

I shall be happy to present you with a table of definitions which I have written out as briefly and succinctly as possible; and though I doubt not the definitions will be well-nigh incomprehensible to the masses, *you are at liberty to make any use of them you please in your literary endeavors to enlighten humanity.*"

John Ernst Worrell Keely, 1894

EDITOR'S NOTE: See pages 91 and 92 for the definitions mentioned above. The following commentaries on the laws were written by Dale Pond one a month beginning in November, 1985.

The famous Musical Sphere which rotates by virtue of proper vibratory chords.
See page 16 & 272 for chart defining these chords.

Law of Matter and Force

"Coextensive and coeternal with space and duration, there exists an infinite and unchangeable quantity of atomoles, the base of all matter; these are in a state of constant vibratory motion, infinite in extent, unchangeable in quantity, the initial of all forms of energy."

Keely, 1894

Commentary November, 1985

Now, from the above, which reads almost identical to the current theory of quantum mechanics, it becomes apparent that if all matter and energy is vibratory motion, then for us to firmly grasp the meaning and form of matter and energy, we must study to learn the laws governing **vibratory motion**, which is what this publication* is all about. To study molecular forms in a test tube or electrical phenomena in a circuit is to ignore the underlying basis of that which we seek, *i.e.,* what causes these things to be?

Indeed, the very next law, number 2, is called the Law of Corporeal Vibrations. That is why we suggested in the first issue[1] for readers to begin reading about music, acoustics and other related matter. The McGraw-Hill *Encyclopedia of Science and Technology* is perhaps the best reference for the lay person that can be had. Your local library may have a copy or can get it for you. Subject headings of special interest would be Resonance, sympathetic vibration, quantum mechanics, oscillation and van der Waal forces.

If everything is vibratory in its inner nature, then we must look to the laws of vibration to explain their behavior. In the late 1800s it was futile to express to the world such ideas, and it proved so. Now, with quantum theories and theoretical work continually beating around the "vibratory bush" so to speak, these things have a ready basis for credulity and applicability.

The first law of sympathetic vibrations says that "coextensive and coeternal with space and duration ..." meaning that as far as **space** reaches and as far as **time** reaches so too do these "atomoles" exist. Never diminishing in quantity nor quality no matter to what extreme they are subjected. Matter has by necessity of being these necessary elucidations of space and time. The law further states that "these are in a state of constant vibratory motion, infinite in extent, unchangeable in quantity, the initial of all forms of energy." As infinite as are the forms and sizes of material objects, so too are the vibrations that make them

up. The vibrations themselves are the "initial form(s) of all manifested energy."

Here of course we run right up against Einstein and his supporters who claim the reverse is true, i.e., that matter is the basis or beginning point of all energy. Take for instance the famous equation $E=MC^2$, which would lead one to believe that energy comes from mass accelerated, the faster it is accelerated the greater the energy. From the first law of sympathetic vibrations however, we begin to see something quite extraordinary - that energy is the cause from which matter is made up!

For those of you set back by utter disbelief I suggest you read McGraw-Hill's description of quantum mechanics and some the properties of atomic and sub-atomic "particles": "It is natural to identify such fundamental constituents of matter as protons and electrons with the mass points or particles of classical mechanics. According to quantum mechanics, however, these particles, in fact all material systems, necessarily have *wave-like properties*."[2]

Yet another McGraw-Hill definition of Wave Mechanics goes like this: "The modern theory of matter holding that elementary particles (such as electrons, protons, and neutrons) have wave-like properties. In 1924 Louis deBroglie postulated that the same wave-corpuscle duality which was then known to exist in the case of light might also occur in matter; this hypothesis was subsequently verified experimentally. With contributions by the mathematical physicists Erwin Shrodinger, Max Born, Werner Heisenberg, P. A. M. Dirac and others, this theory of matter has become the highly successful quantum mechanics of the present day."[2]

Further on, we will look into these phantom particles from the sympathetic vibratory viewpoint. Our approach will culminate with something akin to the "quantized wave" having positive, negative and neutral "charges." These wavelets will have a frequency and hence an energy level equated to that frequency.

Therefore, energy, in the form of vibrating wavelets, *precedes matter* or any "solid" substance. One

96

Universal Laws Never Before Revealed.. Keely's Secrets

must inevitably realize that if subatomic "particles" are wavelets of varying frequencies and that all atoms and molecules are composed of such "particles" then all atoms and molecules (so called materiality) are nothing other than "quantized bundles of vibrating energy," whose all-inclusive existence is determined by the laws of vibrating motion and not by laws of "classical mechanics" as these laws are based on the assumption of a solid materiality. In resolving this paradox, none has given us the answer any clearer or more concisely than Mr. Keely when he stated:

"There is no dividing of matter and force into two distinct terms, as they both are ONE. FORCE is liberated matter. MATTER is force in bondage."
Keely, 1893

Getting back to the Law of Matter and Force, we have now described an universe filled to the infinitely far brim with vibrating corpuscular or spherical globules called atomoles and atomolini. Interspersed between vast distances we have planets, suns, moons and all the other celestial material objects. Since all things and the universe itself is nothing other than vibratory motions, then space (or non-matter) and matter are the same things (vibraotry motions) differing only in quality and quantity. The quality of the vibratory motions and the quantity aer governed by these selfsame laws of vibraotry physics.

Commentary January, 1989

Keely is describing a great unlimited primordial sea of subatomic particles not unlike a vast sea of neutrinos or tachyons or leptons, mesons - you pick which one he is referring to. One thing is quite clear from the law above - *matter is composed of these particles.* In referring thusly, Keely is implying that *matter* is not made of the smaller particles that make up atomoles - atomolini - as these are perhaps too fine to be considered *matter* in his philosophy. In other words, matter, when considered as matter, is made up of the larger particles. Or when considering these particles as a body we are beyond the realms of material manifestations. They are also the basis of energy throughout the universe. Also implying that energy, as defined by man, does not apply to this realm of this atomlinic sea but is confined to the lower realms of manifestation.

Another correlation is to the new theory of strings which has been gathering notoriety of late. However, the string theory is based on a materialistic notion that there must be a *material* connection between these super small particles populating the universe. When push comes to shove - what is the difference between "pure" energy and "pure" matter anyway? Simply rate and mode of vibration. If the string advocates looked a little deeper they might perceive that the connecting link may be something as simple as this and thus be led to believe that maybe the connecting link is not material after all.

Keely's theory (part of which is in this first law) is not unlike the String Theory, Iverson's Crystal Universe Theory (see his article page 11), the old Ether

Theory and the Meson Sea Theory. The fundamental differences are in the overall comprehensiveness of these theories and that which ties them together. To this date the only truly comprehensive theory put forth has been Keely's.

What is there that can tie the minutest particle which fills the universe to the largest Sun?

If everything is composed ultimately of vibrating bundles of focalized energies then the connecting link must be something common to these functionalities. The connecting link must therefore be some aspect of vibration or vibratory manifestations (wave forms, polarities, etc.). Pythagoras mentioned centuries ago that only number had true existence. The only difference between one frequency and another is its rate and mode. What determines rate is density or degree of focalization (degree of integrity), also ambient modulations and what determines mode is direction (relative to the neutral point of focalization and periphery points of expansion).

Also implict in this law is the idea that from each of these atomolini all else is generated - or created - brought into material manifestation in other words. The question then is how does this process of creation (material manifestation) take place? By what mechanism does it operate? Can these be duplicated? What governs them and the relationships between phenomena?

Perhaps the Ancients knew the answers to these questions. After all the Book of Genesis is the story (in allegorical form) of how God (pure energy) became materialized. What is there about Genesis that may be interpreted in modern technical or scientific terms? Perhaps the correlation may be to *periodicity*. This is explored and explained in Mrs. Fitzgerald Hughes' book "Harmonies of Tones and Colors - Developed Through Evolution." She says that the same way music is developed from the process of evolution - matter and light are also developed. Implying that this particular process of evolution is a universal method and is applicable to all things.

Atomoles, Keely maintains, are the basis of all matter and the initial basis of all energy. Can this be true? Matter and energy are derived from the same particle? *The subtance of the atomole evolves into matter whereas its motion evolves into energy.* An extraordinary thought to contemplate. Can we refer to this atomole then as a particle or as a vibration? Is it a "mind" particle? Is it the "spirit" particle or "spirit" energy underlying all Creation?

But there is a definite distinction here, as we are oft commonly finding in all of Keely's work, indicating a separation between what constitutes matter and what is not yet matter. These atomoles are composed of atomolini in his conceptions. Since he indicates the atomole is the basis of matter and energy then atomilini are "beyond" these realms. This is interesting because it may indicate that Keely considered the material and energetic realms as sensorial perceptions or those 'things' which we can perceive with our finite senses. This line of thought then leads one into a

Universal Laws Never Before Revealed.. Keely's Secrets

realm of 'non things' or things beyond man's perception - something akin to radio waves or gamma rays. These things we can perceive with instruments yet they are imperceptible to the commonly acknowledged five senses.

Perhaps these are the particles of mind force which we have yet to empirically substantiate.

(1) *The Journal of Sympathetic Vibratory Physics,* Delta Spectrum Research P. O. Box 316 Valentine, Nebraska 69201 (402) 376-1523.
(2) *McGraw-Hill Encylcopedia of Science and Technology, 6th ed., 1984.*

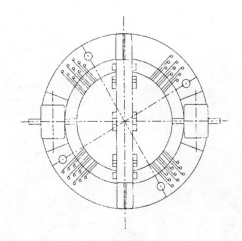

TOP VIEW

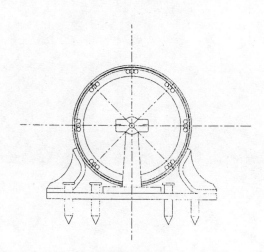

END ELEVATION

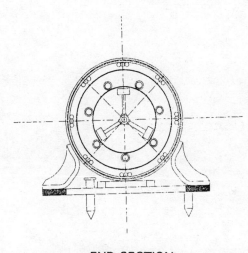

END SECTION

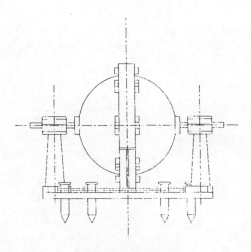

SIDE ELEVATION

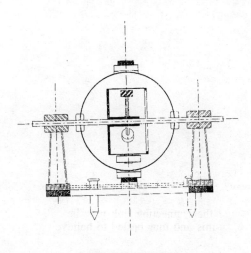

SIDE SECTION

Various views of the Keely Dynasphere construction details.

Mr. Keely, seated. Mr. Crowhurst, standing. Keely actuating the Liberator to release his Etheric Vapor which is the working fluid in the Musical Sphere.

Law of Corporeal Vibrations

"All coherent aggregates when isolated from like bodies, or when immersed or confined in media composed of matter in a different state, vibrate at a given ascertainable pitch."

Keely, 1894

Commentary December, 1985

This law says very simply that everything vibrates at its own frequency when not resonating to a nearby object. Remember Keely's experiment where he floated iron weights in a water filled vessel (Cayce fans may recognize the allusion to "iron floating on water'?) The law says that these iron weights, "when immersed in a media of matter in a different state (liquid, gas, *etc.*), vibrates at an ascertainable rate." This is also recognizable to ham radio operators as the functioning of an antenna. The antenna is an aggregate, usually copper, suspended in media (air) of another state (gas). The length determines the general frequency of resonance. The same holds true with weights in a medium of water and at a later date, Keely was able to do this in the air. Keely apparently could measure the rates of vibration of these weights quite accurately and then alter them (the rates) to suit his purposes; i.e., alter the "predominance from the terrestrial to the celestial."

A very simple law to be sure, but then all true knowledge, when understood, is simple, concise and leaves no room for confusion.

We must, at this juncture, bring into these dissertations some more of Keely's general theories and statements. Last month we gave several words and their definition, some of which may have caused more questions to be raised in your minds, such as atomole or atomolini. In order that we may better grasp these terms in their proper context, we have reproduced, on a CAD computer system, one of Keely's beautiful charts. The "Chart Defining the Arrangement of the Different Areas and Subdivisions of Matter." The detail has not been completely reproduced here, but enough of it is true to the original to convey sufficient comprehension for our discussion.

The Chart...*(see charts end of this book)*

Those who have an understanding of the composition of molecules and atoms as held by conventional science may disagree with the configurations shown in this chart. To those who object to a new viewpoint, let me say this:

First: We are discussing Keely's work as he himself presented it. This is an impartial study intended to analyze what HE did and the explanations he gave of his work.

Second: If we assume, for a moment, that Keely did do some of what is reported, then we have to doubt (or at least temporarily set aside) the conventional stand on these subjects. If he did what he did on one hand and dogmatic science cannot explain why, then we must ask Keely to explain. It is this explanation we are exposing ourselves to in order that we may grasp from it whatever we are capable of. At the very least, Keely has an explanation (though at times bewildering) whereas modern science has none.

Be it further pointed out, that conventional scientific theory of the origin of electricity is founded on the equation E^2/R^2. As Mr. Newman has so plainly shown us, this theory is quite possibly in error, at least in part. If one theory is held to be "somewhat valid" then any other theory must not only be welcome as a furtherance of understanding but may even have as much of this "somewhat valid" credibility as the next.

As has been mentioned in "Keely and his Discoveries" by Bloomfield-Moore and by others in other articles, Keely dealt extensively with his "atomic triplets." These triplets can be readily distinquished from the chart as the three juxtaposed spheres, each repeating itself into the infinite depths of nothingness. This was mentioned in last month's issue. Much indeed can be learned from contemplating this chart. Those of you with a metaphysics background can discern the white and black areas - positive and negative respectively, sometimes symbolized as Yang & Yin.

When considering the chart please understand that as a given length or volume vibrate to a certain ascertainable frequency, then another length or volume resonates to another frequency. The differing sizes of particles as depicted in Keely's chart show

Universal Laws Never Before Revealed.. Keely's Secrets

the relative sizes and this indicates each size has its own frequency range of vibration (bandwidths - see later in this issue under The Bottom Line ... Application). Molecular areas represent gross matter, atomic particles vibrate in the realm of electrical frequencies and lower, the smaller the particle, the higher the frequency. Interatomic sizes are near the microwave bandwidth, the ætheric going far beyond where experimental science has yet reached, gamma ray frequencies and eventually to the frequencies of Mind itself.

Commentary February, 1989

A recent article in Fortune, January 30, 1989, "A Quantum Leap in Electronics," mention was made to "one of man's most brilliant intellectual achievements." The writer is referring to a "new" process called "quantum wells." This process is one where layers of atoms of one material are nestled along or within layers of another atom thus creating a "well" of atoms in which another atom can vibrate "at a given ascertainable rate." They claim that "electrons can be made to resonate like sound inside an organ pipe." By exciting the isolated element tremendous laser power can easily be generated by stimulating the particle into a great quantum leap and thus a release of energy. Sound familiar?

Reread the above law - these quantum wells are a perfect illustration of this law. An aggregate, the ringing electron, is isolated from bodies in a like state, that is they don't ring or vibrate at the same frequency. It may also be said they are immersed (surrounded) by matter in another state (non-resonating).

The quantum leap required to emit the laser beam is then induced from a *known rate* of frequency which has been stabilized within the active element enclosed within the quantum well.

Another example of this law is the doped materials of semiconductor technology. Immerse a douplant into pure silicon and there is an isolated pitch or relative frequency of a known rate. Yet another example is the filament inside an electric light bulb. In this case we have an atomic element(pure element or pure atomic substance) surrounded by a partial vacuum or rarified gases.

Once a pure tone or pitch has been isolated in this fashion it is fairly easy (given our sloppy methods) to cause it and only it to leap to a new energy state. *This is the process by which light and heat are generated in an electric light bulb and also the process in which light and heat are generated when Sun light strikes the Earth's atmosphere.* Is not the Earth isolated within the great vacuum of space? Is there light in the darkness of interplanetary space? Is there any heat there when no molecular or atomic substances are present? Of course not.

This process of frequency modulation was explained very well by Keely when he said:

"Vibrate an atomic substance with an atomic vibration and heat and light are evolved."

And again:

"Light and heat are not evolved until the force of the vibratory sympathetic stream, from the neutral center of the sun, comes into atomic percussive action against the molecular atmosphere or envelope of our planet."

This process was explained by Edgar Cayce in the following reading excerpt:

"As we see manifest in the electrical forces as used by man. This becoming only an atom in motion, and as the atomic force gathers this, producing such vibration as to create heat, light, and of the various natures, by the kind, class or nature of resistance met in its passage in the cycle given, reducing or raising the velocity, or better by the class of atomic force it vibrates, either with or against. These are examples of portions of universal forces." (900-17)

The above quote is rich in vibration concepts. For those who have the training and education in modes of vibration, nuclear and atomic functions and straight elementary physics (refraction, reflection, *etc.*) can see and understand the above.

A good example of this process of evolving latent, interior forces from the neutral center of atoms is the common usage of radiant heat. A heating device may be purchased that does not heat the space in a room but heats the objects in that space. This type of heating is referred to as radiant heat (one of three accepted forms of heat transfer). The heater evidently puts out a lower form of heat than does the Sun. Perhaps this is why only gross molecular objects can release this heat. The Sun, on the other hand, as mentioned above, puts out a higher form of heat that simple atoms can liberate. Perhaps we can safely say that this higher form of heat if og a higher frequency and only resonates "particles" possessing this same frequency range. It is in order to say that this higher and lower form of heis what Keely would have called "undifferentiated" triplets of wave energy. The differentiation does not take place, hence is unnoticeable, until it becomes modulatied by the lower or discordant frequencies of the particles it impinges upon. Then, and only then, do the three coincident frequencies become "knowable" to our senses.

This is the same process taking place in rainbows bursting forth from undifferentiated light sources. One naturally asks but what means does this differentiation take place? What is it that causes the coincidental flows to part in such marvelous exhibitions of colors? From the Keely material we can see that the answer is found in the angle of incidence. If the angle of incidence changes so to does the manner of manifestation.

Vibration

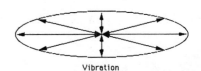

Vibration is the rhythmic motion of a body within itself. This is distinctly different from an oscillation which is the motion of a body about itself.

Vibration

Vibration

Law of Corporeal Oscillations

"All coherent aggregates not isolated from like bodies, oscillate at a period-frequency corresponding to some harmonic ratio of the fundamental pitch of the vibrating body; this pitch is a multiple of the pitch of the atomole."

Keely, 1894

Commentary January, 1986

Throughout mankind's past he has endeavored to assail the enigmas brought before him as a matter of course. Not so much from his desire to know and fathom the depths, but because his inner self stirs his outer self. Not content with outward perspectives of materiality, the inner self's purpose is to establish that which it senses a loss of - Harmony. The creative essence, being a natural and integral part of the inner man, seeks to be more expressive. The inhibition of these creative urges and desires is the cause of man's restlessness and ceaseless effort to **be**. This force from within reaches out in all directions and on all levels of his being, bringing into man's sphere of awareness all that is missing in the attempt by the inner self to find its equilibrium: creative to absorptive, expression to experience.

This reaching out is synonymous to Keely's "sympathetic outreach", *i.e.,* that which is overbalanced reaches for its "sympathetic equalizer". All forces will tend to re-establish the balance from which they originated, therefore we can say that all active forces are balanced forces brought into dis-equilibrium. It is then a logical mode of activity for these unbalanced forces to reach for and find their "sympathetic equilibrium".

This power of re-establishing the balance is as much at work in the subatomic realm as in the human social realms. An atom or electron given a one-sided charge will instantly seek out and adhere to a particle of opposite charge. Likewise with male and female of a species - loneliness seeks company, male seeks female, hunger seeks relief from hunger - the list is as comprehensive as the universe. This balance or harmony and the dynamics of it constitute the initial cause of all active forces in the universe, for when two things are brought into balance all motion ceases as each part has acquired that which it lacked and they now form a coherent whole.

Man, through his ingenuity, can bring a state of imbalance to things around him, and by putting his machinery between the two opposing forces, he can make use of the interplay of energy between them. He can dam a river, put generators between the opposite centers of force and have electricity. Likewise, he can perceive a need. By supplying the need's resolution, interceding with business principles, he can earn himself a livelihood. In this sense the term "middleman" is most appropriate.

Here, then, we have a basis for explaining Mr. Keely's third law of harmony. It states very simply what we have just reviewed, that all things are at a state of rest (their natural eigenfrequency or inborn rate of vibration). This "natural" rate of vibration is modulated by whatever force is brought to bear upon it, either adding to or taking away from the amplitude of that rate.

If any thing has a tendency to behave (oscillate) in any given direction, an appropriate force applied in that direction will augment (increase) that directional tendency. Hence we counsel one another to stress strengths and develop weak areas of our personalities. On the other hand, if strengths are negatized work applied to inhibit a natural talent or mode of oscillation) the opposite is produced. Non-fruitful action or attrition is the inevitable result.

The same holds true with subatomic forces. Add to a charge and that charge-phase is increased; add its opposite and it is brought into an inert state or one of non-action. This can be no better witnessed than by a simple experiment in your own bathtub. With several inches of water in the tub, place your hand in the water horizontally and gently push towards one end, the water will assume a wave form, reach the end of the tub and return going in the opposite direction until it reaches the other end of the tub at which point it will begin to travel in the same direction as before. At this point, give it another push in the same direction - the

Universal Laws Never Before Revealed.. Keely's Secrets

wave will get larger - push added to push will make the wave larger (augmented), stop the motion of the hand or push against the direction of motion (oscillation) and the wave ceases to be coherent and boils and bubbles into stillness.

This is exactly what takes place in a laser ray. All waves are created simultaneously and pushed together at the appropriate frequency. A little photon's worth of energy appears insignificant but when added together with millions of other's, it becomes something to be reckoned with.

The exact same happens with the concept of human action, that called team work. All members of a team when in "sync" can whip the daylights out of a "team" not acting in "sync".

Incidentally, this coherent activity as discussed above, is what Keely meant when he talked about "coincidental action". He said in Keely's discoveries: "Differentiation of mass, *i.e.,* discordant conditions, produce negatization to coincident action." It is the study of harmony and that which causes harmony and disharmony that this newsletter is all about , whether it be in the subatomic realm or the human realm of actions.

Commentary March, 1989

Oscillation is different from vibration. Keely defined an oscillation as "a rhythmically recurring translatory movement." Whereas a vibration is "the rhythmical motion of a body within itself."

From the two definitions we might say (because we lack additional information) that a vibration may be the pulsating motion which is alternatingly center seeking and expansive, something like the motion of a heart. This description would be in line with the Law of One. On the other hand, a motion such as a transverse wave, longitudinal wave or plate wave would be in keeping with the description of an oscillation (as defined above). Perhaps a vibration is the sedate motions of a body while at rest and the oscillation is the motion of a body during outer movements such as when a vibration may be classified as or being in a transmissive mode.

This seemingly oversimplification is of utmost importance not only in quantum physics and acoustics but also in psychology and those other areas dealing with human activity. A vibration maybe compared to an individual's activity within himself. An oscillation maybe compared to that individual's activity with those around him.

Longitudinal waves, transverse waves and all the other manifestations we have come to lump together under the term "vibration" pertain to the outer activities of the individual molecule or atom. The only time the inner activities are studied we are then talking about quantum mechanics or nuclear forces. In this area can be found Planck's Constant at work as the most notable feature of energy measurement. In a following article, Quantum Chemistry, there is being made an attempt to show how these energy states can

be approached from a more wholistic stance than has been evidenced heretofore by way of Quantum Arithmetic. Quantum mechanics admits that these quantum jumps from orbit to orbit (Planck's Constant) are always from orbit center to orbit center. In other words the jump is never from an orbit center to some

Vibration

intermediate point between these orbital layers or shells. The jump obeys a law very much in evidence in Quantum Arithmetic - i.e., the orbits represent whole numbers and not fractions thereof. Let it further be seen that these whole numbers are derived from a common base number and the subsequent derived values are whole multiples of the common base or fundamental. Here, then, is the Music of the Spheres. As has been written in this publication many times before - these values are mathematically determined to be as intervals in music evolution. They therefore represent whole and integral values derived from and dependent upon the fundamental value. All measurements of the orbital physics and all measurements of outside interactions can and do obey this

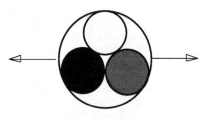

Oscillation

fundamental matrix of <u>relativity of value</u> with the fundamental numbers of the units in question.

The phenomena of periodicity, harmonic reoccurence and commonality of activity appear in any and all quantum existences. Can there be any doubt or question that the greatest story of material creation (the Holy Bible) also demonstrates this Law of the Octave?

The motional differences between an oscillation and a vibration are intriguing indeed. A reading of Buckminster Fuller's book, <u>Synergy</u>, will reveal many of the "hidden" activities of inner vibration mechanics. These inner motions are the inner sanctum of material existence and an indepth study of them reveals the inner activities of Man as well.

Likewise a study of modern nondestructive methodology will reveal many of the outer manifestations occuring in oscillations (which they call vibrations). These are the studies of the outer manifestations of forces. These may be classified as the outer,

dividual. Sympathetic Vibratory Physics is a study of the inner forces as creative influences causing the outer manifestations that materialistic science has er-

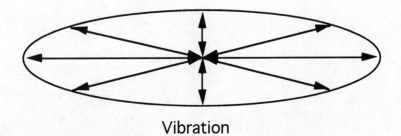

Vibration

grosser more mundane fields of study, a study of the lesser forces in nature.

The real forces in nature come from within the unit. The real force in Man comes from within the in-

roneously considered to be the object of its studies.

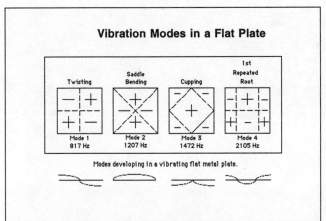

Vibration Modes in a Flat Plate

Modes developing in a vibrating flat metal plate.

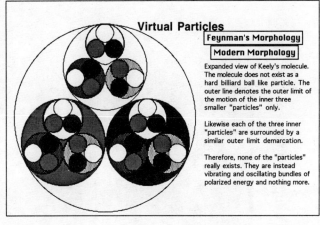

Virtual Particles

Feynman's Morphology

Modern Morphology

Expanded view of Keely's molecule. The molecule does not exist as a hard billiard ball like particle. The outer line denotes the outer limit of the motion of the inner three smaller "particles" only.

Likewise each of the three inner "particles" are surrounded by a similar outer limit demarcation.

Therefore, none of the "particles" really exists. They are instead vibrating and oscillating bundles of polarized energy and nothing more.

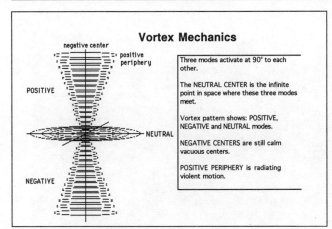

Vortex Mechanics

Three modes activate at 90° to each other.

The NEUTRAL CENTER is the infinite point in space where these three modes meet.

Vortex pattern shows: POSITIVE, NEGATIVE and NEUTRAL modes.

NEGATIVE CENTERS are still calm vacuous centers.

POSITIVE PERIPHERY is radiating violent motion.

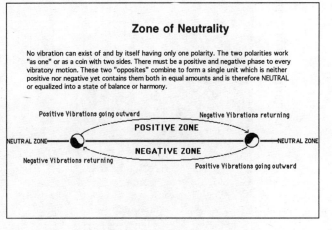

Zone of Neutrality

No vibration can exist of and by itself having only one polarity. The two polarities work "as one" or as a coin with two sides. There must be a positive and negative phase to every vibratory motion. These two "opposites" combine to form a single unit which is neither positive nor negative yet contains them both in equal amounts and is therefore NEUTRAL or equalized into a state of balance or harmony.

Compound Disintegrator. Vibratory Globe & Resonator. Medium for testing vibration under different orders of evolution.

Law of Harmonic Vibrations

"All coherent aggregates are perpetually vibrating at a period-frequency corresponding to some harmonic ratio of the fundamental pitch of the vibrating body; this pitch is a multiple of the pitch of the atomole."

Keely, 1894

Commentary February, 1986

This law (Keely's 4th Law of Harmony) states that everything (any body of whatever composition or size) vibrates at a frequency relative to that of its innermost constituent part, the atomole. The frequency of the atomole representing the fundamental or keynote of the chord (the eigenfrequency of the aggregate). The chord's aggregated rate of vibration is in direct proportion to that of this same atomole. In other words, if the atomole resonates at C^{12}, then the outer body or "coherent aggregate" will vibrate to a note somewhat lower in frequency, say C^2, or any other note forming harmonic relations to that fundamental frequency (see any good book on music theory). Usually referred to as summation or difference tones (beat frequencies), these derived frequencies form the "chord of mass" of any aggregated mass or object.

A prime example is a piano wire which sounds a primary note, the one usually associated with it, yet at the same time, it resonates many partials above and below its fundamental tone (see James Jeans' Science & Music). These partials are related to the fundamental or keynote by definite mathematical ratios, the same ratios that are evident throughout music theory.

As further analogy, a football team, representing a coherent aggregate, resonates to the overall fundamental idea of winning. The team's ideal, then, is the fundamental or keynote. The individual players' ideal is also to win, but must remain subservient to that of the team. In other words, he must follow through with the motions of a given play holding in abeyance his own personal determinations. Whatever he does on the field, must reflect actions harmonious to that of the team as it goes through its coordinated moves. Dis-coordination means failure here.

As no thing can exist of and by itself (it has to come from somewhere), its mere fact of existence tells us it is composed of or derived from something else. Something else being either more or less than whatever it is. Or simply, an object is composed of two or more "substances" or it is derived from something "larger" than itself. Since we all know by now that everything is vibratory in its inner nature, then these sources from which a substance comes is also vibratory. Hence, combining or merging vibrations will create summation or difference tones, therefore, we can safely say, that all aggregated bodies are "chords of vibrations" derived from other "chords of vibrations!" And the rules that define these modes of combination are the same as those found in music theory! (Oh! do I hear pencil sharpeners cranking or rocks beating against the windows?)

Commentary April, 1989

Fundamentally this law shows how the neutral center frequencies resonate throughout an aggregate. Whatever the fundamental pitch of the neutral center or what makes it up constitutes the frequency that permeates from the core outward and it is the pitch upon which the entire existence of the aggregate and its components are based. This may be likened to the manner in which Quantum Arithmetic uses a basic fundamental number from which all the others of a given set are derived.

It must be remembered that a pitch is a *relative frequency* and not just any number of vibrations or oscillations. It is a frequency that is derived much the same way that musical notes in a scale are derived from the fundamental upon which the scale is based. The progression of arithmetical intervals follows natural law and is not deviated from. Since the law of correspondence holds true throughout nature we might assume that the fundamental (when considered as a frequency) is the same thing as the neutral center (if considered as a thing).

Herein lies the key to all molecular substance and may point to the ancient secret of transmutation of elements. If the outer is a reflection of the inner then to change the outer one must change the inner. (Sounds a lot like personal development techniques apply to molecules just as they do to people.)

Universal Laws Never Before Revealed.. Keely's Secrets

The next step would be to calculate these frequencies (beginning with a fundamental) retaining the natural relationships between them. This was done several years ago and the formula was published in SVP, Volume II, Issue 2; Calculating Harmonies of Tones. The process will not be reviewed here as it is a lengthy one and the first article gave sufficient detail.

Suffice it to say that the process follows the naturally occurring evolution of whole numbers.

Another problem yet to be solved is how to calculate the lower frequencies from a high fundamental in a descending manner. (How high does one start?) It was at first thought to reverse the above mentioned sequence but some unusual and unexplainable gliches appeared. No solution to them has yet surfaced.

The computer is a marvelous invention and without it we would be groping in the dark with all these numbers. One can easily build a spreadsheet using any set of mathematical parameters, terms and functions to create instantaneous computations. How it was that Keely could do all this math without benefit from silicon chips can only be accredited to his apparent genius of mind and thought. Another factor maybe his unspoiled mind uncluttered with nonsensical theories and dogmatic "truths" thus he was enabled to think the unthinkable and eventual do the undoable.

We could take a fundamental number (frequency) and compute the higher tones it naturally generates using basic music theory. Once the set of numeric progression has been firmly established it is a simple matter to enter any number as the fundamental and derive the harmonics and partials. These computations are then as natural laws of progressive evolution of musical (sound or vibration) tones.

Keely's ideas concerning the molecule and the structure of its components rests on mathematical clarity. Fundamental to all orbiting bodies are three forces. An outward seeking force, an inner seeking force and a force bridging the two we call a neutral force. These forces act in straight, zig-zag and curved paths. Thus when constructing the model we naturally begin with a dot then use a straight lines to define and then connect the outer limits of activity encompassed within a circle or sphere of activity.

The outer seeking and inner seeking forces are kept in balance by the neutral force. Yet these two forces manifest as straight lines going to and fro thus forming a perfect triangle. It is from this triangle that Quantum Arithmetic takes off and even the construction of musical progressions. The attractive force of th neutral center must balance the centripetal force of inertia. *"When predominance be given to the celestial forces over the terrestrial disruption occurs."* (Keely) The celestial force is the outward seeking force. The terrestrial is the force that attracts towards the center of the mass - we sometimes call it gravity.

The Music of the Spheres can be discerned from the set intervals to which the molecular vibrations are naturally tuned. The various frequencies contained in a molecular structure must obey these intervals and to them they remain forever subservient. As Keely pointed out - any deviance from these intervals constitutes discord and molecular integrity is threatened. Which by the same token indicates to us how and why a molecule can be disrupted or caused to release energy. It is this introduced discordance that is the cause of energy development. And on the other hand this concept of equated forces indicates to us how nature is forever seeking and maintaining balance or harmony within itself. And yet again we can discern that it is number that rules and not matter or force or anything else.

If we can see among God's attributes one similar to harmony - pure harmony or forces - we can picture Keely's idea of the molecule as symbolizing the phrase "Where three are gathered in my name there I be also." The three individuals representing the three fundamental polarities of the same force balance each other out perfectly and perfect harmony is the result.

Harmony in a structure is perfect equation of forces (number or frequency).

Law of Transmissive Vibraic Energy

"All oscillating and vibrating coherent aggregates create, in the media in which they are immersed, outwardly propagating concentric waves of alternate condensation and rarefaction, having a period-frequency identical with the pitch of the aggregate."

Keely, 1894

Commentary March, 1986

The above law (Keely's fifth) dovetails with the 4th law as presented in the last (February) issue. The "pitch of the aggregate" is relative to the frequency of the innermost atomole.

This particular law, as stated above, is a close explanation of the term "eigenfrequency" used every day in physics. Every object vibrates at a given pitch. These vibrations are "waves of alternate condensation and rarefaction". Every acoustic scientist can verify such. In fact, the everyday current explanation of "compression waves" reveals exactly this "alternate condensation and rarefactions." A strongly vibrating string will cause the air to condense on one side and simultaneously cause rarefaction on the other. When considered on one side only, the air is alternately condensed and then rarefied revealing its particular pitch of vibration.

However similar this law may sound to the previous laws (#2 & #3) that is not what is being conveyed here. The law is titled "Law of Transmissive Vibraic Energy", thereby pointing to its real significance. The "alternating waves of condensation and rarefaction" are the transmissive agent in any transfer of energy and a resonance must take place between one or more of the partials of the respective chords involved. It is not the chemical or electrical properties of an atom or molecule but the wave action which constitutes the active or vital essence which causes the various activities associated with atomic or molecular processes. For, after all, is not electricity a high frequency current? According to Keely's theories, so too are magnetism, Van der Wall's forces, gravity and every other force. We will see in subsequent laws that chemicals combine or don't combine entirely dependent on the relative frequencies and harmonics (summation and difference tones) of their constituent parts. Like frequencies combine harmoniously forming stable compound, whereas unlike or discordant frequencies will combine (if at all to form unstable compounds.

As a reinforcement to this idea of atomic harmonics, let me quote from McGraw-Hill Enc. of Sci. & Tech.: "The realization that atoms are continually vibrating in motions that are **nearly harmonic** is essential for understanding many properties of matter, including molecular spectra, heat capacity, and heat conduction." Under HARMONIC MOTION. (emphasis added)

The second part of the law, the scholium (marginal annotation, explanatory remark or comment), points to common knowledge as used today. Ohm's Law, orbital motion of planetary forces electromagnetic wave propagation, weak and strong molecular forces are all part of and fall within this paragraph. In fact, a description of the Inverse-Square Law, (McGraw-Hill Encyclopedia of Science & Technology) reads: "Any law in which a physical quantity varies with distance from a source inversely as the square of that distance." A reading of Coulomb's Law (in the same publication), directly applicable to nuclear charges, is a revelation to the incredulous (if there are any still amongst our readers).

Coulomb's Law. . .

"Coulomb's Law in the rationalized mks system is as in the equation below, where q_1 and q_2 are expressed in coulombs, r is expressed in meters, and F is given in newtons.

$$F = (1/4PIe_0) (q_1 q_2 / r^2)$$

The direction of F is along the line of centers of the point charges, q_1 and q_2, and is one of attraction if the charges are opposite in sign and one of repulsion if the charges have the same sign.

Experiments have shown that the exponent of **r** in the equation is very accurately the number 2. Lord Rutherford's experiments, in which he scattered alpha particles by atomic nuclei, showed that the equation is valid for charged particles of nuclear dimensions down to separations of about 10^{-12} cm. Nuclear ex-

Universal Laws Never Before Revealed.. Keely's Secrets

periments have shown that the force between charged particles do not obey the equation for separation smaller than this." McGraw-Hill Encyclopedia of Science and Technology.

Another example would be Bode's Law.

Here we have again, evidence that John Keely was dealing with tried and true principles. Perhaps not tried in the 1880s but nonetheless, true. It is becoming more and more obvious that Keely was not a fraud as some have stated, he was simply ahead of his time. Each issue, as we progress, adds to this certainly.

Some of these laws are repetitious to current science admittedly, yet we proceed because of that self-same consistency. Keely DID disassociate water, and he DID disassociate stone as was claimed. We know this because modern technology has duplicated these feats to a slightly lesser degree using the same techniques - those of acoustic forces. The question remains, did he disassociate water to such a degree as to liberate tremendous energies? Did he in fact, levitate objects at will? Does NASA? Of course NASA does, not to any practical end yet, but certainly they do levitate small items using the same technique Keely did - acoustics.

If NASA can levitate small objects using an imperfect technique because of their (lack of total understanding), is it too hard to think a man with the proper understanding could not levitate larger objects? The manner and simplicity in Keely's presentation of his laws is ample evidence of his firm grasp of the subject.

What we are trying to say here is simply that you have made a good investment in your subscription to this journal. Your time and effort may be useful elsewhere but it certainly is not wasted being expended on our material. As we progress further and further with these articles you will begin to find ways to apply Keely's laws to your own field and possibly bring about some useful product, service or an improved manner of doing what is already being done. I, personally, have found this material helpful in explaining the workings of ordinary things which has given me insights into many perplexing contrivances or situations.

Commentary May, 1989

This law is typical of Keely's insights - it is so simple as to appear ridiculous that he called it a law. Yet its verity and value can be easily seen to have weight in physics and other areas of application. Isn't it true that the functioning of nature is simple and straightforward once we understand what is happening?

Taking a molecule as an example, according to this law, as it vibrates it creates concentric rings of propagating vibration thus causing its environment to resonate as it does. This is what an antenna does as it broadcasts its radio waves. The metal of the antenna is caused to vibrate and the vibrations travel outward in concentric rings filling its environment with its pulsations. The same happens when a bell is struck or a musical instrument is played.

Taking another law into consideration we can see that any object also in the environment of the above vibration aggregate will be affected by its periodic pulsations. Thus if there is a radio receiver tuned to the same pitch as the vibration aggregate it will "receive" the above propagating waves and the two will vibrate *as one*. Looking at the process as Keely would we must say that the process begins with the vibrating aggregate *creating* a vibration, the environment *transmits* it and the tuned object as *receiving or assimilating* those vibrations. These vibrations are called sympathetic vibrations. The three objects: vibrating aggregate, medium of transmission and receiving or receptive aggregate are all sympathetic to the periodic motion of the vibration. In other words, they all vibrate as one unit or we have three separate objects vibrating in unison.

The MIND
is the guiding influence in
all man's actions
and reactions.

A very important point to keep in my is the fact that a vibration such as we are discussing here is not a simple rate of vibration. There are many partials and harmonics in every periodic motion. These unintentional rates are also propagated throughout the medium in which the transmitting or creative aggregate is immersed. Sometimes these secondary and tertiary vibrations are of such force they may be perceived and sometimes they are mild enough to escape detection. There are also effects from these other vibrations that escape our notice simply because we are unprepared to recognize them for what they are. This is especially true when considering a complex creative aggregate. The task is relatively simple when considering a single hypothetical molecule whereas if we considered a human being as a vibrating aggregate the picture becomes complex indeed.

A human being is in truth a vibrating aggregate immersed in the medium of the atmosphere as well as in the various mediums in which it normally operates such as in the social medium, the family environment and others. Each person does have an affect on his or her immediate environment and those sympathetically tuned to the same interests, ideas and tasks. This proposition cannot be refuted. The single most noticeable means of effect is the voice - a sound vibration. For it is through the voice that man can command his environment and things within that environment to obey his will.

But there are other means man has to command and manipulate his medium in which he is immersed. These are his attitudes and emotions. What governs his attitudes and emotions? The MIND is the guiding influence in all man's actions and reactions. Without mind man is nothing. Mind is a high level vibration or spiritual manifestation. Even the materialistic quantum scientist admit that mind has an effect on quantum subjects under investigation - they call it the Uncertainty Principle. They maintain that it is impossible to study or observe quantum phenomena without bringing a disturbing influence into the picture thus making it an uncertainty as to what is actually happening in the processes under observation.

It has also been well established that the mind is affected by what is happening in its environment even though these forces have yet to be measured empirically. Some examples of this are the effects of the full moon on "unstable" individuals. Another effect is often witnessed in cases of mass panic, hysteria or other forms of crowd reactions.

Yet another characteristic of the mind which has gone mostly unrecognized is its ability to behave in a fashion akin to vibrations. It can and does pulsate as an oscillation. Its three states of "motion" are conscious, unconscious and self-conscious. When conscious or outwardly aware it can and does have a noticeable effect on its environment. This is the transmissive state. When it is self-conscious it is focused on the inner self and has little if any effect on its mediums of expression. This is the receptive or as-

similative state much like a state of studying a matter for absorption. The third state is the neutral state or one of unconsciousness wherein the individual's mind is neither transmitting (expressing) nor receiving (listening, studying, etc.) but is instead oblivious to its environment.

We can see the universal truths of these Laws of Harmony. They are universal because they can be applied *universally* throughout nature showing at once the inter-connectivity of all things.

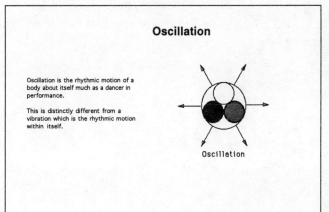

Oscillation

Oscillation is the rhythmic motion of a body about itself much as a dancer in performance.

This is distinctly different from a vibration which is the rhythmic motion within itself.

Oscillation

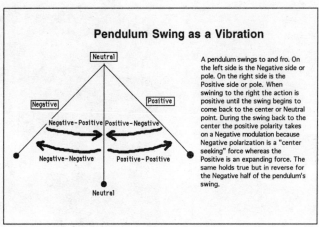

Pendulum Swing as a Vibration

Neutral

Negative   Positive

Negative-Positive Positive-Negative

Negative-Negative Positive-Positive

Neutral

A pendulum swings to and fro. On the left side is the Negative side or pole. On the right side is the Positive side or pole. When swining to the right the action is positive until the swing begins to come back to the center or Neutral point. During the swing back to the center the positive polarity takes on a Negative modulation because Negative polarization is a "center seeking" force whereas the Positive is an expanding force. The same holds true but in reverse for the Negative half of the pendulum's swing.

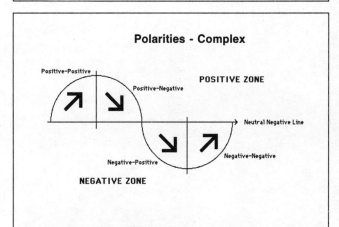

Polarities - Complex

Positive-Positive

Positive-Negative

POSITIVE ZONE

Neutral Negative Line

Negative-Positive

Negative-Negative

NEGATIVE ZONE

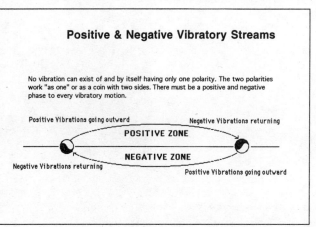

Positive & Negative Vibratory Streams

No vibration can exist of and by itself having only one polarity. The two polarities work "as one" or as a coin with two sides. There must be a positive and negative phase to every vibratory motion.

Positive Vibrations going outward   Negative Vibrations returning

POSITIVE ZONE

NEGATIVE ZONE

Negative Vibrations returning   Positive Vibrations going outward

The Sympathetic Negative Attractor.

Law of Sympathetic Oscillation

"Coherent aggregates immersed in a medium pulsating at their natural pitch simultaneously oscillate with the same frequency, whether the pitch of the medium be a unison, or any harmonic of the fundamental pitch of the creative aggregate."

Keely, 1894

Commentary April, 1986

Any coherent aggregate (any specific body), when immersed in a medium (such as the atmosphere), which is pulsating at the aggregate's natural pitch (eigenfrequency), will cause the aggregate to oscillate with the same frequency (of the atmospheric medium). Regardless whether the pitch of the medium (atmosphere) is a unison (the same frequency) or any harmonic (partial or component) of the fundamental (eigenfrequency) of the aggregate (body).

This law reflects what takes place in a finely tuned antenna circuit, *i.e.*, a finely tuned antenna will resonate to a particular frequency that has been propagated in the atmospheric medium. Let us say an antenna of one meter in length will be particularly sensitive to wave lengths of one meter in length. Whether the length be exactly one meter or ten meters (a harmonic of one) it will still vibrate. We also know that if the atmospheric wave length is more or less than one meter, say 1.2 or .9 meters, then the resonance of the antenna is less than useful, in most cases. Another good example would be two tuning forks of the same frequency; one causes the air vibrate which in turn has this particular effect on the other fork.

Here we have an excellent explanation of synchronous vibrations or sympathetic vibrations.. If the surrounding medium (the air) is vibrating at a frequency identical to or with a harmonic of the natural (eigenfrequency) frequency of the aggregate (antenna) the antenna will oscillate in unison with it (the air vibration). Likewise, if the air vibration is other than this frequency or a harmonic of it, no resonance will be manifested.

This law differs from the second law (see issue 3) in that the second law describes the natural frequency of the aggregate (antenna) alone. That is, the aggregate has its own rate independent of the medium in which it may be immersed.

We may liken this law to McGraw-Hill's definition of sympathetic vibrations which states:

SYMPATHETIC VIBRATION: "The driving of a mechanical or acoustical system at its resonant frequency by energy from an adjacent system vibrating at this same frequency. Increasing the dampening of a vibrating system will decrease the amplitude of its sympathetic vibration but at the same time widen the band of frequencies over which it will partake of sympathetic vibrations." McGraw-Hill Concise Encyclopedia of Science & Technology.

An analogy may be that of entering a quiet forest setting where one feels much peace and harmony. To accentuate this process, the same person should first experience the peace and quiet of a calm forest setting and then proceed from there into the traffic on their way home. Immersing one's self into a traffic jam has an effect of unsettling the quiet previously experienced. Thereby demonstrating the accuracy and validity of Keely's 6th Law of Harmony.

Commentary June, 1989

If a person having a little talent in a particular area is thrown in with a group of people fully exercising that talent the new person will quickly pick up what the others know and soon becomes fully competent in that area. An antenna strung up high in our frequency saturated atmosphere will oscillate and vibrate along with most of the rates it is surrounded with. Two examples far removed from each other in application but exactly the same in *function or cause of activity* - thus demonstrating that here again we have universal application and consequently a *law*.

This principle is also used by the great mystical schools of knowledge when they conduct their worldwide prayer healing sessions. If enough people mentalize what is desired many people will be influenced by that oscillatory or vibratory condition so created and begin to resonate with it. On the negative side we have the detrimental effects of Iran, old Germany and other cases of "mass hysteria." Furthermore, this is

Universal Laws Never Before Revealed.. Keely's Secrets

the basis of family, city and country group karma as outlined by Cayce in several readings on the subject. As a group thinks so they experience - to paraphrase a little. But what a tool for change and development! Imagine if many people's thoughts could be channeled similarly towards positive goals - what great deeds could be accomplished

No less important are the various ways to make this law work for us in a laboratory. By indentifying sources of power in the universe antennas or accumulators can be designed to resonate to those sources thus becoming *as channels* for energy into your next invention. *The little round disks with many thin rods radiating from its circumference found on Keely's machines served just this purpose.* There is enough energy in the atmosphere of varying frequencies to allow an accumulation of them into his spheres and snail-shell resonators thus giving him a source of energy he didn't have to go outside for.

Mechanically we could take this law and engineer a very vibrant device. Making a determination of vibrations active in a given environment (your workshop, home, etc.) and designing a vibrating device(s) that responds to such frequencies. This is what Keely's little disks with rods about its circumference did. Apparently they were sympathetic to certain frequencies and acted as very sensitive receivers of environmental motions. They also behaved like narrow band pass filters and receivers - all these functions rolled up into one simple device. The received vibration was then channeled to the center of the disk and then channeled into his machinery. This is how he could stand across a room and sound a harmonica or violin or even whistle and the device would begin its motions. In short, using this law, he was able to build a *microphone* that only responded to certain chords of frequencies and no other. This is also how radio antenna work from transmitter to receiver.

This law illustrates very well what a sympathetic vibration is: an object in accord, in harmony, in unison or of a harmonic with another are then sympathetic to each other. They are *sensitive* to each other.

They vibrate as *one unit* and not as two separated by a distance. The key then to utilizing this principle is to make the components *sympathetic* to each other and energy is then easily transferred between them.

Through sympathetic association it can be seen that everything in the Universe is connected at least in some degree. All hydrogen atoms, all atoms (because of their commonality of component sub atomic parts) are linked together through sympathetic vibrations and oscillations. Whatever is done in one place can and does have an effect elsewhere. Because of this sub atomic connection (referred to by Keely as etheric or inter-etheric) there is a "high level" or what some would call *spiritual* connection between all things. This spiritual connection some call Christ Consciousness as it permeates all things. Is this not what Christ was: sympathetic to all around Him?

This sympathy of vibration permeates the Universe from end to end and is the connecting link between Man and the Spiritual things of life. Sympathetic vibrations are obedient to the laws of harmony thus it has been rightly pointed out by Edgar Cayce and others that music is the connecting link between material and spiritual (energetic states) realms.

This one law and the one preceding it state and reinforce this awesome and all-important concept of connectivity. It is indeed a shame on the face of Man that this simple *mechanical* idea has so long escaped his notice and embrace. This simple concept destroys the warring between the Creationists and the Evolutionists at once giving the answer to their arguments - which turns out to be the same answer in both cases. The material world was both created and is evolved according to the principles of music or more properly - the science of vibration.

Small wonder then that so many new books are being written and consumed that tie quantum physics with metaphysics - because they are discussing the same principles only in different contexts (they think).

Over Unity is Recognized in Conventional Science

FLOURESCOPY: When a phosphor or other luminescent substance emits light, it gives, in most cases, an emission according to a fundamental law known as Stokes' Law. This law states that the wavelength of the flourescent (emitted) light is always greater than the wave length of the exciting radiation. It was first observed in 1852 in the memoir "On the Change of Refrangibility of Light" by Sir G. G. Stokes. In terms of energy the relationship states

$$\varepsilon\, em < \varepsilon\, ab$$

While Stokes' Law holds true for the majority of cases it does not follow in certain instances. In some cases the wave length is the same for both the absorbed and emitted radiation. That is, the efficiency appears to be perfect or unity. This is known as resonance radiation. In the other case Stokes' Law does not hold where *energy emitted is greater than the energy absorbed.* This is known as Anti-Stokes Emission. In 1935 Prileshajewa showed that there is an energy difference as much as 1.1v between the exciting light and the flourescence of aniline vapor. This added energy is attributed to additions from the internal energy of the molecule. [1]

1 Dake, H.C. & DeMent, Jack; *Fluorescent Light and Its Applications*, Chemical Publishing Company, Inc., 1941, Brooklyn, New York; pages 51-52.

Law of Attraction

"Juxtaposed coherent aggregates vibrating in unison, or harmonic ratio, are mutually attracted."

Keely, 1894

Law of Repulsion

"Juxtaposed coherent aggregates vibrating in discord are mutually repelled."

Keely, 1894

Commentary May, 1986

We have taken the liberty of discussing these two laws as they are mutually agreeable in subject matter; *i.e.,* attraction and repulsion. These two laws reflect the universality of Keely's laws of harmony. When two differing bodies associate (juxtaposed or relative in space and time), like attracts like and unlike repel (like or unlike in rate or frequency of vibration). Many of us know that we are attracted to others who resonate to our wavelength and we have also experienced the opposite when others disagree with our stance on various subjects. The same takes place in the atomic or subatomic realm. For instance mercury adheres strongly to mercury but does not always adhere to other substances as readily. Certain elements used in crystal growing (silicon & iron oxide + amethyst) readily combine while others need a complex process to bring them together. The latter can be witnessed when a crystal is desired from a solution, either liquid or gas, that is not naturally homogeneous and must be made so artificially.

These two laws lay at the foundation of sympathetic vibratory physics and other fields of study, such as chemistry, psychology, mathematics. Like in nature (inner constitution) attracts while unlike in nature (inner constitution) repels. Opposite poles of a magnet attract because they are (conceptually) alike in their inner constitution yet opposite in polar orientation. Male and female dogs, cats or humans are attracted to each other **in species** because the inner constitution is similar but the orientation (sex) is opposite.

The general discussion of polarity is fundamental to a more comprehensive understanding of John Keely's discoveries and the work of others.

Commentary July, 1989

The first law describes how and why crystals are what they are. The second law describes how a pressurized gas is what it is.

The two laws describe two opposite states of matter under two opposite states of association. Harmony is opposite from discord - one attracts the other repels.

This concept of polarity brings to mind a great many questions. For instance; do atoms join together because of their ion valency as is being taught in conventional physics or are they united because of harmonic relations of their respective vibratory makeups? What is electrochemical valency? What causes two opposite charges to unite? Why is one charge positive and the other negative? Is there an isolatable characteristic causing polar opposition that can be defined and studied?

Quantum mechanics (the study of sub-atomic phenomena) founds its very existence on vibratory forces. Mechanical concepts such as Newton's Laws of Physics are founded on gross material ideas. The idea that *an object or mass tends to remain at rest until acted upon* does not take into consideration that every tiny component making up that mass is under such tremendous vibratory and orbital motion that science can not determine to any great degree of accuracy where those components are at any given time!!! Soooo - is the mass at rest or does it just seem (to our senses) merely so??? The Newtonian concept as embodied in its very own laws is a gross material viewpoint and suffices when speaking in and with material terms. However once the veil has been lifted from our unseeing eyes into the realms of sub-atomic phenomena a new approach must be taken if an understanding of the *actuality* of the phenomena is to be had.

Even more absurd is the accepted idea that atoms can even hold themselves together at all!!! An electron spinning around a nucleus (conventional model) would or should flee its orbit due to centrifugal force.

Yet it doesn't. What force could there be sufficiently strong to hold this atom together?

Even the unimaginable forces of hurricanes, earthquakes or volcanic heat cannot break down these bounds which are indeed stronger than the strongest steel.

The idea of weak and strong molecular forces just does not hold up when imagining the forces at work in nature. What is there about harmonic and enharmonic frequencies that can bind or repel objects? Why does a harmonic chord pull objects together? Why does an enharmonic chord cause the same objects to repel each other?

Perhaps the individual particles (when in harmonic relationship) create a series of node points surrounding themselves. These node points are in set about the center of the forces as would be orbital rings or concentric rings equidistant from the center. Because a node point is a place of least activity (least vibratory motion) that any surrounding object would tend to move into this place and remain there. It would be at relative "peace" or quietude. If several objects were arranged around each other in a three dimensional matrix pattern each and every one would seek to come to rest on a node ring relative to each other. Thus a vector alignment would result and we could see that the objects would naturally form in a crystalline pattern. This pattern would be formed of lines 90° to each other and the center of each particle would align itself along these lines. Any particle center that was temporarily not aligned along these lines would eventually come into sync along a line of least resistance.

Just the opposite is experienced in a repellent situation. If a change in frequency chord is sent into this "hard alignment" the concentric ring radii would vary and the three directional vectors would change relative to each other. The centralizing tendency of the particle centers would vary and eventually break down would occur. According to Keely's work - the breakdown would occur when one directional distance exceeds a 4 to 1 ratio with another directional vector.

These concentric ring formations are a three dimensional configuration. They would represent a "shell" or a zone surrounding the center of activity of the particle fixed at a given distance from the particles' center. The next furthest ring would be at a fixed distance and this second ring's distance would also be a place of relative quiet. Orbital particles would settle on these rings and the distance between them could only be spanned as a "jump" or what has been come to be known as the Quantum Leap. A certain quanta or quantity of energy is required to be absorbed or released from the orbital conglomeration depending on whether the orbital unit is riding one concentric shell zone or another zone. Each orbit of the unit can be considered as a unit of frequency - either the velocity is increased to cover the same time of orbit on a longer or shorter orbit path or the different length of path is covered in a different time or orbit. Transition orbit time and length of vibration are interchangeable. Thus each side of the equation must remain in balance or relative.

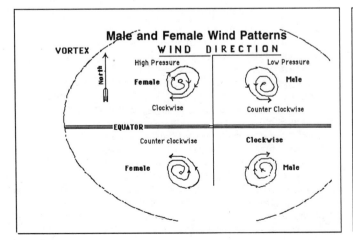

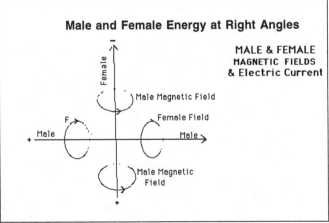

Law of Cycles

"Coherent aggregates harmonically united constitute centers of vibration bearing relation to the fundamental pitch not multiples of the harmonic pitch, and the production of secondary unions between themselves generate pitches that are discords, either in their unisons, or overtones with the original pitch; from harmony is generated discord, the inevitable cause of perpetual transformation."

Keely, 1894

Commentary June, 1986

Pythagoras stated that the greatest harmony is evidenced when the ratios of the vibrations are lowest, *i.e.*, 3 : 4 : 5 for an example, whereas a ratio of 243 : 128 has less harmony and may be considered a discord. If we take three bodies (aggregates) one with a fundamental pitch of D, one with a fundamental pitch of G and the third with a fundamental pitch of E and bring them together, they will come together harmoniously because D, G, and E are harmonically related to and derived from the keynote of C, which becomes the fundamental pitch of the united aggregate. One of the basic principles of music teaches us that when any notes, harmonically related, are simultaneously sounded, the fundamental or keynote will arise spontaneously of this sounded chord. The simplest ratios in our example are C to D or 8 : 9 (a Major tone), C to G or 2 : 3 (a Perfect Fifth) and C to E or 4 : 5 (a Major Third). Very small ratios indeed, all of which are related to the fundamental pitch or the lowest pitch to which the two or three may sound or have in common, in this case, the keynote of C.

Thus we can see that these three bodies are then in a state of harmony because of their relative fundamental pitches. The picture begins to change when we look at the higher harmonics each one of these bodies has on its own. Because the law states that these bodies are in harmony in so far as the fundamental pitch is concerned, the combinations taking place with the higher harmonics begin to bring about action, or motion because as they (the higher harmonics of each fundamental tone) join together, the resultant or summation tones are no longer simply related and are therefore called discords. This too is a fundamental principle of music, that any tone when sounded will cause its harmonics to arise simultaneously in the higher octaves. In this example we have the simultaneous generation of the higher harmonics of C, D, G, and E. As these higher harmonics begin to relate we see beats, the cause of dissonance.

Tyndall, in his book Sound, says of ratios: "The simpler the ratio of the two (or more) parts into which the string was divided, the more perfect was the harmony of the two sounds. Ratios with smaller numbers are less apt to have beats or dissonance." Once again we quote McGraw-Hill on Harmonics: *"If a violin string is bowed steadily, the frequencies of the partials of the resulting complex tone will be integral multiples of the lowest (fundamental) frequency, and the partials may properly be called harmonics. If however, the same string is struck or plucked and then allowed to vibrate freely, the frequencies of the partials in the airborne sound and the frequencies of the corresponding modes of vibration are, in general, no longer exactly in the ratios of integers, and the partials and modes of vibration are inharmonic."* In other words, beats or summation tones causes discord or a discordant pitch.

From the MacGraw-Hill definition we can see at a glance that "from harmony is generated discord, the inevitable cause of perpetual transformation."

What this has to do with Chernybol and latent energy is this: Uranium or any other element is in a state of relative harmony (a state of rest) until acted upon as above described. The phenomena known as "critical mass" comes readily to mind. Activated uranium, U_{235} for instance, is composed of tiny particles NOT in a high state of balance or harmony. The component particles are not simply related to the fundamental pitch of the aggregate. When the mass is increased, the fundamental pitch changes until such a point is reached that no harmony can be discerned, the mass becomes total discord (chaos) and we have the inevitable result action or the release of tremendous energy. With the above fully impressed on our minds let us read what John Keely says about latent energy:

LATENT FORCE IN INTERSTITIAL SPACES
by John Ernst Worrell Keely

"If latent force is not accumulated and held in corpuscular aggregations, how is it that progressive or-

116

Universal Laws Never Before Revealed: Keely's Secrets

ders of disintegration of water induce progressive conditions of increased volume and higher power?

"How is this sympathetic power held in the interstitial corpuscular condition?

"Answer: By the incalculable velocity of the molecular, atomic and etheric capsules (the ether is the capsule to the molecules and atoms all the way up to the perfect stream of structural ether) which velocity represents billions of revolutions per second in their rotations. Imagine a sphere of 12 in. diameter, a magnified molecule surrounded by an atmospheric envelope of 1/16th inch in depth, the envelope rotating at a velocity of the same increased ratio of the molecule's magnification. At the very lowest estimate it would give a velocity of 600,000 miles per second. An atmospheric film, rotating on a 12 inch sphere at the same ratio as the molecular one, would be impenetrable to a steel pointed projectile at its greatest velocity, and would hermetically enclose a resisting pressure of many thousands of pounds per square inch. A rotating envelope such as this would hermetically enclose an internal pressure of several thousands of pounds per square inch, especially when we consider that the ether, unlike the atmospheric film which has inertia and consequently centrifugal force, has centripetal force or neutral attraction in direct proportion to its velocity. This is the explanation of the wonderful pressures evolved by aqueous disintegration, which have been measured on a lever specially built for this purpose, strong enough to stand three times the explosive power of gunpowder. The evolution of power from the latent condition in interstitial space by the proper exciter in all its multiplicity of forms proves the "connecting link" between the celestial and terrestrial, the infinite and the finite. The absence of latent energy in matter would make life an impossibility.

"There would be no life, and therefore no action in aggregated matter, had the latent negative force been left out.

"The magnet arouses the interstitial latent action in a bar of iron. This is the power I am now getting under control (using the proper exciters as associated with the mechanical media) to do commercial work. In other words, I am making a sympathetic harness for the polar terrestrial force; first, by exciting the sympathetic concordant force that exists in the corpuscular interstitial domain, which is concordant to it, and secondly, after the concordance is established, by negatizing the thirds, sixths and ninths of this concordance, thereby inducing high velocities with great power by intermittent negation, as associated with the dominant thirds.

"Again: Take away the sympathetic latent force that all matter is impregnated with, the connective link between the finite and the infinite would be dissociated and gravity would be neutralized, bringing all visible and invisible aggregations back into the great etheric realm (read: dissolved into its subatomic components).

"What is cohesion, the power holding the molecules together, but electromagnetic negative attraction? What is the state that is brought about by certain conditions of sympathetic vibration causing molecules to repel each other, but electromagnetic radiation?

"It must not be understood that the character of the action of the latent force liberated from liquids and gases is the same in its evolution, as that of the latent force existing in metals. The former shows up an elastic energy, which emanates from the breaking up of their rotating envelopes, increasing, at the same time, the range of their corpuscular action, thus giving under confinement, elastic forces of an almost infinite character. By liberation from the tube it is confined in, it seeks its medium of concordant tenuity with a velocity greater than that of light.

"In metals, the latent force as excited by the same sympathizer, extends its range of neutral sympathetic attraction without corpuscular rupture, and reaches out as it were to link itself with its harmonic sympathizer, as long as its exciter it kept in action. When its exciter is dissociated, its outreach nestles back again into the corpuscular embrace of the molecular mass that has been acted upon.

"This is the polar sympathetic harness, as between metallic mediums and the polar dominant current - the leader of the triune stream of the terrestrial flow.

"The velocity of the sympathetic bombarding streams, towards the centers of neutrality in the corpuscular atoms, during sympathetic aggregation of visible molecular masses (in registering the latent force in their interstitial spaces) is thousands of times greater than that of the most sensitive explosives. An atmospheric stream of that velocity would atomize the plate of an ironclad, if brought to bear on it.

"All these conditions of evolution and concentration are accomplished by the celestial mind force, as associated with terrestrial brain matter.

"Latent force is accumulated and held in interstitial space by corpuscular aggregation, otherwise the progressive disintegration of water could not induce increased volume and pressure.

"The latent force liberated from liquids and gases differs from that liberated from metals in that it is elastic, giving an infinite variety of pressure, whereas in the metals, vibration simply extends the range of neutral sympathetic attraction without corpuscular rupture as it reaches out for concordance in the sympathizer.

"This sympathetic latent power is held by the incalculable velocity of the molecular etheric capsule and the atomic etheric capsule, which rotate at billions of times per second, in interstitial corpuscular aggregation.

"The mighty forces latent in corpuscular matter - and all matter - are held in oscillating vortex action, this latent, registered definite power interchanging sympathetically with the celestial radiating stream (renewing loss in radiation through absorption by receptiveness) whereby light, heat, electricity and magnetism are propagated in their different orders, vitalizing Nature with their life giving principles."

"The first seal is being broken, in the book of vibratory philosophy, the first stepping stone is placed toward reaching the solution of that infinite problem, the source of life."

After having explored, in a preliminary sort of

way, the concept of latent forces, I'd like to present some of Cayce's readings dealing with the human body as a composition of molecular, atomic and subatomic particles. With the introduction of these readings we are opening up a whole and vast area to be explored in subsequent issues, that of the correlations between mind, body and health. The human body cannot be considered separate from mind and its latent forces, nor can mind be considered wholly a psychological phenomena without that which it uses as its intermediary for its expression, the body. These two organism function interdependently, one without the other is as improbable (in the healthy creative individual) as the sun would be without sunlight.

THE ROLE OF ATOMIC FORCES
IN HEALING

Below we quote a few of the many readings given by Edgar Cayce on the role atomic forces have in the field of healing. Much thought and research have gone into these readings in the attempt to decipher the uncanny accuracy that was sometimes evidenced in the healing manifested through following material from this source. When one realizes that the human body is composed of molecular, atomic and subatomic particles and that energies are manifested in these particles, one can then begin to see that to evoke a harmonious condition (health) in the bodily functions these particles must not be left out of any prognosis. Next month we will publish a series of readings wherein many conditions are described as being the result of sympathetic conditions arising from disharmony in other parts of the body.

"In every physical being, the whole body is made up of the atomic forces of the system, with the mind of each atom, at it is builded, supervised by the whole mental mind of the body, varied by its different phases and attributes, for, as is seen in its analysis, an atom of the body is a whole universe in itself, in the minutest state. The attitude, then, of all the attributes of the mind toward self, and the forces as manifest through same, become paramount. As to any healing in the body, or any application of any source, nature, character, kind, or condition, is only to create that incentive in that same atomic force to create the better condition in a body, whether it be medicinal properties, whether it be of manipulation to induce incentive reaction, whether it be of an operative nature, or what not, is to create that same condition in the atomic forces of the body to bring about the better physical conditions in the system. Then, necessarily, it is paramount. How to go about same? May be through self and self's attitude towards those conditions which are of the physical and spiritual natures in an individual, and to this individual especially." (137-81)

"The consideration that is to be given in making any application for corrective forces, that there may be the better coordination in the mental, the superficial, the imaginative and the physical being, would be to create within the system itself that as makes for the proper coordination of atomic forces as control the functioning of, and the changing of, those material conditions, as are taken, for substance, into the physi-

cal body, into such vibratory forces as to create a normal equilibrium between the matter in the body and that of a normal, or near normal functioning of that matter in a material plane and in a material body.

"As is seen and known, all atomic forces are of an electrical nature in their effect and effect upon a physical organism. Not all portions of the system function in the same vibratory rate, as the nerves of the sensory organism are made - as it were - in a series of necessary portions of system for the proper alteration of vibration of atomic forces to create either that of vision, hearing, so also, in the assimilation as for gland functioning - as creates in the system those elements that add to either the nerve energies in their activity those necessary elements for the coordination of the muscular forces within the system, as to produce functioning in a nominal or normal manner, or they are overcharged or undercharged - that prevent their functioning in a nominal manner. Hence, as is seen, in a manner, as how the activity of the physical body can be altered by the concerted activity of minds that are directed to the atomic forces of an individual, in raising their vibrations to a normal or normal manner. Hence we have that of spiritual healing to a body.

"Now, the same vibrations may be raised for a physical body, in the physical sense, as may be raised in a mental or spiritual body by its association or its connection with that that creates a necessary element of vibration for corrective forces in a system.

"Then, to find the correct vibration for elements that are lacking in their sustaining forces for a living organism, and to create that within the enlivening portions of the system in such a way and manner as for same to be assimilated by, or become effective in, a living organism, is to be able to change that environ of that physical organism as to be creative and evoluting in its activity in that system.

"For this body, then, we would find that we would add those vibrations from the low form of the electrical vibration as comes from that known or called in the wet cell vibration from those atomic forces necessary in the forces of the body itself." (5576-1).

"As is understood, Life - God - in its essence is Vibration, and - as the physical beings are of that atomic force, a portion of the same - the awareness of same is as to how conscious that vibration may be made, even as we find in the physical body that sight, hearing, taste, speech, are but an alteration of vibration attuned to those portions in the consciousness of the physical body, becoming aware of things, of vibrations, reaching same from within or from without. Hence one may not hear the prayer or the thought sent by an individual whose attunement is not sufficient to raise that vibration in an individual, but the combined - as we have in numbers - raise to such an extent that the awakening comes by this continuing of this direction of the spiritual forces to an individual; even as the small drop may wear away the hardest stone." (281-4)

"Here, let's analyze for the moment, to those that must consciously - as this body - see and reason, see a material demonstration, occasionally at least! Each atomic force of a physical body is made up of its

Universal Laws Never Before Revealed: Keely's Secrets

units of positive and negative forces, that brings it into a material plane. These are of the ether, or atomic forces, being electrical in nature as they enter into a material basis, or become matter in its ability to take on or throw off. So, as a group may raise the atomic vibrations that make for those positive forces as bring divine forces in action into a material plane, those that are destructive are broken down by the raising of that vibration! That's material, see? This is done through Creative Forces, which are God in manifestation! Hence, as self brings those little things necessary, as each is found to be necessary, for position, posture, time, period, place, name, understanding, study each, and assist each in their respective sphere. So does the entity become the healer." (281-3)

Keely's Frequencies. . .

Last month we published a listing of some of the frequencies mentioned throughout the Keely literature. Subscribers have written in with some accurate observations and a few valid questions that need answering. Even though we don't possess the right and proper answer, we will attempt to arrange things in order that these questions can best be addressed.

To begin with we list again the same frequencies as before, with a few additions:

Commentary August, 1989

Taking an aggregate, say a molecule, and analyzing its component frequencies one would, according to this law, find many frequencies *other than harmonic derivatives* of the fundamental. This may explain why it is difficult to find harmonic derivatives in such an analysis just as it has often proven to be.

This law embodies the ideas previously and repeatedly stressed herein about musical note progressions. Hughes' *Harmonies of Tones and Colors*, Ramsay's *Scientific Basis and Build of Music* and Harris' *Acoustics* all give substance to unravel this "discords from harmony."

It is not such a difficult concept to grasp. It is, however, complex and exacting. The Musical Ratios spreadsheet found in the SVP catalog was designed to derive these ratios of one frequency relative to another. The above mentioned books also give illustrated essays on the subject.

It is believed that this is perhaps the greatest "secret" to be revealed concerning Keely's work. Once these musical progressions are deciphered in a coherent and logical manner - all sorts of "mysteries" are to be revealed to the seeker of truth.

Electrical and mechanical engineers are all very familiar with finding the harmonics of fundamentals. The harmonic is an obvious discernment and it is easy to divide or multiply by 2. However, to find a *third* or *sixth* or *Perfect Fifth* is not as easy - unless one is trained to discern them - much as a musician is trained in the art. Remember that Keely was a musician before he became a physicist!

The exact deciphering of this problem has eluded this author for a number of years. Hughes comes the closest to giving the exact methodology yet. The basic premise is that a fundamental, in its progression to a higher frequency, creates from within itself these higher frequencies such as its octave. The other notes or frequencies produced are similar or inverse to the Fibonacci series. If these notes are constrained to a single measure as is used in music notation we would see within this measure the seven basic notes of an octave with the octave appearing in the next measure. Now these seven notes are not written down from the lowest to the highest in an ever increasing (in frequency) manner. They are however, evenly spaced, linearly speaking, from the left side to the right side of the measure. These spacings are referred to as "periods" or "steps." The fundamental occupies the first period, space or step of the measure. This progression is better illustrated in the evolution of keynotes and not through individual notes. Hughes has some beautiful charts clearly illustrating this concept.

One interesting metaphysical correlation derived from all this is F is the root of C and C is the root of G. Each step being a Fifth and one of great harmony. F whose color is green may be symbolic of Eden giving birth to Man (C or red) who in turn gives birth to Women (G or blue). So we may say that F being the fertile neutral center first expands out (male-ish activity) creating an everlasting male influence in the environment. All the while this male influence continues expanding it causes its own pole to be created as no thing can exist in and by itself. The female counterpart is thus called into existence. This is something like minting coins - as soon as one side of the coin is minted the other side comes into being simply because no coin can possess one side only.

Looking back to the beginning it has been stated that darkness was in the beginning. Ultraviolet may be taken as dark because the human eye cannot really see deep ultraviolet. Ultraviolet corresponds to B. B is the root of all keys (frequencies, notes, etc.). From B the second step in our progression is the note E - its color is yellow. Yellow of course is the Sun or the light of day. Hence was created day and night *at the same time* because day cannot exist without the lack of day or night. Thus we can see the development of the first trinity of the greatest harmony - C, red, man; E, yellow, sun; and G, blue, woman. This trinity also corresponds to the Holy Trinity of the Bible as "Him first," the son of God; "Him midst," the Almighty Father, and "Him last," the Holy Spirit, proceeding from the Father and the Son, Trinity in Unity. The correlation with the biblical scenes as depicted in Genesis (first three octaves of creation) is plain to see. Remember that Genesis is the story of creation - *creation of the material realm* and is part of our study of how atoms and molecules evolve themselves. This understanding will help to understand how atoms and molecules may be taken apart and modified in our materialistic world. It is this study of the creative forces to which we have devoted ourselves.

Though at times it appears as though I write about religion - *this is not so* - I write about the creative forces. Religious teachings have preserved these ideas through the centuries because they tell of man's association with and how he is part of these forces

119

and processes. By understanding the above creation
and progression of forces one begins to grasp the idea
that *nothing is by accident* - that each and every thing
is done *according to Law* - natural Law as it unfolds
itself through time and space.

Rotating Resonator, weight, 780 lbs., and Vibratory Globe.

Keely's final motor on left. This machine operates via amplified gluonic bonding/repulsing forces as near as we can understand Keely's explanations.

Law of Harmonic Pitch

"Any aggregate in a state of vibration develops in addition to its fundamental pitch a series of vibration in symmetrical sub-multiple portions of itself, bearing ratios of one, two, three, or more times its fundamental pitch."

Keely, 1894

Commentary July, 1986

What we begin to see through this law is the unfolding of the inner relationships between the evidenced eigenfrequencies of an aggregated mass and the subtler, less evident vibrations of its makeup. Quite clearly we have seen and discussed the vibrations and the fundamental origins of those vibrations. This law indicates there are more vibrations not necessarily perceived as such. We perceive here a series of motions that may be categorized as a quality perpetuating itself by simple number ratios, i.e., a "quantization" (condensation and rarefaction) seems to be taking place. What are being described here are the harmonic pitches that arise from the fundamental pitch of the aggregate. However, in reviewing last months law, "The Law of Cycles," we see that there are also, in any given aggregate, another parallel group of vibrations. These other vibrations, we saw, are developed as BEAT frequencies, summation or resultant tones. See issue 9 for examples.

So here we have a description of two types of frequencies arising from the same fundamental or source of all other vibrations as appear in a given aggregate. Harmonic pitches and summation or difference pitches make up the whole of the vibrating spectrum.

The next step in dealing with these multiple frequencies is to determine how and why any given vibration of frequency arises from another or in this case the fundamental. The answer lies in Music Theory. A fundamental will, when sounded, give rise to its harmonic and the other summation or beat tones. Any sophomore music theory student knows this! The Key question still remains - HOW DOES ONE NOTE BECOME ANOTHER? The creation of harmonics is simply the fundamental dividing itself by two over and over again. The next step is the harmonics sounding together and with the fundamental causing the summation and difference tones. For instance: 2 as a fundamental gives rise to 4 or 8 or 16 as harmonics. 8 minus 2 gives us a difference tone of 6

whose lower harmonic is 3 and several higher harmonics of 9, 12, 18 etc. Where these frequencies match we get higher amplitudes or lower amplitudes as they "mis-match". Below we have a listing done by Sir James Jeans of music theory renown wherein he calculates some of the generated frequencies from a fundamental. The root is C at 64. Ramsay and Hughes both differ from this system.

C	64		x1
C1	128	Harmonic	x2
E	162		
G	192		x3
C2	256	Harmonic	x4
E2	324		
C+E	290	Summation	
E+G	354	Summation	
C+G	320	Summation	x5
C-E	34	Difference	
E-G	30	Difference	
C-G	64	Difference	
C3	384	Harmonic	x6
E3	486		
G3	576	Harmonic	x9
C+E+G	482	Summation	
C2+E	418	Harmonic + Summation	
E2+C	452	Harmonic + Summation	
E2+G	516	" "	
G2+E	546	" "	
G2+C	512	" "	x8
C2+G	448	" "	x7

The above list of frequencies is only partially complete. It is revealing to note that all these notes are generated from sounding the single note of C (64 cps). This single fundamental gives rise to its harmonics C1, C2, etc. and all the rest are derived from it "spontaneously". Therefore, when we say no thing can or does exist in and by itself, the evidence is now before us. All things are related SYMPATHETICALLY. One can even say that all the above notes are ONE, because they have arisen from ONE source, C.

Universal Laws Never Before Revealed: Keely's Secrets

A more accurate statement would be that they are from ONE family or ONE origin, but not ONE single separate unit. This evolutionary process of musical notes will be further explored in future issues.

Commentary September, 1989

This law of one of the more recognized and accepted laws in use today. All fields of engineering use it extensively in calculations both derivative and functional.

The use of the word pitch is also accurate as a pitch is a relative frequency where frequency alone is simply a number of cycles per second. Again the use of musical terminology is fundamental to the in-depth study of vibratory phenomena. Being relative is the state of relating to something else - another frequency, the fundamental or key note, in this case.

It is not known when electronic and other engineers began using harmonics in their work. Certainly this usage began some time ago. What is even more puzzling is why hasn't this well-known law of physics been identified as a law? When something always and invariably takes place as a result of a given action it is without a doubt a law. A vibratory occurrence will always and at all times produce these harmonics. They can be calculated by doubling the frequency and the subharmonics can be calculated by halving the frequency. The Electromagnetic Scale commonly seen in school class rooms and engineering departments is based entirely on this concept. These scales begin with 1 cycle per second and doubles at each octave resulting in a sequence of numbers: 1, 2, 4, 8, 16, 32, 64... .

All of the above is just dandy - what is a vibration anyway? Is it a periodic motion back and forth or to and fro? Or is it an alternating pulsation? It may be either, both and even other modes of periodic *changing of state*. Various objects in motion and under consideration may behave in different motions. However, what remains the same in all cases is the object changes state from what may be considered a positive state, to a negative state and also the neutral state. For instance a stretched piano or guitar wire may be said to swing back and forth. Upon consideration it may be seen to also shorten and length as the string increases its swing further away from the neutral or rest position. Thus a simple guitar string vibrates in at least two different directions at 90° to each other. As the string moves towards is furthest distance away from the neutral position the ends tend to draw closer together simultaneously (if they were not rigidly fixed they would approach each other).

Another fundamental principle of harmonic creation is that of tension. Increase the tension the string and the frequency also increases. Therefore as the string swings again to its furthest extension away from the neutral position it tends to increase the tension. as it approaches its furthest extension the frequency again changes to a higher rate.

The law of harmonics even applies to gravity. For every 16 feet an object falls its velocity doubles. Would this mean that gravity is a function of velocity? Accelerate an object to a given velocity (escape velocity) and it will escape the pull of gravity. Velocity therefore may be a rate of change from one polarity (state) to another. Polarity is a difference of state, harmonic, dominant (neutral) or enharmonic.

To say that a complex shaped piece of metal vibrates to a given frequency is misleading. It would, however, be correct to say that the piece of metal does have a fundamental pitch. From this fundamental pitch are developed harmonic pitches, enharmonic pitches and a wide assortment of node configurations. The various wave forms and frequencies constitute a chord of pitches. Thus this complex assortment of wave forms constitutes Keely's "chord of mass."

To sum up a little, even though a vibrating aggregate does indeed create a series of harmonic pitches, it also creates a series of enharmonic pitches. These various forms of evolved pitches constitutes the vibratory composition of the aggregate. Harmonic pitches alone do not reflect the true vibratory nature of any aggregate. They but represent an over simplification of the analysis. Small wonder then that "modern" science has done so little when it could do so much more. Their analysis has been confined to harmonic analysis, without recognizing this function as a law of nature, and have lumped all the other noted frequencies derived from their analysis as unrelated mathematically to the fundamental. These other frequencies have been classified with statistical methods alone. Statistical methods are nothing other than various ways to average indeterminate numbers. Averaging does not recognize the individuality nor interrelatedness of a set of numbers. Music terminology and methodology makes no such error. It recognizes a given frequency for what it is and how it may relate to others. Music (SVP) is broad-minded enough that it can give credit where credit is due. If it didn't music (SVP) would have no basis to exist as its very existence is founded on the idea that all things *do* exist and *do* have a meaningful relation to all other things.

This may be the salvation for dogmatic and differentiating science. If an object sounds a fundamental it also sounds all of its harmonics and enharmonics as an infinite chord of frequencies. *Radionics has long recognized and worked quite successfully with this fact.* Since this chord is really an infinite series of pitches it therefore stands to reason that all things have an infinite effect - not just the effects found within a certain and limited spectrum of frequencies.

Law of Force

"Energy manifests itself in three forms: *Creative*, the vibrating aggregate; *Transmissive*, being the propagation of isochronous waves through the media in which it is immersed; *Attractive*, being its action upon other aggregates capable of vibrating in unisons or harmony."

Keely, 1894

Commentary August, 1986

If we take the analogy of two finely tuned tuning forks and set one to vibrating, is manifesting the Creative form of energy alluded to in the above law or that which creates the other two forms of energy. The next manifestation of energy would be a continuous series of waves set into motion by the vibrating fork, these are the Transmissive energy mentioned above propagating through the air surrounding the fork. The third manifestation of energy is manifested after the second fork begins to vibrate which is caused by the impinging Transmissive energy, this is the Attractive energy, because of its affinity for that particular frequency it tends to have an attractive quality to which said frequency of vibration readily seeks.

There is a lot implied here and we will explore the method of "guidance" or means these forks use to identify and then communicate with each other as we develop our sensitivity to the subject matter. It is the Dominant current of the triune chord which is suspected as the supra-light velocity means of touch or sympathy attunement. I will devote a full journal to this subject of sympathy later.

It may be added here that the two finely tuned forks, are in sympathetic attunement because of their resonant character; *i.e.*, they are in sympathy because of their likeness insofar as inherent frequency sensitivity goes. Any number of items so attuned are therefore said to be sympathetic or they possess this quality of sympathy.

Commentary October, 1989

This law of one of the more elegant of Keely's 40 Laws of Harmony. In it are embodied the fundamental basics of sympathetic vibrations - their theory as well as their actual function. This law is also a perfect descriptive of the multi-phenomena called cause and effect. What is wrong with the concept of cause and effect is answered in this law; *i.e.*, what happens between the cause and its effect?

Any engineer possessing an open mind must admit that energy must first be created or made manifest. This manifested energy possesses discrete and identifiable characteristics. A good analogy familiar to many engineers it that of a radio transmitter-send-receiver setup. All sorts of mechanical, electrical and other processes are involved in developing the power and signal preparatory to broadcasting. This is a highly complex and exacting preparation. An even more common analogy would be common speech or conversation between two or more parties. One formulates an idea and prepares the subject and method (infliction, tone, emotion, etc.) for delivery one's own spoken word before the first word is uttered. This can be a carefully cultivated speech designed to have a special effect on the listener or it can be a careless "engage mouth before engaging brain" action. Part of the process of preparation involves allocation to ambient noise (ever try to talk in a discotheque?), hearing acuteness of the recipient, language used and understood by the recipient, *etc*. It too is a highly complex and exact preparation.

Notice in the foregoing preparation process attention is given by the talker (*Creative*) to the environment and to the capabilities of the listener. These are the second (*Transmissive*, ambient conditions) and third (*Attractive*, listener) parts of the above law. The same process is taken under very serious consideration by a radio technician when engineering and installing a radio transmitter-send-receiver setup.

According to Keely's philosophy and that of MacVicar (Sketch of a Philosophy) all things regardless of location are intimately connected. All organized bodies are permeated and surrounded with the æther. The æther is a super fine subatomic substance from which the subatomic, atomic and molecular particles are created. This is a primordial "soup" composed of many differing particles possessing many differing characteristics. Hence, as we have said herein, there is no such thing as a perfect vacuum (ab-

Universal Laws Never Before Revealed: Keely's Secrets

sence of any and all material objects) - there is *something* permeating interplanetary space - long held to be a perfect vacuum.

Because of this omni-connectivity, any action or cause has an effect on everything else. Conventional science is beginning to realize this in their studies of the environment. Pollution is not a personal and isolated cause with localized detrimental effects. It permeates the entire bio-sphere of our earth having diverse origins and effects. This environmental situation however is found within a narrow range of action - the subatomic through the molecular. The æther, on the other hand, permeates all this range and ranges far beyond the ability of Man's instruments to yet detect.

This ætheric environment is so fine a substance that it possesses a an æthereal pressure of 122,400,000,000 times that of the atmosphere, according to MacVicar or is 986,000 denser than steel, according to Keely. With such an intimate contact with and between its component particles how could everything not be in contact? A slight breathe on a dandelion would be instantly transmitted to the far reaches of the universe. An eruption on Mars or Neptune would have an effect on affairs on earth.

This ultrafine medium of transmission, the æther, behaves in a unique manner. Unique in the eyes of Newtonian/Einsteinian physics that is. Current paradigms invest the transmission of energies as an applied force expanding outward after this force has been created or generated from somewhere else. Thus the Law of Conservation of Energy is an absolute and essential part of the existing paradigm. It is doubtful that æther works solely on these premise. In fact, because of its nearly infinite density it behaves quite differently. According to Keely and MacVicar the æther has what they both call "sympathetic negative attraction." This is embodied in the one great law of the universe that all objects tend to assimilate themselves to themselves and to each other in successive moments. Thus the universe, and all that it contains, is permanently and forever seeking to co-exist in harmony and oneness because of this all-pervasive connectivity.

What is done in one place is transmitted instantly to every other place and there, at that point, is felt the effects of the original causative motion. The mode or arena of transmission is the ætheric realm of substances. If one finds or constructs a *channel* from the ætheric to the molecular - the effects can then be observed. This is the principle of the so-called radionics devices. A bridge is constructed from the finite molecular realms of substances to the infinite ætheric realms of substances. The principles governing the construction of such a bridge can be found in music. Music is the harmonizing of vibrations. A vibratory motion is self-creative and will sound all of its higher harmonics even to the highest ætheric realms. Keely built such a bridge in his devices 100 years ago.

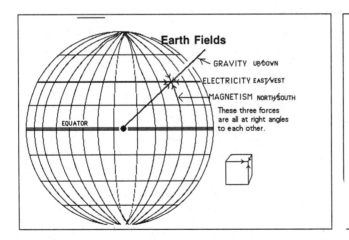

Earth Fields

GRAVITY UP/DOWN
ELECTRICITY EAST/WEST
MAGNETISM NORTH/SOUTH

These three forces are all at right angles to each other.

EQUATOR

Ether or Æther

"The luminiferous æther - the compound interetheric element - in other words, celestial mind force - is the substance of which all visible and invisible things are composed." Keely

Steiner's Four Ethers

Life Ether
Light Ether
Chemical or Tone Ether
Warmth Ether

Æther is an atomolic substance 986,000 times the density of steel." Keely

"The fundamental mode of vibration changes as we reach the fifth subdivision of matter, to the dominant, the diatonic third of the mass chord, which controls the vibratory states of both the etheron and interetheron. The awful might concealed in the depths of the etheric and interetheric subdivisions utterly transcends anything Science has ever known. Even the theoretical energy value of radium now accepted by Science, pales into insignificance in comparison to the energy value of an equal amount of water subdivided to the etheric or interetheric state." Keely

Law of Oscillating Atomic Substances

"Coherent atomic substances are capable of oscillating at a pitch varying directly as the demsity, and inversely as the linear dimensions from one period of frequency per unit of time to the 21st octave above, producing the creative force of Sonity, whose transmissive force (Sound) is propagated through the media of solids, liquids, and gases, and whose static effect (Sonism) produces attractions and repulsions between sympathetically vibrating bodies according to the Law of Harmonic Attraction and Repulsion."

Keely, 1894

Commentary September, 1986

The Law of Harmonic Attraction and Repulsion we take to be the laws discussed in issue #8 and possibly the law discussed in issue #10. Please review these. These laws for a comprehensive WHOLE and should be considered so. (Unlike conventional science wherein there are so many laws scattered amongst the various disciplines.) Keely seemed to have created a truly unified approach that promises to bring many different subject areas into a comprehensive paradigm.

In this law we can begin to see and understand Keely's classification process of matter. Material aggregates labeled "atomic" are those substances that have a natural frequency range of from 1 to 3,145,728 cps (see Keely's Frequencies in issue #9).

Herein he also differentiates between a "creative force" called Sonity, the "transmissive force" called Sound, and the "static force" or "attractive force," Sonism. We can see at a glance that this does not coincide with modern theory. We may even begin to perceive the idea of why Keely claimed sound, a transmissive force, travels at 20,000 fps in a vacuum. This may be true if one considers sound to be an aggregation of phonons just as light is an aggregation of photons or electricity is an aggregation of electrons. An unhindered phonon (lacking molecular interference within a vacuum) may very well travel at this rate! Besides this, sound is a conscious perception, *i.e.*, it is only sound if it is audible to the human ear. Anything traveling at 20,000 fps isn't going to be audible! On top of all this, a phonon, being an interatomic or subatomic particle wouldn't necessarily be hindered by a gross molecular substance such as the vacuum chamber's walls, but would, theoretically, pass right through it lust as light photons pass through "solid" glass unhindered or even as magnetic particles pass through "solid" steel.

Getting off the subject (but still within it's scope) regarding perception, I'd like to make a case for supra light speeds, or the possibility of something traveling faster than light. Light is a sensory perception, which means the eyes are capable of receiving photons at this rate and has the ability to convert them into nerve signals, *etc*. Because electromagnetic phenomena also travel at this speed, the visual perception apparatus of man is marvelously suited for this purpose. However, in the hypothetical case of something traveling faster than light and/or electromagnetic speeds, they cannot be perceived because they out race the visual apparatus of man. This also holds true for any instruments he may use which are based on electrical circuits for measuring such a supra-light velocity. Logically, there could be many things traveling at these incredible velocities, but because of the aforementioned restrictions it is doubtful they can be readily perceived and measured. This difficulty nevertheless does not preclude the existence of such entities.

The first part of this law, "Coherent atomic substances are capable of oscillating at a pitch varying directly as the density, and inversely as the linear dimensions from one period frequency per unit of time" reads very much like Tesla's description of energy quoted below:

"The kinetic and potential energy of a body is the result of motion (vibration) and determined by the product of its mass and the square of its velocity. Let the mass be reduced, the energy is diminished by the same properties. If it be reduced to zero, the energy is likewise zero for any finite velocity."

Nikola Tesla

Energy, of course, is an equation of motion (velocity or vibration), Einstein's Theory of $E=MC^2$ quite clearly exemplifies this. That Keely classifies "atomic substances" by and within a given frequency range is almost unintelligible until we come to realize that an atomic substance is different than a molecular substance in his way of thinking. A pure crystal may be called an atomic substance when it is composed of a single atomic substance or element, whereas a molecular substance is composed of two or more atoms

126

Universal Laws Never Before Revealed: Keely's Secrets

(atomic substances of elements), according to modern chemical theory. It is logical to think that two different atoms, vibrating at different chords, will have a modulating effect on each other that may lead to a lower frequency range due to harmonics but also because the linear dimension has INCREASED and the density has decreased, each of which by itself, would have lowered the frequency. So the second part of his statement appears to be true.

That an atomic substance can have more density than a molecular substance is not quite as far out a concept as it first appears. There can be fitted far more atoms in a given space than can molecules and the "empty" spaces between such atoms is also smaller than the "empty" space surrounding the molecules. Following this concept further one could grasp, at least conceptually, why Keely claimed æther is 987,000 times denser than steel, because more æther particles can be placed in a given volume than steel molecule (a complex molecule, meaning LARGE molecule) and the resulting surrounding "empty" space is almost non-existent or at least not measurable. It is also logical to think that some atoms are as large as some molecules and vice versa because Keely claims the frequency bands of atomic vibrations and molecular vibrations overlap to some degree.

Commentary November, 1989

Coherent atomic substances are capable of oscillating (oscillation is a rhythmically recurring translatory movement) **at a pitch (pitch is the relative frequency of vibration) varying directly as the density** (a coherent substance is like a crystal of a pure atomic element. The atoms are all the same and are ideally situated within the crystalline structure. The oscillations of this substance increase in frequency directly in relation to the crystal's density - the higher the density the higher the frequency) **and inversely as the linear dimensions** (as the linear dimensions increase the frequency diminishes and as the size diminishes the frequency increases) **from one period of frequency per unit of time to the 21st octave above** (the oscillations begin at one cycle per second or whatever time unit is employed and continue up to the 21st octave or to the middle of the electromagnetic wave spectrum, *i.e.,* radio, at 2,097,152 cycles per second - this is the limit of atomic oscillations), **producing the creative force of Sonity** (this produced force is a new complex action resulting from the interactions of these frequencies resulting from homogeneous oscillations of this coherent medium - lattice structure - which bears these particular characteristics), **whose transmissive force (Sound)** (Sound is the propagating or carrying medium that is the vehicle through which this new complex creative force - sonity - is transmitted) **is propagated through the media of solids, liquids, and gases, and whose static effect (Sonism)** (Sonism is a new complex assortment of forces or rather effects of the force sonity possessing attributes some of which we have come to recognize as short and long atomic and molecular forces - atomic and molecular cohesion in other words when attractive and fission or dissociation when disruptive) **produces attractions and repulsions between sympathetically vibrating bodies** (the particular character - attraction or repulsion is a function of the degree of sympathy or like vibratory characteristics of the aggregated bodies or atoms in which the creative force sonity has been introduced) **according to the Law of Harmonic Attraction and Repulsion** (the character of the attraction or repulsion is dictated by the atom's degree of conformity to the Law of Harmonic Attraction and Repulsion - see SVP July, 1989).

This is a complex law. It entails the creative force, the transmissive force and the effects of these forces on third party coherent particles. Remember particles are really vibrating bundles of energy each possessing its own particular range and assortment of vibration frequencies, modes and other particulars.

Each will tend to react to the creative force, sonity, impinging upon it in a slightly different manner. The creative force, sonity, is also unique in its characteristics dependent upon the nature of the initial make-up of the aggregates from which it originates and of course the transmissive force, sound, is again entirely characterized by the media in which it finds itself.

A good analogy is a speaker, creative, speaking through the medium of the atmosphere, sound, and the listener passively being effected, sonism, by that which was created - the lecture - then transmitted through the air by way of sound.

The inner nature of that which was meant is not that which is being conveyed by the air and may not be that which is understood. A good speaker, on the other hand, is one that can maintain the integrity of that which is in his mind through the entire process of communication. When the speaker (that which is creative), the medium of transmission (quiet, still air) and the listener (that which is receptive) are in a high degree of sympathy then perfect transmission can and does take place. If on the other hand, the speaker is incoherent, the room is noisy and the listener is bored or distracted then perfect sympathy is disturbed and the integrity of the message is likewise destroyed. The listener no longer hears or understands that which is meant to be conveyed. And likewise the speaker is no longer being received or understood according to that which he intended.

This law specifically refers to sympathetically tuned aggregates or those aggregates that have the same pitches of vibration such as components of crystal-like substances. Even though it does not pertain directly to people engaged in conversation the analogy is nonetheless valid. This is because two or more people can be sympathetic to one another. When their ideals, goals, likes and dislikes are similar they are drawn naturally together - they are repelled from each other to the degree that their ideals, goals, likes and dislikes are dissimilar. This law *is* a law because it embodies common sense and it can be seen to apply to every situation involving two or more similar interacting things. Common sense and universal applicability are imperative.

Law of Sono-thermity

"Internal vibrations of atomic substances and atomic molecules are capable of vibrating at a period-frequency directly as their density, inversely as their linear dimensions, directly as the coefficient of their tension from the 21st to the 42nd octaves, producing the creative force (Sono-thermity), whose transmissive force (Sono-therm) is propagated in solid, liquid, gaseous, and ultra-gaseous media, statically producing adhesions and molecular unions, or disintegration, according to the Law of Harmonic Attraction and Repulsion."

Keely, 1894

Commentary October, 1986

In issue #9 was published a complete list of Keely's frequencies. The list shows the 21st octave having a frequency of 2,097,152 Hz. The 42nd octave has 4,398,046,511,104 Hz. This frequency band, according to Keely, comprises the range of frequencies in which what he calls Sono-Thermity, Sono-therm and Sono-thermism have their manifestations. The term sono comes from the Latin, sonos, meaning sound. The term therm comes from the Greek, word for heat. In the New Century Dictionary it is defined as: THERM: *"In physics, a unit of heat or thermal capacity; a thermal unit, as the small calory or the large calory, or unit equal to 1,000 large calories; sometimes, a unit equal to 100,000 British thermal units."* One is reminded of the modern term SONO-LUMINESCENCE: [Physics] *"Luminescence produced by high-frequency sound waves or phonons."* McGraw-Hill Dictionary of Scientific and Technical Terms.

In recent issue of one of the popular science magazines there was an article about the sound waves detected in the sun. It seems there are a great number and quantity of sound frequencies present on the surface of the sun. Do you suppose these waves are what gives rise to the heat we perceive coming from the sun and not actually from nuclear activity? Some of the literature I have indicates this may be so. We'll have to dedicate a future issue to solar and planetary phenomena as seen by Keely and others.

Those of you familiar with the ordinary Electromagnetic Scale will see that these frequencies mentioned by Keely, especially the higher ones, are within the Infrared frequency range. I think we can surmise from what Keely says that he considered heat or the generation of heat nothing other than sound waves vibrating at a quicker rate. This I have heard from many different scientists and engineers. But if this is true, then the idea that heat causes things to rise is a fallacy! Because heat is a manifestation of high frequency sound waves and not something in

and to itself. Just think, if heat applied to a substance causes it to rise and we see it rise such as air or water, then we would be tempered to say that heat causes levitation. Indeed, heat applied to air will cause it to rise. But heat applied to a pound of water in a pan on a stove top doesn't make it any lighter! NASA has shown us that sound applied to solids causes them to rise. Might it not be something within heat or the cause of heat that contains the "levitating effect"? If heat and sound are vibrations, then this "levitating effect" is caused by vibrations or some kind of mode of vibrations and not by heat alone.

In the case of heated air rising, it would be better to say that heat is present in air as it levitates or rises. The atomic and molecular vibrating structure we call air, when immersed in a media vibrating between the 21st and 42nd octave, will become modulated by those same frequencies. The result will be an air atom or molecular vibrating or resonating to those same frequencies which then emits "heat" (or the same rates of vibration recognized as heat) and at the same time this air particle will have a tendency to rise vertically.

Therefore, in summation, heat and levitation may be the results of modulating the atomic frequencies of the air with the frequencies between the 21st and 42nd octaves.

Heat and levitation then should be recognized as two separate and distinct phenomena arising from the same frequency. This of course, leads us to think that there are at least two distinct types of vibration at work. One causes heat the other levitation. Water atomized by an ultrasonic humidifier is cold and has a tendency to float and the fall in the air. Whereas water atomized by heat has a tendency to rise. Discover the difference and your fame and fortune is guaranteed!

Law #11 The Law of Force, issue #11, tells us that "Energy manifests itself in three forms: Creative or Sono-thermity, the vibrating aggregate; Transmissive or Sono-therm, being the propagation of isochronous waves through the media (atomic substances and

Universal Laws Never Before Revealed: Keely's Secrets

atomic molecules) in which it is immersed: Attractive or Sono-thermism, being its action upon other aggregates capable of vibrating in unisons or harmony." I think this law is more or less self explanatory, once one becomes comfortable with Keely's jargon that is.

Taking logic a little further with what Keely lays out before us I would say that heat is an atomic phenomena. That means that a molecule does not possess heat but it is the atoms of which the molecule is composed that manifests this rate of vibration we perceive as heat. Or we might say that it is the molecule vibrating at the atomic frequency rates which gives rise to thermal outreach (heat). In one of Keely's papers (to be published in its entirety at a later date) he claims that when a molecule is submitted to supercooling as in cryogenics, the thermal outreach nestles into the intermolecular realm remaining latent there until the cold has been withdrawn. The thermal outreach (heat) then reasserts itself and becomes evident again as "latent heat". "Latent heat" is not the same as "specific heat". A strange concept when first approached but not so improbable as "heat causes air to rise".

Commentary December, 1989

This law is fundamentally the same as the law reviewed in the November, 1989 issue. The major difference is this law covers the phenomena of the next set of octaves from the 21st octave to the 42nd octave. The other difference is here we will be discussing vibrations while in the previous law we discussed oscillations. See SVP, March, 1989 for a discussion of the difference between these two forms or modes of rhythmic motion.

"Internal vibrations (vibrations are internal rhythmic motions whereas oscillations are the whole body moving from side to side) **of atomic substances** (crystalline like materials) **and atomic molecules** (substances composed of unlike atoms but not possessing molecular properties) **are capable of vibrating at a period-frequency directly as their density** (the higher the density the higher the frequency and vice versa), **inversely as their linear dimensions** (the greater the linear dimension the lesser the frequency and vice versa), **directly as the coefficient of their tension** (the greater the tension the higher the frequency and vice versa) **from the 21st** (2,097,152 cps) **to the 42nd** (4,398,046,511,104 cps) **octaves, producing the creative force (Sono-thermity),** (from this idea we see that Keely interpreted the frequency as a cause of these forces - the frequency is separate from the force - the frequency is not the force of and by itself) **whose transmissive force (Sono-therm) is propagated in solid, liquid, gaseous, and ultra-gaseous** (plasma-like materials) **media, statically producing adhesions and molecular unions** (a result or effect of these frequencies brings about the aggregation of the associated particles), **or disintegration, according to the Law of Harmonic Attraction and Repulsion."** (This law implies that like vibrations cause aggregation and unlike - discordant - vibrations produce repulsion or disintegration).

There does not appear to be any conflicts between this law with modern concepts. The only area a conflict could result in the calling of this phenomena a LAW. However, a review of what constitutes a law would settle that conflict in short order because this phenomena is a constant and does not deviate.

To make this law and the one before it useable one would find themselves emerged in atomic and nuclear physics. Mathematical formulae used in this field of research reflects the use of frequency as an essential component of their calculations. A place that has been using this phenomena but without the knowledge of the greater paradigm is in excimer lasers. This particular laser can and does cause a dissociation of molecular and atomic bonds without the generation of heat. This laser is the closest thing I've seen or heard of resembling Keely's stone disintegrator device used to mine hard rock gold in 1883. The introduction of a high frequency vibration into a coherent chord of vibrations possessed by the stone caused a strong discord and disintegration was the result. The gold, being a metal, has a strong property Keely called *negative attraction*. This apparently is more or less an opposite state or inverse state of coherent chordal factors. Thus a metal is not affected in the same way that a crystalline substance (granite) is. The metal "absorbs" the frequencies and becomes more "compact" a thus may break itself in much the same way that has been demonstrated in exploding wire experiments instead of disintegrating by atomic or molecular bond weakening which is the cause of disintegration.

Later in this issue are listed the known musical intervals. These are to be identified in molecular and atomic chords. It is these intervals that we speak of that compose the chords of molecular and atomic bonding. The more concordant the bond or interval the more compact and the stronger the bond is. A more discordant bond is weaker and aggregations formed around such bonds are not strong and may be disrupted with much less effort.

The idea or key in this matter is not to hammer away at a substance to effect a break in the bonds. A much subtler and more effective method would be to "tickle" or modulate the bonds into a discordant state. Hugh results can be discerned from a small energy input. Dissociation would be the inevitable result. The requirement of hugh amounts of outside energy to effect such changes comes from the lack of understanding concerning the real cause of the bonds' existence. Thus "art" and skill can easily supplant the "sledge hammer" approach to molecular and atomic disintegration.

It is an easy thing to say bonding is caused by valence, short and long molecular forces because there is no real understanding of what valence, short and long molecular forces are. This is like saying gravity causes things to fall to the earth - without giving a description of what gravity is. All things vibrate - therefore we must look to the vibrations as the common denominator between all things.

129

Law of Oscillating Atoms

"All atoms when in a state of tension are capable of oscillating at a pitch inversely as the cube of their atomic weights, and directly as their tension from the 42 to 63 octaves per second, producing the creative force (Thermisim), whose transmissive force (Rad-energy) propagated in solid, liquid, and gaseous æther, produces the static effects (Cohesion and Chemism) on other atoms of association, or dissociation, according to the Law of Harmonic Attraction and Repulsion.

Scholium: Dark radiant heat begins at absolute zero temperature, and extends through light, chemical rays, actinic rays, and infra-violet rays, up to the dissociation of all molecules to the 63rd octave."

Keely, 1894

Commentary November, 1986

The Law of Harmonic Attraction & Repulsion was discussed in issue #8. Keely indicates that atoms oscillate within and just around the visible light frequencies depending on the weight of the atoms. This is a simple statement and one that is easily verifiable by consulting any good reference work on atomic resonances.

The unique idea here is the separate distinction between creative force (Thermism) and the Transmissive force ((Rad-energy). Thermism as we have already seen, is or can be associated with heat. We may (with tongue-in-cheek) associate Keely's Thermism with the modern term of "latent heat." The other force, Rad-energy, we may conceptualize as that force or energy that radiates from given atom and causes the effects an atom has on its neighbors. If the atom was very dense as in uranium or other radioactive substances, then this effect is very noticeable. We call it radiation. The term radiation implies a force that radiates. Rad-energy is also a force that radiates. The term are more or less synonymous. When considering heavy element radiation, the force is considerable and has a considerable effect on its neighbors. When the radiating forces are weak as may be from a light element, the effect may not be noticeable, yet the effect is still there. Hence we cannot say that gold, for instance, does not have a radiating force or that hydrogen (the lightest of recognized elements) does not also have this quality. Keely tells us that they all do according to their tension and atomic weight. With these numbers in hand it should be easy to determine any element's radiating force (rad-energy or radioactivity coefficient).

According to the Laws of Harmonic Attraction and Repulsion, if these radiating forces are in a harmonic ratio with a neighboring substance, the two will join and be held together by cohesion. In fact, according to Keely, it is this harmonious relationship between resonant substances that is cohesion (see Law of Attraction, issue #8). If the radiating frequencies are not in harmony, the two substances will be repulsed (see Law of Repulsion, issue #8). Thinking along these lines one is enlightened as to what Keely means when he uses the term Chemism. Chemism is chemical action. We know from even a simply study of chemical actions that these actions are an association or dissociation of atomic and subatomic particles and very little else. So the study of chemistry must be the study of harmony, *i.e.,* the attraction and repulsion of particles which are governed by the frequency of the associated substances. Atomic substances that have a harmony with each other will be attracted and form new substances whereas atomic substances having an inharmonic or non-harmonious relationship will be mutually repulsed and will not form a new and unique substance. It follows that a complex chemical substance can be broken down by increasing the inharmony present in one or more of the substances thereby causing them to mutually repulse one another. Take a stick of dynamite for an example: the chemicals are held in a stable (balanced, harmonious) state until they are violently shaken (read vibrated) by an impulse from a detonator. This is the sole purpose of a detonator - to cause a sharp and violent high frequency impulse. This impulse modulates the relative chemical (atomic) frequencies of the compound bringing about an inharmonious association - the elements become repulsive to each other and rapidly expand away. Ask any good chemist to describe a chemical association or dissociation and he will first look to the atomic weights of the substances to be associated.

Some interesting work done by John Dalton nearly 100 years prior to John Keely's describe this exact idea of elementary atoms radiating "rays" of energy, the number of which contributed to the ability or inability of various elements to associate into new chemical substances. We aren't dealing with anything new and bizarre here, only a clear and effectual of fundamental principles.

The scholium given above is recognized by all physicists in that any element does have a "latent

Universal Laws Never Before Revealed: Keely's Secrets

heat" factor (Thermism or thermal factor) from absolute zero. Cryogenologists recognize and deal with this every day.

Commentary January, 1990

All atoms when in a state of tension are capable of oscillating at a pitch inversely as the cube of their atomic weights, if we take the first 8 elements according to their atomic weights we can calculate their pitch (relative frequency):

Element	Atomic Weight	Cube Atomic Weight
Hydrogen	1.00797	1.0241010689616
Helium	4.0026	64.124881137576
Lithium	6.939	334.110914019
Beryllium	9.0122	731.96862049585
Boron	10.811	1263.565041731
Carbon	12.01115	1732.8212769962
Nitrogen	14.0067	2747.9414856808
Oxygen	15.9994	4095.5392172798

Assuming the tension is 1 then we might say that for every oscillation experienced by Hydrogen, Oxygen oscillates 4095:1 times. In other words, Oxygen is 'deader' than Hydrogen and does not respond as well to a vibratory influence. To say the same thing in another fashion - Hydrogen can oscillate 4095 times greater than Oxygen - *it is an extremely active element.* See SVP March, 1989 for a descriptive difference between a vibration and an oscillation. **and directly as their tension from the 42** (4,398,046,511,104 cps) **to 63** (9,223,372,036,854,775,808 cps) **octaves per second, producing the creative force (Thermism), whose transmissive force (Rad-energy) propagated in solid, liquid, and gaseous æther, produces the static effects (Cohesion and Chemism) on other atoms of association, or dissociation, according to the Law of Harmonic Attraction and Repulsion.** The above implies that cohesion between atoms takes place between the frequencies mentioned. This band of vibrations spans the infra-red up to the gamma rays. Is it coincidence that heat and laser energies can bring about dissociation? Excimer lasers are widely known for their ability to dissolve chemical bonds and heat is used everyday to dissociate chemical compounds. Infra-red is the scientific term used to describe *heat* first discovered and used by Herschel 200 years ago. Keely uses the term *Thermism* to describe the same thing or range of frequencies.

Scholium: Dark radiant heat begins at absolute zero temperature, and extends through light, chemical rays, actinic rays, and infra-violet rays, up to the dissociation of all molecules to the 63rd octave.

It appears as though what Keely calls *dark radiant heat* is very close to what we call *latent heat* which is present in all substances regardless of their temperature. This latent heat is functional in all equations of chemical association and dissociation.

What is most evidently different about Keely's approach to chemistry and the modern approach is his insistence on the vibratory aspects of the substances involved. His approach is more like a quantum mechanical viewpoint than physical chemistry. It seems that he elevated the science of chemistry to and beyond our current accepted system of materialistic chemistry. By bringing an understanding of vibratory sciences to bear on this matter of the formation of molecules we can discern the music of the molecules - indeed the musicology of all material existence. Small wonder then that his charts are replete with musical notations. These notations show the relative discords and concords active in the associations and dissociations of molecular structures the very fabric and fibre which binds the Universe together. Which brings me to one of my favorite subjects: intervals.

The Bible, particularly Genesis, the first three chapters, is a description of the formation of the Universe. When studied with care and an eye for the significant meanings behind the descriptions the days of creation are exact descriptions of manifested intervals of which there are six. In music development there are six intervals (and seven notes) in an inclusive octave. *The eighth note is really the first note of the next octave.* All counted there are three octaves described in Genesis. Here we have Keely describing the formation and dissociation of matter and on the other hand we have Genesis describing the formation of the material universe. They are both using musical terminology describing the same thing.

It has been pointed out in the literature that Keely studied the ancient writings which led him through his work. This should not be a point of contention to religionists or materialists. For here we can see a bridge - a divine bridge - spanning the two realms that have ever warred with each other. Music is that bridge so often referred to by Edgar Cayce: *"For music alone may span the space from the realms of the divine to the spheres of activity."* (3509-1)

Law of Vibrating Atomolic Substances

"Atoms are capable of vibrating within themselves at a pitch inversely as the Dyne (the local coefficient of Gravity), and as the atomic volume, directly as the atomic weight, producing the creative force (Electricity), whose transmissive force is propagated through atomolic solids, liquids, and gases, producing induction and the static effect of magnetism upon other atoms of attraction or repulsion, according to the Law of Harmonic Attraction and Repulsion.

Scholium: The phenomena of Dynamic Electricity through a metallic conductor and of induction are identical. In a metallic conductor, the transmission is from atom to atom, through homologous interstices, filled with ether, presenting small areas in close proximity. In crystalline structures, heat, which expands the atoms, by twisting them produces striæ, increases the resistance, *etc.* Between parallel wires and through air the induction takes place from large areas through a rarefied medium composed of a mixture of substances, whose atoms are separated by waves of repulsion of various pitches, discordant to electric vibrations; the said atoms sympathetically absorb the vibrations and dissipate from themselves, as centers, concentric waves of electric energy which produces heat and gravism."

Keely, 1894

Commentary December, 1986

A Dyne as defined by McGraw-Hill Dictionary of Science and Technology is: [MECH] *"The unit of force in the centimeter-gram-second system of units, equal to the force which imparts an acceleration of 1 cm/sec² to a 1 gram mass."* Since Keely had a much different idea of gravity than we do (if we do at all) he lumbers into this law without hesitation. However, we must take our time with it (see article this issue GRAVITY QUOTES). I believe from a more careful reading of the body of this law what is really being pointed out here is the relationship between electricity and gravity. We all know that electricity is considered a flow of electrons (herein described not as an electron or electron-like particle flow but as a vibrating force). The above law says this vibration takes place within the atom. Lattice vibration theories regarding charges that are transmitted in very small semiconductor (chip or crystalline) configurations. The charges or charged electrons seek out holes in the material and are repulsed by non holes. Extrapolating Keely, we would say that these non-holes are another atom (electron, atomole) vibrating at a discordant rate when compared to the charged atom (electron, atomole) and repulse that atom and its charge. The holes are atoms (electrons, atomoles) that vibrate in unison or harmonically with the charged atoms (atomoles or electron) (see Law of Harmonic Attraction and Repulsion issue #8).

Heat buildup according to Keely twists the atomic structure and creates these striae producing resistance. I have come to more or less equate resistance with Keely's "interference to coincident action." As he describes above, this electric flow is from atomole to atomole when vibrating in unison or harmoniously. In other words there is a "coincident" or harmonious action between them. Resistance of course would be as an interference to this activity.

STRIA: pl. STRIAE, [LATIN, a furrow, channel, flute.] A slight furrow or ridge; a linear marking; a narrow stripe or streak, as of color or texture, especially one of a number in parallel arrangement.
STRIA: [BIOL] A minute line, band, groove, or channel.
STRIATION: [ELECTR] A succession of alternately luminous and dark regions sometimes observed in the positive column of a glow-discharge tube near the anode.
STRIATION TECHNIQUE: [ACOUSTICS] A technique for making sound waves visible by using their ability to refract light waves.

Transmission of electricity through the air or gases is from sympathetically vibrating atom to atom. The gas particles are vibrating in discord thus repulsing each other, yet their atomic structures (atomoles) can and do vibrate sympathetically with the electricity current. Would we say that atmospheric transmission is then due to sympathetic vibrations and not by a wave of some sort? The electromagnetic wave may

Universal Laws Never Before Revealed: Keely's Secrets

then be considered as an accumulation of the individually vibrating atomic structures. The atoms first absorb the vibrations and then dissipate this electronic flow in concentric waves which is another way of stating an interpretation of the quantization of electron activity as viewed by and with planck's quantum theories. It further appears that it is this absorption and dissipation frequency, when in unison with neighboring atoms, that constitutes the propagating wave. In other words, the time taken for an atom to absorb and then dissipate this energy establishes the velocity of wave propagation. If the medium of propagation is molecular or atomic the speed of assimilation and emission is slower (as in sound waves) and when the medium of propagation is of a finer substance such as interatomic particles (electrons, atomoles) the speed of assimilation and emission is quite faster. This gives us an idea of why Keely claimed sound travels 20,000 fps in a vacuum. (A vacuum being the lack of molecules and atoms only, it is still replete of subatomic particles all of which can and do vibrate to different frequencies. Proof of this assertion can be seen every time we send a space probe out into the vacuum of interplanetary space and communications with it are maintained through electromagnetic waves.)

NOTE: According to the McGraw-Hill Encyclopedia of Science and Technology, the electron was *"Discovered in 1895 (one year after Keely's laws were first published) by J.J. Thomson in the form of cathode rays, the electron was the first elementary particle to be identified."* The article goes on with "Electrons contribute the bulk to ordinary matter, the volume of an atom is nearly all occupied by the cloud of electrons surrounding the nucleus, which occupies only 10-13 of the atom's volume. The chemical properties of ordinary matter are determined by the electron cloud." And "the electrons have magnetic properties" and "spin (vibration) is one of the permanent and basic properties of an electron." Since the electron wasn't "discovered" and named until after Keely's discovery, he had to call it something and he apparently choose to use the word atomole. The derivation of the word appears to come from a combination of atom and mole. The term mole comes from the Latin moles meaning; mass, massive structure, mole. So we might, with tongue in cheek, say that an atomole is an atomic mass of a mass within or of the atom. In today's physics, we make a distinction between electrons, protons and neutrons which go to make up the substance and mass of an atom. Keely made a similar distinction when he described the three revolving bodies making up the atom as positive, negative and neutral atomoles. Let us review some of Keely's descriptions of the atomole:

LAW OF MATTER AND FORCE: "Coextensive and coeternal with space and duration, there exists an infinite and unchangeable quantity of atomoles, the base of all matter; these are in a state of constant vibratory motion infinite in extent, unchangeable in quantity, the initial of all forms of energy."

"**Atomoles** are elementary units of matter uniform in size and weight, and exist in solid, liquid, gaseous, and isolated forms."

"**Atomolini** are ultimate units of atomoles, and when in a liquid state are the media for the transmission of gravism. The illimitable divisibility and aggregation of matter is a logical sequence."

"**Atoms** are multiple combinations of atomoles, and they also exist in solid, liquid, gaseous, and isolated forms."

"**Electricity** is the oscillation of the atomoles of an atom."

"**Gravism** is the transmissive form (of energy) through a medium of atomoles in the fourth state, or a medium composed of atomolini."

"**Gravity** is the mutual attraction of atomoles."

Keely describes electricity as "the oscillation of the atomoles of an atom" and the gravity as the attraction between atomoles of the atom. I would think that he means these "atomoles" have a very high rate of vibration and it is this vibration, transmitted by sympathetic vibrations to neighboring atomoles, what he considered electricity to be and not an actual flow of electrons from atom to atom or molecule to molecule. This of course is different from excepted theory then all that modern science has is a theory. One could ask Joseph Newman what he thinks of the modern electron theory.

Perhaps we should review what Keely described as being electricity, the following quotes are from Bloomfield-Moore's book, Keely's Discoveries and elsewhere.

"There are three kinds of electricity, the harmonic and enharmonic, which, with their leader, the dominant, form the first triple. Their sympathetic associations evolve the energy of matter. The dominant is electricity luminous, or propulsive positive. The harmonic, or the magnetic, which is the attractive, with its wonderful sympathetic outreach, is the negative current of the triune stream. The enharmonic, or high neutral, acts as the assimilative towards the reinstatement of sympathetic disturbance. In electric lighting, the velocity of the dynamos accumulates only the harmonic current - by atomic and inter-atomic conflict - transferring one two hundred thousandth of the light that the dominant current would give, if it were possible to construct a device whereby it could be concentrated and dispersed. But this supreme portion can never be handled by any finite mode. Each of these currents has its triple flow, representing the true lines of the sympathetic forces that are constantly assimilating with the polar terrestrial envelope. The rotation of the earth is one of the exciters that disturbs the equilibrium of these sensitive streams. The alternate light and darkness induced by this motion helps to keep up the activity of these streams, and the consequent assimilation and dissimilation. The light zone being ever followed by the dark zone, holds the sympathetic polar wave constant in its fluctuations." **Keely**

133

Universal Laws Never Before Revealed: Keely's Secrets

"Electricity is but a certain condensed form of atomic vibration, a form showing only the introductory features which precede the etheric vibratory condition. It is a modulated force so conditioned, in its more modest flows, as to be susceptible of benefit to all organisms. Though destructive to a great degree in its explosive positions, it is the medium by which the whole system of organic nature is permeated beneficially; transfusing certain forms of inert matter with life giving principles. It is to a certain degree an effluence of divinity; but only as the branch is to a tree. We have to go far beyond this condition to reach the pure etheric one, or the body of tree. The Vibratory Etheric tree has many branches, and electricity is but one of them. Though it is a medium by which the operations of vital forces are performed, it cannot in my opinion be considered the soul of matter." **Keely**

"Keely has discovered and was the first to demonstrate that electricity has never been handled; that it is in principle as material as is water; that it is not merely a force or a form of energy,- that it is matter; and that what we call electricity, and have diverted 'for commercial use in electric lighting, is but one of the triune currents, harmonic, enharmonic, and diaphonic, which are united in pure electricity; that the enharmonic current seems to be sympathetically and mysteriously associated with the dominant current; and that the dominant current can no more be brought under control than can the lightning itself. The diversion of the dominant current would mean destruction to any mechanical medium used for that purpose, and death to the operator. The intense heat evolved by the electric stream Keely attributes to the velocity of the triple subdivision at the point of dispersion, as each triple seeks its medium of affinity. Sudden union induces the same effect, but demonstration shows that the concentration of this triple force is as free of percussion as is the breath of an infant against the atmosphere; for the three currents flow together as in one stream, in the mildest sympathetic way, while their discharge after concentration is, in comparison to their accumulation, as the tornado's force to the waft of the butterfly's wing. The enharmonic current of this triple stream, Keely thinks, carries with it the power of propulsion that induces disturbance of negative equilibrium; which disturbance is essential to the coordination of its flow, in completing the triune stream of electricity. When this fluid is discharged from the clouds, each triplet or third seeks its terrestrial concordant, there to remain until that supreme law which governs disturbance of equilibrium again induces sympathetic concordant concentration, continuing to pass through its evolutions, positively and negatively, until the solar forces are expended." **Bloomfield-Moore**

"The flow of electricity, as set down in Keely's system, is governed by triple conditions; 1st. the dominant or high vibratory; 2nd. the sub-dominant or low vibratory; 3rd. the harmonic or undulatory; In combination one flow. Keely writes: "When electrical experts can construct a mechanical device whereby the low vibratory conditions of the sub-dominant can be assimilated to the harmonic undulatory, by thirds, they will be able to run their dynamos without any extraneous appliances. An introductory impulse, on a certain order of vibration, being all that would be required to give the sub-dominant a concordant relation to the dominant; which would more effectually operate the dynamo than any number of steam-engines; allowing the harmonic stream to be the governor. This concordance, as towards the dominant, would only excite its sympathetic action in a way that would divert the ruling conditions of the two, without being submitted to the destructive effects of the dominant current. I think many lives will be lost before such a position is attained. Tesla has reached out almost to the crest of the harmonic wave, leaving all electrical explorers far behind him. It is only when such a condition is reached that the true value of electrical lighting will be understood, and extraneous power dispensed with; but, in my opinion, the present conditions for transferring power will remain unaltered, in the use of electricity, for generations.

"There is but one position to arrive at, that will redeem the many failures of the past decade, in attempts to find an economizing medium for commercial benefit in regard to power; and that position will be attained when the polar sympathetic harness is completed, which will give to the world the control of the polar forces."

"In reply to the question, "What do you include in the polar forces?" Keely, answers, "Magnetism, electricity, and gravital sympathy; each stream composed of three currents, or triune streams, which make up the governing conditions of the controlling medium of the universe; the infinite ninths that I am now endeavoring to graduate to a sympathetic mechanical combination, will, if I succeed, close my researches in sympathetic physics, and complete my system. These sympathetic streams from celestial space, percussing on the dense atmospheric environment of our earth, by their infinite velocities, wrest from their atomic confinement the latent energies which we call heat and light."

"Question: And where do these sympathetic conditions or streams of force have their origin?

"Answer: "`So God created man in His own image, in the image of God created He him; male and female created He them, ' Genesis I : 27." All sympathetic conditions, or streams of force, are derived (if we dare to make use of such a term in speaking of Deity) from the cerebral convolutions of the Infinite; from the center of the vast realm of the compound luminous. From the celestial intermediate, the brain of Deity, proceed the sympathetic flows that vitalize the polar terrestrial forces." **Keely**

"Electricity is the result of three differential sympathetic flows, combining the celestial and terrestrial flows by an order of assimilation negatively attractive in its character. It is one of Nature's efforts to restore attractive differentiations." **Keely**

GRAVITY QUOTES...

Below are some quotes from the Glossary of Sympa-

Universal Laws Never Before Revealed: Keely's Secrets

thetic Vibratory Physics. They are included here as a reference for understanding the law as given above.

GRAVISM: "Gravism is the transmissive form (of energy) through a medium of atomoles in the fourth state, or a medium composed of atomolini." **Keely**

GRAVITATION: What is gravitation? "The centralization of vibratory forces, ready to be changed in power by non-activity." (195-54)

GRAVITATION, CHEMICAL: "The problem then, is whether he should make a casting for the tank and bearing stand, as a unit, and use the old revolving drum, or whether it would be better to discard this machine, as built, in its entirely, and build another motor, using direct gravitation forces instead of using those of chemical gravitation." (195-60)

GRAVITATION DIFFERENTIATION: "In each atomic force has its energy, as is seen in that of the variation of the force as would be by the fall of an apple or that of an orange from the same distance. Or, to put it in a different degree, would be as it seen in the ability of force to cast off a metal - or to cast off a wooden ball. Each weighing the same, the metal can be cast off farther on account of the variation in atomic energy (See **MASS**), as is exercised through that of the force itself, and the variations in these are as the variations as are shown in the activity of the force as seen in gravitating towards that thrown off or that drawn to by the activity of the energy itself; for, as is and as has been given, the atomic force - with which gravitation in space, as is seen, as related to the earth's atomic position (See **FORCE-ATOMIC**) - is with that ability of the rotating energy to produce to other conditions and other elements, of which it is a part in its relative position. Hence we find that the earth's forces are as in the same relation to those elements as is a portion of that center about which it rotates.

"Then, in the varying elements as are kept in their activity, in keeping these in that same rotary motion, are those as produce the varying conditions through which the varying changes come to the various portions of the surface. (See **FORCE-RADIAL**) Hence, as gravitation is produced, so does the element - or the air - as brings gravitation - in its elemental activity - bring about or create about, that from which the radiation is thrown off, or we have air about the earth. As we have in other elements - created then in its own activity, and the variation in the gravitation, as is seen from the surface of those elements or those planets, are as the variation - or that attractiveness from which the radiation comes to produce its gravitation; that is, as would be seen - one that would be able to leap in the air in the earth's gravitational force would be able say six feet - would be able in another sphere to leap only, one two, three - while in others would be that of four, ten, twenty-four, thirty. This is a variation in the attractiveness, or attractability, of that from which the radiation comes - as to that which produces its force.

"As is seen here in this application of this same here to the motor: As the race through which the element of the gravitating force brings one into the contracting, throwing off of one portion, rotates the other in that it pulls while the other pushes, keeping that continued motion as would prevent the throwing off or the drawing to of the active principle in the rotary forces." (1955-57)

GRAVITY: [MUSIC] The downward effect, to the ear, of a sound in a key.

GRAVITY: "Gravity is the mutual attraction of atomoles." **Keely**

GRAVITY: "Gravity is an eternal existing condition in etheric space, from which all visible forms are condensed. Consequently, it is inherent in all forms of matter, visible and invisible. It is not subject to time or space. It is an established connective link between all forms of matter from their birth, or aggregation. Time is annihilated by it, as it has already traversed space when the neutral centers of molecules were established."

GRAVITY: "Gravity is transmissive inter-etheric force under immense etheric vibration." **Keely**

GRAVITY: "Gravity acting through space on everything has no action on space itself." (195-57)

GRAVITY: "The Amount of Aggregation reached by any system of bodies at any point in time depends upon the relative proportions of its Forces and its Energies at that moment."

GRAVITY: "Gravity may be considered a negative force, for it tends to balance the positive forces. Gravitational forces are vibratory forces and might be defined as the centralization of vibratory forces ready to change into power by non-activity." (195-70)

GRAVITY: "Gravity is nothing more than an attractive, sympathetic stream, flowing towards the neutral center of the earth, emanating from molecular centers of neutrality; concordant with the earth's center of neutrality, and seeking its medium of affinity with a power corresponding to the character of the molecular mass. Gravity, he defines as transmittive inter-etheric force under immense etheric vibration. He continues: - The action of the mind itself is a vibratory etheric evolution, controlling the physical, its negative power being depreciatory in its effects, and its positive influence elevating."

GRAVITY: "The force of gravity may be considered to have elements in octave of density, and these in relativity to same of forces - Now let this apply to what is commonly considered as octave (meaning vibration thrown off as sound), but as an octave or a vibration as would be set in motion by this vary activity of the gravitation in its activity - as pushes up as well as pushes down. Not until you have overcome gravitation. Now you are beginning to understand the law of gravitation. So as the raising power, there must be the opposite power, (See 18) understand these, then we begin to see how the vibratory forces is the active principle all radiates from.

What is gravitation? The centralization of vibratory force, ready to be changed in power by non-activity, see?" (195-54)

GRAVITY: "Any visible molecular mass of metal can be so impregnated by triple orders of sympathetic vibration as to give it the same sympathetic transmissive qualities that exist in the mental forces, which make such mass subservient to either the attractive or repulsive conditions of terrestrial sympathy.

"Gravity is nothing more than a concordant attractive sympathetic stream flowing the neutral center of the earth. This force is inherent in all visible and invisible aggregation forms of matter, from the very birth of a planet, around whose center the molecules cluster by the sympathetic affinity which is thus induced. If these conditions had always maintained a neutral position in etheric space, no planet would ever have been evolved. These conditions have been fixed by the Infinite. These rotating neutral centers, set in celestial space, have been endowed with the power of rotation to become their own accumulators. It is through the action of these sympathetic forces of the Infinite etheric realm that planets are born, and their volume of matter augmented.

"If we pick up an object we feel a resisting power in it which physicists call gravity; but they do not explain what gravity is. It is simply a sympathetic flow, proceeding from the molecular centers of neutrality; which flow is concordant with the earth's neutral center of same, seeking this medium of its affinity with a power corresponding to the character of its molecular mass. There is no actual weight in the molecules of the mass of which the earth is composed. If the sympathetic negative polar stream that flow towards the neutral center of the earth were cut off from it, the earth's molecular mass would become independent, and would float away into space as would a soap bubble filled with warm air.

"The gravital flow comes, in this system, under the order of the sympathetic concordant of the 9ths, and belongs to that third of the triune combinations called polar propulsive.

"Magnetism is polar attraction.

"Gravity is polar propulsion.

"Both magnetism and gravity can be accelerated by the proper medium of sympathetic vibratory influences." Keely

SOURCES:

1) Bloomfield-Moore, Clara Jessup, Keely and His Discoveries, Delta Spectrum Research P. O. Box 316, Valentine, Nebraska 69201 (402) 376-1523.

2) Edgar Cayce Readings, Edgar Cayce Foundation, A.R.E., Inc. 57 & Atlantic Blvd., Virginia Beach, Virginia 23451

8) Ramsay, Dougald Carmichel, The Scientific Basis and Build of Music, Delta Spectrum Research P. O. Box 316, Valentine, Nebraska 69201 (402) 376-1523.

18) Allen, Grant, Force & Energy the Theory of Dynamics, Delta Spectrum Research P. O. Box 316, Valentine, Nebraska 69201 (402) 376-1523.

POLARITY OF SCIENCE

Fundamentally there exist two basic types of scientific activity. The educational areas or static science and the exploratory areas or dynamic science. These two areas represent the male and female of this universal principle as it manifests throughout the wide ranges of scientific activities. The innate natures of these two are diametrically opposed to one another, yet neither could exist without the other. Just so in any field, area or realm of activity. There must be a matching yet opposite counterpart in polarity for anything to have an existence.

The first polarity, that of educational science, strives to propound the fruits of the exploratory science. It will, with alacrity, use its best efforts to show how this or that scientific fact is valid and worthy of teaching and especially of learning by its students. It will defend to the last any knowledge it proposes because this knowledge is its *raison de vie*. Without which educational science would have no justification for existence. Because of this, it will defend to the last man any thing it perceives as an encroachment on the "facts" that it strives so well to impart to others.

On the other hand, it is the prime goal and ideal of exploratory science to debunk existing paradigms as taught and held so dear by the educators. They must question every thought, every idea, every fact in its efforts to arrive at new and novel discoveries. These too, will fight to the last man to defend this right to question and to propose new research. The very idea of a fixed opinion in the face of new discoveries smacks of narrow-mindedness and demonstrates to them an unwillingness on the part of the educators to accept their new discoveries. Which to them, are their reason for existence.

Problems arise in the scientific society when one of the two polarities cease working together and one of them gets the upper hand of authority and tries to defend their position with too much enthusiasm and the result is the oppression of the other's activities. An example of this is when Galileo (a dynamic explorer) found some new facts that the educators (the Church, static) perceived as a threat to their superior position, that of educator. The Church being vested of an inordinate balance of power succeeded in supressing (jailing) the dynamism of the exploratory sciences. This reoccurring behavior became over a period of years the Dark Ages. Other examples of this same imbalance of power can be seen in the relationship of Tesla, Keely, Moray, Reich and many others. In these cases the vested authority was in capitalism or rigid scientific circles supported and defended by capitalism being no less dogmatic than the aforementioned religious organization (each being the preservers of education of the day).

Universal Laws Never Before Revealed: Keely's Secrets

When the opposite takes place, when the explorers gain the upper hand of authority quite a different result comes about. When Columbus, a scientific explorer, secured the backing of regal power a whole new world was literally opened up. When Edison, another explorer, gained the backing of capital, the world became a new place in which to live. When capital backed Tesla's AC ideas the world became illumined.

Authority is vested with the capitalist today. Another type of authority is that of public opinion. Publishers have been wielding this power for quite sometime. When the press backed de Broglie, Bohr and Einstein, the known realms of scientific knowledge literally took a quantum leap forward. When these public opinion authorities withheld their patronization as in the case of Tesla, Keely, Moray, etc. what could have happened didn't.

This curious balance of authority and dynamism is synonymous with Bloomfield-Moore's description of the force Keely called negative attraction. The withholding of authority is the same in its activity as the negative attractive force. Those in control of authority seemed to have desired (consciously or unconsciously) that the known realms of science and knowledge will be allowed to expand "this far and only this far," there to remain for a time until another quantum leap is allowed to take place. That is when the dynamic force of free discovery again reasserts itself by again securing the blessing of authority. This is what took place in the USA during the beginnings of the Great Space Race which culminated with men actually reaching the Moon. Authority turned off all controls and unbridled the exploratory forces that they may be unhindered in their expansion. The result is there for all to see.

However, speaking of authority, it has been known and taught for many centuries that the ultimate authority lies with the people. You, I and our neighbors. It is this popular authority that holds supreme command over all man-created authorities. When Apple Computers unleashed the MacIntosh computer into the free market place, the general field of computers was forever changed. The advent of the personal computer represents a true quantum leap in social and scientific activity. The semi-controlled field of knowledge and its assimilation burst open with such force and speed that few realize the ramifications of it yet. The common man in the street can now do what was reserved for those in authority. He can now have easy access to vast stores of knowledge previously unattainable and with it, as a base, and his unfettered creativity, literally create a whole new age for us all to live in and enjoy.

The sword of authority is being passed to the man in the street. We hope he uses it wisely.

When the two opposing forces meet in a cooperative fashion for their mutual benefit all sorts of things begin to happen. When the exploratory forces represented by Cortez met with the educational authorities of the church whole nations died while others were given birth. This symbiosis takes place today in two very distinct realms. On the educators side we have an excellent example set by the university laborato-ries. Wherein exploratory research is conducted for the purpose of gaining new knowledge that is nearly always immediately included in the curriculum of studies gaining more knowledge for the purpose of gaining still more knowledge. The opposite but identical process takes place in corporate research laboratories. Research is done there for the purpose of acquiring new products or services that are immediately added to the corporate ideal of acquiring more capital for more research to make more products. Both polarities in the equilibrium of scientific forces are working to expand their influence and natural talents, one to educate, the other to explore. They are both educating themselves and exploring at the same time. They are only different in their ideals, manners of attaining them and the purpose for attaining those ideals.

As the balance are maintained the result is not a quantum leap per se but a steady upward spiralling of gain, both in education and exploration. The quantum leap only comes when one of the forces as been "suppressed" or otherwise held at bay. It appears that the future portends a more balanced cooperation between these forces simply because people have seen the advantages to their self purposes by doing so. The New Age promises to be an era of cooperation whereas the past has been marked by contention and aggravated antagonism, first by one side, then the other.

Commentary February, 1990

Atoms are capable of vibrating within themselves at a pitch inversely as the Dyne [the higher the coefficient of local Gravity the lower the atomic frequency] **(the local coefficient of Gravity), and as the atomic volume** [as the atoms' volume goes up so too does the frequency - the greater the volume the greater the frequency], **directly as the atomic weight** [as the atoms' weight goes up so too does the frequency; does this mean the atomic weight as used as a measure imply higher frequency?], **producing the creative force (Electricity), whose transmissive force is propagated through atomolic** (subatomic - atomoles are of the same range of "particle" as are electrons and protons) **solids, liquids, and gases, producing induction and the static effect of magnetism** [magnetism is herein described as *static* because it possesses *both positive and negative polarities at the same time* thus can be neither positive nor negative alone as electricity is] **upon other atoms of attraction or repulsion, according to the Law of Harmonic Attraction and Repulsion.**
Scholium: The phenomena of Dynamic Electricity through a metallic conductor and of induction are identical. In a metallic conductor, the transmission is from atom to atom, through homologous interstices, filled with æther, presenting small areas in close proximity. [Keely indicated metals are negative attractive - attractive to each other - thus forming together into close proximity possessing a more or less uniform lattice structure. Because of this uniformity the electric current can and does travel much easier than through a non-uniform gas such as the atmosphere.] **In crystalline structures** [structures possessing a lattice or vector polarization between com-

Universal Laws Never Before Revealed: Keely's Secrets

posite particles] , **heat, which expands the atoms, by twisting them** [bending or distorting the lines of vector polarization increases "resistance"] **produces striaæ, increases the resistance,** *etc.* [This maybe an explanation of why certain ceramic materials are efficient in superconductivity work - their crystalline structures resists twisting.] **Between parallel wires and through air the induction takes place from large areas through a rarefied medium composed of a mixture of substances** [this "rarefied medium" may be the atmosphere or other medium of transmission], **whose atoms are separated by waves of repulsion of various pitches** [gases are gases because their atoms mutually repulse each other to some degree which surpasses their cohesiveness, this repulsion is a result of discordance between atomic centers manifesting in concentric waves], **discordant to electric vibrations; the said atoms sympathetically absorb the vibrations and dissipate from themselves, as centers, concentric waves of electric energy which produces heat and gravism.** [Here is the first reference I've noticed that electricity produces gravism or that which is the cause of gravity.] A correlation between heat and gravity has been explored herein in earlier issues. What is it about heat that causes gases to rise? Is it really a virtue of expanded volume relative to specific gravity of the atmosphere or is it something else?

Notice in the first part of this law: it is the vibrations of the atoms that *creates* electricity, magnetism and gravity. If this is so and logic indicates that it does then these three forces are a natural part of every atom - a truth science has known for decades yet has failed to grasp its significance except in nuclear detonations.

Given this idea how, is electricity "generated" in a generator? Why isn't spontaneous electricity more evident? Does this explain the Tucker Energy Accumulator? The Tesla Coils' zap? Lightning?

Electricity is produced and then it is "transmitted" or communicated from atom to atom. The degree of conductivity or induction is dependent on the degree of sympathetic resonance of each atom in the electrified medium. If there is only a small degree of sym-

pathetic association great resistance will be encountered and the "current" or sympathetic flow will be hindered. On the other hand if sympathy between particles (centers of vibration) is increased the transmissive form of electricity will easily propagate (be communicated) throughout the medium. Sympathetic transmission is increased in homogeneous lattice structures with relative ease - while a non-homogeneous structure inhibits association lessening sympathetic communication or transmission.

An example of this law can be seen in electrolysis. As a DC current is applied to the water the atoms begin to twist, heat builds up, resistance increases and more "current" is required to accomplish the same effect that a smaller current accomplished before the lattice structure began to distort. In superconductivity experiments the structure is frozen thus preventing the twisting action between atoms thus maintaining a path free of interference - the current flows with little or no resistance.

This flow is between particles. First one vibrates, causing a sympathetic response in its neighbors, thus forming a continuous chain of sympathetic response from atom to atom. The atoms, while sympathetically linked in motion, will continue to vibrate until a difference in lattice structure is encountered, either in time (distortion or breakdown) or in space (change of substance). Thus minute cracks in a wire will cause an interruption of flow of the sympathetic current or when it reaches the boundary of the vibrating medium and encounters another substance of different structure which may or may not respond sympathetically with that of the first transmitting medium.

The above law is somewhat unlike current electron theory. This law does not state anything resembling the "jump of electrons" from atom to atom although this may be implied. A careful study of the electron theory will reveal that it is *only a theory* subject to much debate especially when considered from a quantum mechanical viewpoint such as the one continually expressed in this column. Much work and thought needs to be applied to these matters before we can say which ideas are good and which need be forgotten. Time and patience are our best allies.

Over Unity is Recognized in Conventional Science

SOUND WAVES: "The mean force acting on a rigid sphere placed in a progressive spherical sound field has been obtained by integration of the individual contributions from the velocity potential and particle velocity acting on each element of the sphere's surface. Motion of the sphere under the action of the first order pressure variations in the sound field has been taken into account. The radiation force has been expressed as an infinite series of inverse powers of the source distance, each term of which is multiplied by an infinite power series in terms of sphere radius. *At very large distances from the source the radiation force obeys an inverse square law of repulsion. As the source of the field is approached, the repulsion decreases to zero and then becomes a force of attraction.* The extent of the region of attraction is determined both by the frequency of the sound field and by the size of the detecting sphere; lower frequencies and smaller spheres both extend the region. Even when allowance is made for an inverse square law, *the attractions may be many times greater than the repulsions in the same sound field.*"

(1) Embleton, T. F. W., *Mean Force on a Sphere in a Spherical Sound Field I & II*; The Journal of the Acoustical Society of America, Volume 26, Number 1; January, 1954, page 40-50.

Keely's Planetary Globe Device. Supposedly all the smaller spheres rise into the air and rotate about the larger sphere depending on the vibratory chords applied to them.

Law of Oscillating Atomoles

"Atomoles oscillating at a uniform pitch (determined by their uniform size and weight) produce the creative force *Atomolity*, whose transmissive form, *Gravism*, is propagated through more rarefied media, producing the static effect upon all other atomoles, denominated *Gravity*."

Keely, 1894

Commentary January 1987

A great portion of the literature extant today tries to equate gravity as a force, something to be aligned with electricity, magnetism and molecular forces forming the four basic forces of the universe. We have seen some laws as given by John Keely where these forces are indeed related as Creative, Transmissive and Receptive. However, he equates Electricity as a Creative force, Magnetism "the mutual attraction of juxtaposed bodies vibrating at unison or harmonic electric pitches," and Gravity as "the mutual attraction of atomoles." Electricity and Atomolity are Creative forces whereas Magnetism and Gravity are Static forces. Furthermore, he makes a distinction that electricity and magnetism originates from vibrating atoms while gravity arises from vibrating atomoles. We can then say that electricity is the active half of the electromagnetic duality while magnetism is the non-active or static half. Atomolity is the active force of the Gravitis dual and Gravity is the non-active or static half. We will quote from Keely himself again on electricity and gravity.

What is Gravity?

"Gravity is an eternal existing condition in etheric space, from which all visible forms are condensed. It is inherent in all forms of matter, visible and invisible. It is not subject to time or space. It is an established connective link between all forms of matter from their aggregation. Time is annihilated by it, as it has already traversed space when the neutral centers of the molecules were established. It is nothing more than an attractive, sympathetic stream, flowing towards the neutral center of the earth, emanating from molecular centers of neutrality, concordant with the earth's center of neutrality and seeking its medium of affinity with a power corresponding to the character of the molecular mass."

Commentary March, 1990

Levitation anyone? This law may help us to understand the cause and eventual control of gravity.

Before we can grasp these insightful concepts we must understand the terminology used. What is an "Atomole?" Keely defined this term as: *"Atomoles are elementary units of matter uniform in size and weight, and exist in solid, liquid, gaseous, and isolated forms."* The word atomole is derived from the Latin and Greek meaning "unit of energy." This atomole resembles our quarks in that there are three quarks contained within an electron and we may suppose also in the proton and maybe even the neutron. However the distinctions made in this law refer primarily to the three modes of energy: *Creative, Transmissive* and *Receptive* or *Static*. This concept of three modes of propagation or types of energy is the greatest difference between Keely's view of atomic physics and that of modern science. Modern science does not yet recognize these three forms *as three distinct parts of a whole*. However, exploring Ohm's Law brings one face to face with this reality of three-ness. $V = IxR$. V is the resultant of a force after it has passed through a media having resistance. I is the originating current flow (Creative); R is the resistance this force encounters as it passes through the "conductor"; and V is the quantity remaining of the original force. Herein we have a confirmation of the ancient and fabulous *Law of Three*. This law was much spoken of by the famed English physicist John Dalton around 1600.

These three aspects of a given "force" can be arranged together to better show their relationships:

Creative	I	Atomolity	Sound
Transmissive	R	Gravism	Sonism
Receptive	V	Gravity	Sonity

Of course, this is an over simplification. Each of these three "states" of the force are much more com-

Universal Laws Never Before Revealed: Keely's Secrets

plex than at first appears. But the simple can and does lead to the more complex. A complex description of the force can be made at each and every "state." This would entail a great deal of research and meticulous notation. Also there needs to be a rewrite of the basic premises from which Ohm formed his law.

Atomoles [quantized units of energy] **oscillating** [oscillation is a rhythmically recurring translatory motion] **at a uniform pitch** [pitch is the relative frequency of vibration] **(determined by their uniform size and weight) produce the creative force** *Atomolity,* [Atomolity is the activative or Creative force] **whose trans-missive form,** *Gravism,* [Gravism is the radiative or radiating energy] **is propagated through more rarefied media,** [this transmissive energy propagates through a less dense media such as electricity traveling through the vacuum of space] **producing the static effect upon all other atomoles, denominated** *Gra-vity.* [Static refers to the receptive or female aspect of this same energy].

This law describes the origin, function and *modus operandi* of gravity. It (gravity) is, as some profess, a vibratory (sound) phenomenon. It is also a push and a pull motion. But there is something different here and that is this idea of the transmissive gravism passing into more rarefied media. This is not so commonly noticed because we tend to think of electricity (for example) as traveling through more dense media such as the atmosphere or along (within) solid metallic conductors.

A really good example of this is a tuning fork?! It is used to vibrate (*Creative atomolity*) thus in turn causing the air to vibrate (*transmissive gravism*) rendering an effect on the air molecules (*a less rarefied media*) the result is an alternating condensation (a pulling together of the molecules or *static gravity*) and rarefaction (a mutual repelling of the air molecules).

The "how does this happen" needs to be explored before this law can successfully be used. How can a more dense vibrating substance effect a less dense substance? The answer lies in atomic dissociation (destruction). This was a common subject of discussion in the late 1800s. It was found that sound is actually created and propagated by atomic destruction thus liberating sub-atomic particles which radiate outward effecting neighboring atoms - in this case other sub-atomic particles. Keely often mentioned this fact and said that a bell left to vibrate over a period of centuries would eventually cease to exist having given up all of its sub-atomic and atomic substances to this process of dissociation.

This being true - it can be seen that the vibrating aggregate, as it changes from a condensed to a rarefied state, actually dissolves thus liberating its component particles which travel through space acting against sympathetically aligned atoms in the vicinity causing them to resonate similarly and eventually going through the same process as the first atomic structure, if allowed to behave in accord with their natural tendencies to do so.

Further thought shows us that this *transmissive gravism* travels through vacuous space (from a more dense body such as the Sun) and acts on any atomic structure possessing these atomoles. It also travels through the interstices of molecules (a less dense media) to effect atomic structures beyond them. Thus Gravity cannot be shielded or detoured around any known substance because all known substances contain atomoles. Keely also maintained that the dynaspheres of an atom are composed of atomoles or an atomolic substance - this would further facilitate the *transmissive gravism* to travel through these interstices between the molecules.

Atomolity may be likened unto sound (in function). The difficulty is we have no word (commonly accepted) for the form of sound that travels or the form that is passive. Sound may be the creative form of a force which creates alternating zones of condensation and rarefaction. Sound may also be considered as a current or flow of phonons. The same holds true for atomolity whose active particles may be atomoles. Gravism is its form that travels or is transmitted and gravity is the passive form or the result of its having traveled and its (atomolitic) effect. In the case of sound, Keely defined the traveling or transmissive form as sonism and its passive form as sonity.

Modern physics does not yet recognize any but the originating form of an energy. Keely recognized three distinct and discrete forms of force acting as one force. Ohm's Law can be used as a guide in developing an intricate equation which defines these three forms of this one force from its creation, during its transmission and its resultant state or condition.

Another comparative force can be examined that also reveals this triune condition - that of light. It originates (as far as we are concerned herein) in the Sun, travels through space and impinges on atmospheric molecules and atoms. We are uncertain how this light force is created; we are uncertain how it is transmitted (wave or particle?) but we are familiar with its resultants - heat and colors, each possessing vast varieties of modes of manifestation. For the most part science has concerned itself with the resultant or symptom of this solar created light force and not with its cause or method of transmission.

It may take years for science to recognize, define and accept a triune paradigm of forces operating within and throughout our Universe.

Law of Transformation of Forces

"All forces are different forms of *Universal Energy* unlike in their period-frequency, merging into each other by imperceptible increments; each form representing the compass of 21 octaves. Each form or pitch may be transformed into an equivalent quantity of another pitch above or below it in the scale of 105 octaves. The transformation can occur only through its static effect, developing vibrations of harmonic pitches above or below their fundamental vibration, or developing with juxtaposed aggregates, resultant and difference, or third order, as the case may be.
Scholium: A table of the intervals and harmonics of the normal harmonic scale will indicate the ratios in which the transformation of forces will occur."

Keely, 1894

Commentary February, 1987

This law tells us that the manipulation of energy and force can take place at certain numerical relations between vibrations. The numerical intervals at which this transformations may occur may be synonymous with the musical intervals. Tyndall says in his classical book "Sound": *"The simpler the ratio of the two parts into which a string is divided, the more perfect is the harmony of the two sounds. Ratios with large numbers have overtones with beats. Ratios with smaller numbers are less apt to have beats or dissonance."* We have assembled a list of these musical intervals in this issue as an aid in organizing this knowledge and presenting it to those who may learn to apply it. Keely's Scale of Octaves was printed in the September, 1986 issue. This scale of octaves designates the 21 octave compass of each energy type.

A point to keep in mind is the relative harmoniousness of various intervals. The lower the two numbers on each side of the colon determines the concordance of the ratio. For example a Perfect Fifth at 3 : 2 is much more coincident or harmonious than say the Greater Chromatic Semitone at 135 : 128. From the Law of Attraction & Repulsion given in issue 8, May, 1986 it follows that the lower the numbers, the greater the harmony and the greater the attractive force between vibrating aggregates. Higher numbers have greater degrees of dissonance and cause a repellant action between aggregates. This is like the old adage "birds of a feather flock together" and also may be a clue in understanding why people of "like mind" tend to join in groups of mutual activity. It may also explain why elements such as gold will aggregate about themselves forming larger quantities of itself and tends to not join together with other elements. When the elements naturally aggregate together as in an amethyst crystal with iron and silicon, the joining takes place by virtue of the relative intervals of frequencies of the atomic iron and atomic silicon. In other words, if the relative intervals of frequencies of the substances to be combined are at a low enough ra-

tio, the substances will combine readily. If, on the other hand, they are at a greater numeric ratio, it will be more difficult to combine them into a stable form as they may be combining about the resultant or difference harmonies created. It appears from Keely's law that beat frequencies may be responsible for repellant actions.

In a more practical vein, we have seen before that a gas is composed of repellant particles. Therefore we may assume that the relative intervals between these particles is of a high numeric ratio. When the ratio has been brought into a lower numeric equation - the gas particles become less repellant and more attractive and will eventually form into a liquid state. Continue lowering the ratio or increase the number of coincident ratios and the liquid condenses into a solid

This law has tremendous implications for interpersonal relationships whether they be one-on-one, one-to-many or many-to-many as in society at large. Any leader of persons knows intuitively that when desiring action from a group the group must first be brought into some form of coherent harmony or agreement. Once this point of cooperativeness (harmony or purpose) is reached, the groups force can very easily be directed either into the same area with renewed activity or into a new direction. The same process takes place between a salesman and a new client. The first step is to bring the client into as harmonious state as is possible with the salesman before making the pitch. The salesman or speaker before a group makes light and agreeable conversation to relax the wary or dissonant attitudes before launching into his topic. This is the transformation of force in actual every day usage.

Relaxing into a lower ratio is one way of bringing the multiple aggregates into coincidence. Another way is to raise the numeric ratio of one to that of the other. This is done by adding "heat" (a vibration) or another vibrating influence such as water or other substance, to one or both elements of the mixture. If two ratios one of 3 : 2 and one of 135 : 128 are brought together, one may be either raised, the other

Universal Laws Never Before Revealed: Keely's Secrets

lowered or both brought to some mutual numeric ratio relative to one another. The result would be the same excepting that if either reverts to its natural state or ratio, the mixture will breakdown or dissolve back into its individual components.

Commentary April, 1990

This law is a description of the process of transmutation of forces and hence transmutation of things.

It has been written that Keely was able to transmute elements into other elements and was thus able to create some exotic materials for some of his devices. One of these materials was his Trexnonar - a wire composed of platinum, gold and silver alloyed together in a special manner. It took Keely eight years to create this wire through which he transmitted his etheric force. In another device - his famous motor for domestic energy development and use - he "planished" the metal in such a way that the etheric force developed within it could not escape through the metal. Yet another material was used in his magnets - reported to be strong enough to hold several hundred pounds of weight and could be turned on or off at will.

"All forces are different forms of *Universal Energy* unlike in their period-frequency, merging into each other by imperceptible increments; [these period-frequencies (if they could be seen) would look much like the light spectrum where one color imperceptibly merges with the next] **each form representing the compass of 21 octaves.** [See the Scale of Forces published in SVP December, 1989 where these octaves have been defined by 21 octaves, labeled and measured) **Each form or pitch may be transformed into an equivalent quantity of another pitch above or below it in the scale of 105 octaves. The transformation can occur only through its static effect,** [the key here is "static effect"; the cause or the force itself cannot be transformed but its static effect can be - this is like the story of Adam and Eve - mankind cannot be transformed solely through the male force but can be changed by way of the posers of the female - the progeny will be like the male and female but of a new order - fundamentally like its parents yet different - remember Fibonacci and Pythagoras with their work with numbers used as bases and generated resultants? Quantum Arithmetic is also founded on this principle. The fundamental creative forces here are 1, 2 and 3 - God, Male and Female. The static effects of a fundamental vibration can be created or brought into manifestation by evolution or progression into sub or super harmonics, modulation or demodulation of another frequency giving rise to resultant or difference tones and even tertiary harmonics. See earlier issues of SVP for discussion of these secondary and tertiary vibrations.] **developing vibrations of harmonic pitches above or below their fundamental vibration, or developing with juxtaposed aggregates, resultant and difference, or third order, as the case may be.**
Scholium: A table of the intervals and harmonics of the normal harmonic scale will indicate the ratios in which the transformation of forces will oc-

cur." [Some of the older music theory books have tables demonstrating this vertical (sub and super harmonics) and horizontal (secondary and tertiary harmonics) harmonic generation. Some of these older books are in the process of being re-published by Delta Spectrum Research - watch the catalogue for them.]

This law is really important because it is the key to discovering how to take a super high frequency and have its effects demonstrated within the lower frequency ranges. Likewise a lower frequency can be made to act upon the higher domains.

Many people have asked me how Keely was enabled to work in such tremendously high frequency ranges - within this law are the keys to that enigma. He used a set of vibrating plates tuned to each other such that the lower plate created vibrations of a given pitch that acted directly on the resonance of the plate above it (with a higher fundamental) causing it to vibrate. This process continued to the 40th plate in the set thus transforming a lower audible frequency into a frequency well beyond the x-ray and gamma ranges. This process no doubt worked in reverse as well.

The small disk resonators having rods of different lengths in its periphery were no doubt another set of "progressive resonators" used by Keely to attain the same end but using a different waveform (rods and plates vibrate with a different set of intervals and waveforms - any book on music synthesis plainly points this fact out - hence the manner of progressive harmonic generation will be different between rods and plate resonators - thus the need for multiple tables of these rates).

The proof for the assertions of this law can be seen in the article "Chladni Plate Modes ... An Exercise in Musical Derivation" published in SVP December, 1989 where frequencies can be very accurately predicted from a known fundamental. This method was also successfully employed several years ago to predict and verify a progressive series of vibrations emitted from a cement truck as part of an experiment performed by Shine Richards and Dale Pond. The mathematical basis for that experiment was given in SVP November, 1986 in an article titled "Calculating Harmonies of Tones".

Entire scales of musical notes are naturally derived in this same fashion. The fundamental is sounded and the full collection of notes are derived from this one tone - all remaining relative to one another. "Harmonies of Tones and Colours" and "Scientific Basis and Build of Music" both go into this process with great depth and thoroughness. It is suggested these be reviewed to better understand the process of harmonic creation. Harmonic here does not necessarily mean a doubling or halving of a frequency alone - it relates to any mathematically defined and relative pitch with the fundamental. As we have stated before - consideration solely of doubled or halved pitches is only a small part of frequency modulation and demodulation and will not yield a complete picture of the vibratory nature of anything.

Therefore when exploring mathematically the pitches from a vibration or cyclical signature one must involve these other partials as important factors

Universal Laws Never Before Revealed: Keely's Secrets

to derive meaningful relationships and not just the doubled and halved harmonics. Isolating the even harmonics alone will not only be inaccurate because it leaves out the odd harmonics but will ultimately lead the investigator astray because he does not see the entire picture of what is going on. This narrow vision will result in incomplete synthesis and conclusions regarding his experiments. In fact a picture derived from such narrow consideration will only reveal $1/7$th or $1/12$th (depending on the degree of accuracy sought) of the entire picture. Where would music be if it only considered the doubled and halved octaves of the fundamental? A keyboard consisting of only "C" notes would be boring indeed. The other notes are ALL derived from calculations of the odd or enharmonic intervals between the "C" keys thus giving rise to the full complement of notes found on an ordinary keyboard. The very same can be said of a vibrating plate such as was analyzed in the afore mentioned article. How boring vibration analysis is without these wonderful middle notes. Enharmony or discord can be a disturbing influence and the spice of life, vibration and music.

Combination Tones

A Combination Tone is a third sound, which may be heard or measured, when two tones of different pitch are simultaneously sounded, and which are not heard, when either of these two tones is sounded alone.
The two tones which give rise to a Combination Tone are termed its generators.
There are two kinds of Combination Tones:
Differential Tone: the vibration number which is the difference of the vibration numbers of its generators.
Summation Tone: the vibration number which is the sum of these generator vibration numbers.

Differential Tones may be of various orders:
A Differential of the **1st order** is that tone produced by two independent tones or generators.
A Differential of the **2nd order** is that tone produced by the Differential of the 1st order, and either of the generators.
A Differential of the **3rd order** is that tone produced by the Diffferential of the 2nd order, and either of the previous tones being either the Differential of the 1st or 2nd orders and/or one of the generators.

Compound Difference Tones

Interval	Difference			
	1st Order	2nd Order	3rd Order	4th Order
Fourth 4:3 G:C 512:384	1 = 128 = C			
Major 3rd 5:4 E:C 640:512	1 = 128 = C	3 = 384 = G	2 = 256 = C'	
Minor 3rd 6:5 G:E 768:640	1 = 128 = C	4 = 512 = C"	2 = 256 = C' 3 = 384 = G	
Major 6th 5:3 E:C 640:512	2 = 256 = C'	1 = 128 = C	4 = 512 = C"	
Minor 6th 8:5 C:E 1024:640	3 = 384 = G	2 = 256 = C'	6 = 768 = G' 1 = 128 = C	7 = 896 = B' 4 = 512 = C"

Diatonic Scale

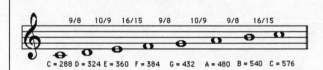

9/8   10/9   16/15   9/8   10/9   9/8   16/15

C = 288   D = 324   E = 360   F = 384   G = 432   A = 480   B = 540   C = 576

DIATONIC: 1) One of the three genera of music among the Greeks, the other two being the chromatic and enharmonic. 2) The modern major and minor scales. 3) Chords, intervals, and melodic progressions, etc., belonging to one key-scale. A diatonic chord is one having no note chromatically altered. A diatonic interval is one formed by two notes of a diatonic scale unaltered by accidentals.

Difference Tones

Interval	Ratio	Rate : Rate	Calculate Difference	Difference Tone
Octave	2:1	512:256	256 - 128 = 128 = 1	C
Fifth	3:2	384:256	384 - 256 = 128 = 1	C
Fourth	4:3	512:384	512 - 384 = 128 = 1	C
Major Third	5:4	640:512	640 - 512 = 128 = 1	C
Minor Third	6:5	768:640	768 - 640 = 128 = 1	C
Major Sixth	5:3	640:384	640 - 384 = 256 = 2	C'
Minor Sixth	8:5	1024:640	1024 - 640 = 384 = 3	E
Major Second	9:8	1152:1024	1152 -1024 = 128 = 1	C
Diatonic Semitone	16:15	2048:1920	2048 -1920 = 128 = 1	C

The vibration number of a differential tone is the difference between the vibration numbers of its generating vibration numbers. It is easy therefore to calculate what differential any two given generators will produce. Further, if the two generators form any definite musical interval the differential tone may be easily ascertained, though their vibration numbers be unknown.

Enharmonic Scale

ENHARMONIC: 1) One of the three genera of Greek music, the other two being the Diatonic and Chromatic. 2) Having intervals of less than a semitone, e.g., an enharmonic organ or harmonium is an instrument having more than twelve divisions in the octave, and capable, therefore, or producing two distinct sounds where, on the ordinary instrument, one only exists, as, for instance a scale having both G# and Aflat. An enharmonic scale is one containing intervals less than a semitone.

Fibonacci Numbers

Fibonacci is Music

Fibonnaci was a monk who lived about 1100 AD. When studying the reproduction rates of rabbits he came upon a method of calculating natural progressive rates. You can see how this works by typing any two sequential prime numbers into the first two fields to the right then click on the Create Numbers button above.

The process used is simple: add the second number to the first number to create the third number until infinity is reached (never). See SVP Compendium of Terms for greater detail.

Create Numbers

3
4
7
11
18
29
47
76

144

Keely, much older in this photo, seated by his final motor to his left. This machine operates via amplified gluonic bonding/repulsing forces as near as we can understand Keely's explanations. See other photo on page 207.

Law of Atomic Pitch

"**Atoms have each a different and definite pitch, at which they naturally vibrate.**

Scholium: Atomic pitch is determined directly from its simple spectrum.

Scholium: Atomic pitch is determined by computations from its associate spectrum with all other atoms, as in known spectra.

Scholium: Atomic pitches are more important working data than atomic weights; tables of atomic pitches *must* be precise."

Keely, 1894

Commentary March, 1987

Around the turn of the century there was a great debate as to whether atomic pitches represented harmonics of one another or not. According to the available data the question was never resolved to anybody's real satisfaction. I uncovered a paper in the Applied Spectroscopy magazine wherein this harmonic relationship was eluded to by a more recent writer when considering the Hydrogen and Oxygen, components of water. The writer indicated he would explore this phenomenon in a later article. A later article was never found.

Now, the issue died around the turn of the century because scientists were looking for a HARMONIC relationship instead of a MUSICAL relationship. A harmonic relationship, according to the rules of music, is a doubling or halving of the frequencies under study. They were looking for a 1, 2, 4, 8, etc. series of relationships. This is well but there are more relationships than this simple obvious series. What Keely is talking about in the phrase "computations from its ASSOCIATE spectrum with all other atoms (frequencies)" is what the relationships are even though they aren't strictly a harmonic one. For instance we have a relationship of a Perfect Fifth = 3:2 or a Perfect Fourth = 4:3. How do these relate to atomic frequencies? What can they mean? All along we've pointed out that Pythagoras stated the lower the numbers in the relationship, the greater the harmony between the two frequencies. According to Keely's scientific philosophy this translates into greater bonding force or denser material aggregation. The opposite applies to greater number relationships.

Now, in order to determine what the relationships are one must first have the atomic frequencies which can be easily acquired from a table of Nuclear Magnetic Resonances or spectra of the elements. In the last issue was published a table of musical intervals. Match the two tables and you have the true and proper relationships as spoken of by Keely in this law. I have assembled all the known musical ratios onto a lotus 1-2-3 spreadsheet (IBM or MS-DOS or PC-DOS compatible) in such a fashion that ANY numbers may be used on it and their respective relationship may be determined. I also have a great number of the spectra assembled though more is taking than I've been able to acquire. The insights given about elements when run through this spreadsheet is mind boggling! Though little is yet understood at this point everything points to a facility of being able to do things approaching on the magical.

A fine example of what may come to light using this spreadsheet is the example of the Fibonacci series of numbers. Currently we use PHI as the derivative of this series but this number is irrational (never ending series of decimals places), but once it is run through the musical spreadsheet we get WHOLE NUMBERS. Exactly what we need to compute finite qualities as for instance when working with Quantum Arithmetic. Here is the series and their musical intervals:

Fibonacci Series: 1, 1, 2, 3, 5, 8, 13, 21, etc.

$1:1$ = Unison
$2:1$ = Octave (harmonic)
$3:2$ = Perfect Fifth
$5:3$ = Major Sixth
$8:5$ = Minor Sixth
$13:8$ = Major Sixth

All subsequent ratios oscillate from a Major to a Minor Sixth always approaching what would be termed a Perfect or Harmonic Sixth. What does this mean? Keely maintained:

"The rhythmic relations in which force acts are everywhere, under all conditions, and at all times, the same. They are found experimentally to be universally expressible by the mathematical relations of thirds."

According to musical theory, a **Third** is the **inver-**

Universal Laws Never Before Revealed: Keely's Secrets

sion of the **Sixth.**

Keely worked, without success, on the theory that polar and depolar current actions were circular. He found success when he found and proved that these forces act with a SPIRO-VORTEX motion. Since we can now see that spirals are governed by Sixths (inversion Thirds) we begin to get an idea about his "Triune Polar Flow."

We can now begin to understand why the Ancients could do things eluded to by so many unexplained monuments, etc., and we haven't been able to duplicate their feats. They did it with simple WHOLE NUMBERS, which can be calculated on the fingers, whereas we can't with our high-powered computers trying to work with irrational unworkable numbers. As Inverson has so long maintained, we can skip all the heavy unworkable math when we work with whole numbers. This also helps us grasp why Keely was able to do so much with so little one hundred years ago.

Commentary May, 1990

Looking at this law we can see that Keely raised the science and art of atomic physics to a very high level perhaps even higher than modern science has yet reached. Modern science uses atomic spectra to determine exactly what atom is being investigated. Chromospectroscopy, Glow Discharge Spectroscopy are both standard procedures for investigating atomic identities by virtue of their spectra. This is an ordinary everyday tool today - but 100 years ago?

What is unique and interesting about this law is it goes a couple of steps further. Keely recognized the relative pitches between atoms and states that this is just as important as the spectra (vibrational frequency) of the atoms themselves. After all - what value has a frequency when it is not relative to another frequency? Not much and probably no value whatsoever.

That an atom can be identified by its spectra is no mystery. That this work was done so long ago is astonishing.

It is curious that modern chemistry still uses atomic weight in their calculations so much when atomic physicists use the spectra in their calculations. This is probably because we have become so specialized now days. It is not right and proper for a chemist to poke his nose in atomic physics and vice versa. However, you will notice, that great breakthroughs of science come usually when someone dares to go against custom. Some brave soul will one day make the effort to bridge this gap between these two noble sciences and Keely's law may be seen to be true and accurate. Logic tells us this is not too far in the future.

For years now I have been writing about the relativity between pitches - is anyone listening? This relativity is all important. The pitches themselves are of little consequence when viewed by themselves. But once they are brought together we have music intervals, modulation and demodulation of each other and the whole host of phenomena associated with such merging of vibratory influences. Without the relativi-

ty of pitch there would be no world because the world is a result of the pitches associating with one another. If the spectra are viewed exclusively as separate from one another how then does this association happen? Isolating things from one another is one of sciences greatest mistakes - one that has established the world order that we now experience - cold, hard and without love.

Keely's paradigm contains *sympathetic association* - what I refer to as love. Through association do things happen and have their existence. This new paradigm reflects the teachings of ancient science (seen everyday hidden in the world's great religions) showing love (sympathetic association) as a prime mover or factor in the forces at work throughout the universe. Without this constant interaction between focalized sources there would be no universe.

The idea that there are only four fundamental forces at work in this vast universe is a joke. Where do emotions and love fit into the picture? Are human beings something foreign to the universe? Of course not, we are a part and parcel of all that there is. Are we not composed of these same fundamental particles? Emotions, love and Will are fundamental forces in human activities - are they not important to human activity? Can this activity continue if these forces were removed from the human politic? Human existence would cease without them therefore they are fundamentally important to our existence. Therefore they are fundamental forces in our universe. Outside of the older philosophies which expound such things who is championing these concepts today? What paradigm of science embraces these other forces and makes them an integral part of itself? Sympathetic Vibratory Physics does. The scientific paradigm exposed and by John Keely and bequeathed by him to future generations.

For these reasons and many more I hold tenaciously to what can be found in his work. This is not an arrogant or self-centered project.

The world is in deep trouble brought on from a lack of seeing or understanding that there is more to life than lifeless matter and energy.

We have ignored nature and those things that are truly important to the survival of the species and the planet. To assume and propound that nature is lifeless and everything must be separated from everything else is preposterous and has proven a deadly paradigm.

It is held and taught that only organized biological structures have life. How does the organized structure become organized if the parts are without some kind of intelligence. If intelligence is a sign of life then even the smallest subatomic structure possesses some degree of intelligence. Since all forms of these particles associate with something else then they must possess love or sympathy one to another. The degree of sympathy can be calculated by comparing their individual pitches one to another. The more concordant the relationship the greater degree

Universal Laws Never Before Revealed: Keely's Secrets

of attraction. The greater the discords found in this relativity constitutes the degree of repulsion between focalized aggregates. The principles of music can get us this understanding. Because inherent in music is an understanding of what constitutes harmony and discord. Music is structured around this idea of relativity of pitches - without it there would be no music just as there would be no universe if atomic pitches did not relate to one another. We may even say, with accuracy, that the universe is music personified.

If there were a Grand Unifying principle tying all molecular, atomic and sub atomic activity to the colossal activities of the planets it would be music or those principles which go to make music a living vibrant concern. Polarity, relativity, time and periodic change of state combined with number and progressive vibration evolution all go to make music what it is. Making these factors vibrant and dynamic is the concept of sympathetic association. These are the same constructive characteristics of all known ele-

ments or parts found anywhere in the known universe. Without any one of the aforementioned factors no thing would have an existence and with these factors all things are vibrant components of an astonishingly active and organized universe. All things change and all things remain the same. All materiality and all forms of activity owe there existence to these factors and probably a few more I haven't mentioned.

Someday - hopefully not in the too distant future, mankind will come to recognize the principles that bind him to everything else. When this day comes (what some call Christ Consciousness) a new and extraordinary time will burst forth. Nothing like it has ever been experienced in the history of the world. When man sees that he is indeed part and parcel of the universe about him he will then find his rightful place at the right hand of God (Universal Creative Force).

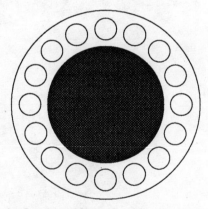

Etheric Chord 8th Octave

Quadruple Chord 3rd Octave

An inside look at the working resonators of the Musical Sphere.
More photos can be seen on pages 95 and 99.

Law of Variation of Atomic Pitch by Rad-energy

"The higher harmonics and overtones of projected rad-energy are of a pitch sufficiently high to cause the atom to expand; by causing the atomoles to vibrate systematically the same influence will cause the atom to contract, and thus by changing the volume, atomic pitch is varied."

Keely, 1894

Commentary April, 1987

Rad-energy (radiant-energy), according to Keely's Scale of the Forces in Octaves, begins on the 43rd octave or what we term infra-red frequencies just below those of visible light. It is also at this point where "chemism" begins. Chemism is chemical activity. Modern chemists associate ion exchange with chemical activity. According to McGraw-Hill Dictionary of Science and Technical Terms an ion is "an isolated electron or positron or an atom or molecule which by loss or gain of one or more electrons has acquired a net electrical charge."

Following the Keely physics philosophy of low and high frequency ratio as causes of aggregation and separation we can see a convergence and divergence of frequencies happening periodically thus resulting in the contraction and expansion mentioned in this law. The atomoles (subatomic particles) when vibrated sympathetically (in unison or harmony) cause the atom to contract - if convergence of frequency causes a contraction then this is true. A node point is a place of contraction whereas the place of maximum displacement causes disruption. A synchronization of wave fronts produces a contraction and non-synchronization causes the opposite. This is the old push added to push story all over again. Synchronize the vibrations (frequencies) and contraction results just as when vibrations are out of sync we have expansion. Perhaps here we can have a theory of superconductivity actions? By cooling the molecular structure we are actually bringing the vibrations into sync. Go back and reread the Law of Vibrating Atomolic Substances given in the December 1986 issue for an explanation of electrical conduction and resistance. These two qualities are properties of concordant and discordant frequencies respectively.

Keely mentions the harmonics and overtones of rad-energy what one would assume to be frequencies higher than infra-red or light. He also mentions the pitch of the atom changing. I have no current research information on this particular subject. Do atoms change Frequency say during an atomic reaction? Do molecules change pitch when subjected to X-ray frequencies? Long term X-ray exposure does heat up molecular structures - increasing the "rad-energy" quantities. Perhaps this expansion is part of molecular and atomic disintegration caused by high powered laser beams which operate in the frequency band mentioned. The laser light causes the atoms and or molecules to expand until they rupture and release their bound up inter-particles or plasma like matter.

An obvious correlation of what Keely says about expansion can be seen every time something is heated (infra-red frequency), it expands. But is there a contraction more or less simultaneous or periodically with the expansion? I read of some experiments where a candle flame was shown to be periodically lit and then "out" all the time looking as though it were a continuous uninterrupted flame. This is something like an ordinary light bulb which appears to be continuously lit but is in fact flashing on and off 60 times a second. Our eyes can't assimilate the image fast enough (about 30 times a second) to discern this rapid on-off sequence.

Perhaps one of our readers more versed in atomic or molecular physics could shed some light on this subject. There are simply to many details unavailable to this writer at this point in time.

The Cayce quote on the front cover is an exact analogy of this law. Just as the atomoles (that which the atom is comprised of) sync or unsync their activity so goes the whole structure. The relativity of influence is as like begets like or degrees of harmony and/or discord causing attraction of like particles (aggregation) or repulsion by discord.

Commentary June, 1990

Rad-energy has a frequency beginning just below those of the visible light spectrum and extends into the far vacuum ultraviolet ranges. (See SVP 12/89, pg 5, 6 & 7, Scale of Forces in Octaves) This rad-

Universal Laws Never Before Revealed: Keely's Secrets

energy is then the same range of energies as are used in laser technology today. In this range of frequencies modern science and technology have developed the areas of atomic emission spectrochemical analysis which is a technique for analyzing elements based on there emitted light when excited by various means. Analysis of emitted light is really the analysis of the frequencies being emitted. It is also the range in which atomic transitions (substances change from one state to another, *i.e.*; solid to liquid or from one crystal structure to another) take place. Coincidentally this is exactly what Keely is referring to above.

However, there is a major difference in what he is saying and what modern science "knows." Keely was a manipulator of matter and energy. Modern science works more with measuring and testing because they have not yet learned to approach matter and energy in the way they will in the not too distant future - with the approach outlined herein. They have not yet attained the level of knowledge where they can manipulate the elements as Keely did. Therefore, he is describing how to manipulate the latent states of matter in order to bring about a desired result. The atomic spectrochemical analysis process being used today is simply a method of measuring light spectra emitted from aggregates for the sole purpose of determining their chemical or elemental makeup. Apparently Keely could determine an aggregates constitution already - he went further and desired to make changes in that chemical or elemental structure. Since an aggregate is really a composition of frequencies he could identify and then modulate those frequencies. The law being discussed herein describes the methodology of modulating frequencies and the result that can be expected.

We have discussed in these pages to great length the subject of harmonics and partials. Let's cover it again that others unfamiliar with earlier issues can catch up.

When a given frequency is caused to vibrate it causes its own harmonics to (a double of frequency or halving of wavelength) to take place. This double or halving does not stop with the creation of just one or two harmonics but causes them all - all the way to infinity - to occur. The progression of harmonics can and does create the higher tones or super harmonics as well as the lower ones called sub harmonics. This is why Cayce said over and over again that music is the bridge between the material and spiritual realms. This also explains how and why vibrations possess so much power as evidenced by their destructiveness to vibrating media such as springs. Any tone being sounded will create a series of tones from the lowest to the highest frequencies imaginable. Just as a string on a piano or guitar vibrates so too do all of the higher harmonics and partials vibrate all relative to the fundamental tone or pitch or frequency of the string. I say partials because more resultant frequencies occur than just even doubling or halving of the fundamental frequency. Other ratios of vibration also rise up to fill the whole realm of motion. These can and do include thirds, sixths, sevenths, elevenths, etc. So when modern science refuses to recognize the odd or uneven partials and only focuses on the even harmonics it is missing the greater view of the phenomenon under study.

This is not a new revelation - this has been written about extensively in 100 year old books on music and vibration theory. To create really good music one must have a really good background in vibration theory. Modern music is bereft of this greater knowledge that for some reason is not being taught extensively. When music, such as we hear every day, is created with a scale that has been arbitrarily established (the chromatic or evenly spaced notes) the resultant sounds may be pleasing to the human ear but they fail as burning hail on nature because nature obeys subtler directives than sensual feedback. The even tempered scale is designed to sound good this is done by evenly measuring the frequencies of the notes in such a way that beat frequencies are kept to a minimum and hence the naturally occurring uneven partials are not allowed to manifest themselves.

The atomoles are the generic vibrating bundles of energy we call sub atomic particles. The harmonics and partials of the rad-energy cause these inner particles of the atom to vibrate or to change orbital characteristics such that the composite particle, the atom, changes in size and maybe even shape but without destroying the atom itself. Now these subatomic particles are not always equally affected by the influential rad-energy. They will change their frequency rates in accordance to their degree of sympathetic resonance. If a particle is greatly sympathetic to the influential vibration it will be affected greatly. If a particle is not sympathetic it will not be affected at all. Hence each one will change differently and we can then say that their relative frequency one to another changes. This relative frequency is called pitch. Once the size has been changed its overall characteristics or chord of mass also changes. This is what happens when a laser beam is played upon atomic elements or molecules. The subatomic particles begin to excite and disruption of the composite particle is inevitable - dissociation of the aggregated subatomic and atomic particles takes place.

Simple logic and observation substantiates this phenomenon. What does modern science use to modify atoms and molecules? In most cases it uses fire - the great transformative element. Fire is heat from a Bunsen burner or a laser and sometimes from chemical activities. And what is fire or heat but a high frequency vibration? A curious thing about the thermal vibrations known as heat is they do not have much if any effect on subatomic particles or particles making up subatomic particles. Heat frequencies manifest mostly on the molecular and atomic aggregates. What does this tell us? That the frequencies of heat are not high enough to have a direct effect on the structures of subatomic and quantum particles because there is little if any sympathetic association or resonance with them. So therefore, if one desires to tap into the subatomic and quantum levels of matter one must resort to frequency ranges far in excess of those commonly used such as X-Ray, Gamma or ultraviolet bands. Likewise to affect solid matter one would use the lower band levels such as heat (therm) and sound (sono) ranges. Keely indicated these ranges extended

151

21 octaves each and he may be right.

Another consequence of influential vibrations is that of mode changes. This is a rather complex development and will be discussed in future articles. Let it suffice that we dwell on the rainbow - God's gift to mankind. Through which he has and is showing us a very valuable lesson in how Harmony manifests as discord and as a non-color is manifest as infinite colors so too does the non-energy or zero-point energy manifest as the infinite range of materiality we call the Universe.

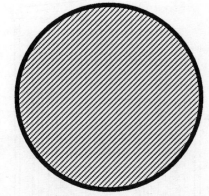

Chord of Equation 5th Octave

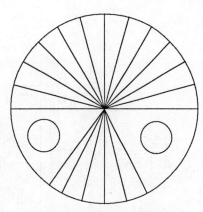

Sympathetic Chord of Transmission

Chord of Radiation 1st Octave

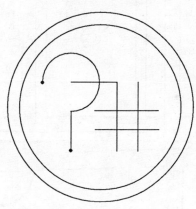

Chord Aflat 1st Octave

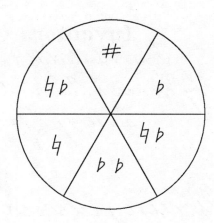

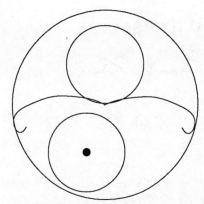

Neutral Chord any Octave

Keely's Secrets

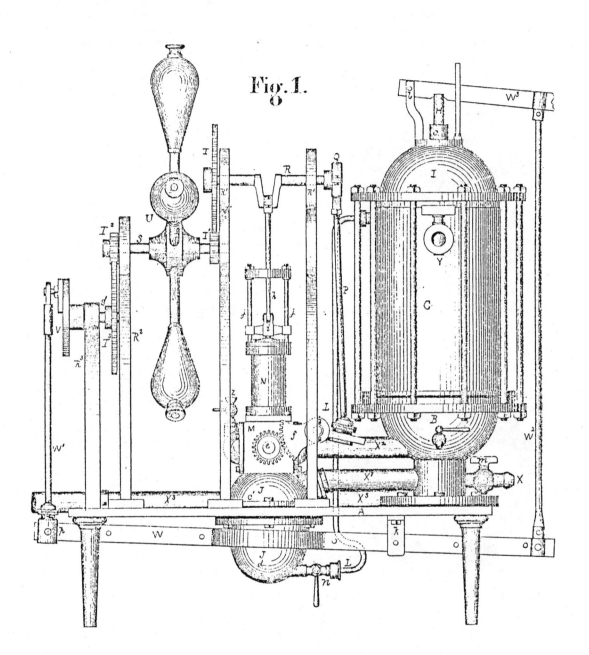

Fig. 1.

Witnesses.

J. Snowden Bell

G. W. Schuckers

Inventor.

John W. Keely

by Francis D. Pastorius

his Atty in fact

Hydro Pneumatic Pulsating Vacuo Engine

Law of Variation of Atomic Pitch by Electricity and Magnetism

"Electricity and Magnetism produce internal vibrations in the atom, which are followed by proportional changes in volume and, therefore, pitch."

Keely, 1894

Commentary May, 1987

A change in volume of course is a change in wave length. According to the change so to does the frequency change. Laws numbers 20 (April ' 87 issue) and 15 (Dec. ' 86 issue) give more background on this particular law and how it works.

Not knowing a great deal about Nuclear Magnetic Resonance I can't say much except that a tremendous magnetic field is used in conjunction with radio waves to produce the imaging capability. Perhaps the magnetism synchronizes the multitude of frequencies found in the body according to material types thus rendering contrast.

One thing to notice in this law is the reference to changes internally of the atom. In other words, on the components making up the atom. Electricity and magnetism, according to this law, have an effect upon the inside of an atom and those components found there. According to Keely's system of subatom-ic physics, the inside of an atom is called the inter-atomic and the next size of particles below that of atoms are called inter-atomic particles as are all phenomena associated with them. Therefore, we can see why Keely said electricity and magnetism are inter-atomic phenomena and they must also be some sort of vibration themselves. In modern parlance electrons are inside of an atom (when not wandering around randomly) and also may be seen as an "inner atom" particle with relative "inner-atomic" activities.

The next level of particles Keely called "etheric." From recent discoveries in quantum physics we are told that photons come from within electrons. Therefore, a photon is an "etheric" particle and all photon (light) associated phenomena are of the etheric realm of activity again according to Keely's philosophy. Muons, mesons and the different varieties of quarks are then of the next level of materiality or the "inter-etheric" realm. These levels aren't pertinent to this law as it is stated and therefore further discussion will be left for a more appropriate time.

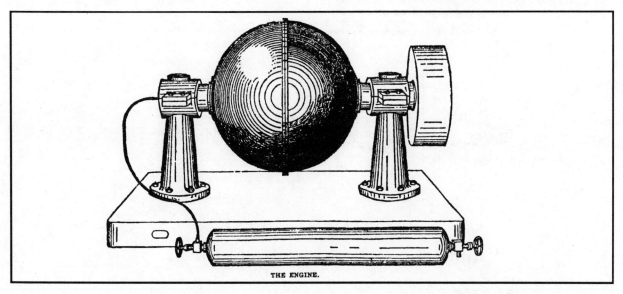

THE ENGINE.

Keely's Secrets

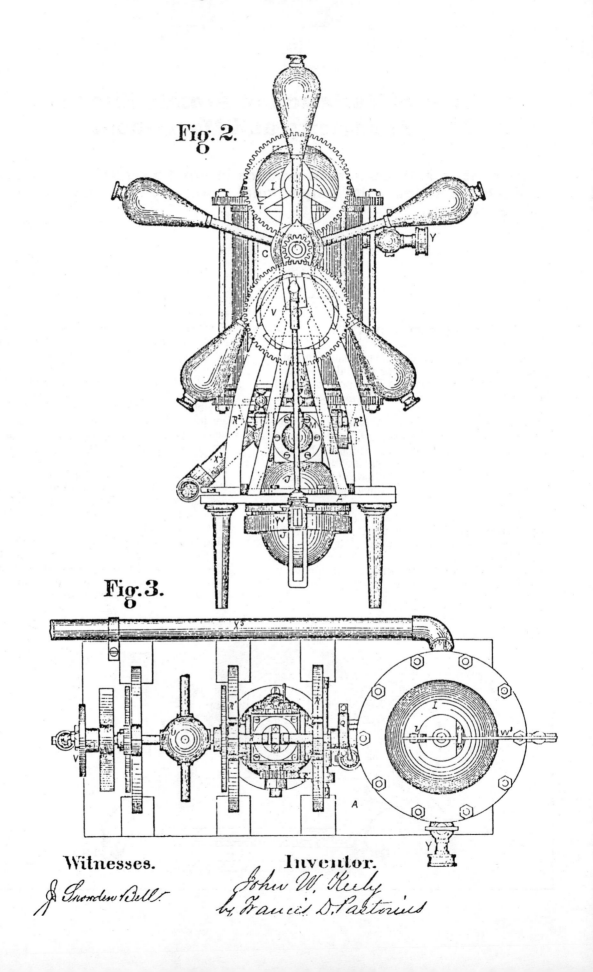

Fig. 2.

Fig. 3.

Witnesses.

J. Snowden Bell.

Inventor.

John W. Keely
by Francis D. Pastorius

Law of Variation of Atomic Pitch by Temperature

"Atoms in chemical combination oscillate with increasing amplitude directly as the temperature, and simultaneously absorb overtones of higher harmonics, producing expansion of volume and diminution of pitch.

RULE: The gradual approach of the temperature of harmonic combination can be observed by mutually comparing superimposed spectra; chemical combinations commences when the fundamental lines of each spectrum bear harmonic ratios by linear measurement."

Keely, 1894

Commentary June, 1987

One must remember that we are discussing atomic pitches and not molecular pitches. There appears to be some minor discrepancy between Keely's definition of molecules and atoms and our own. I haven't yet deciphered the difference enough to be able to explain it fully. However, the difference isn't great enough to prohibit us from attaining a good feel for what is being discussed.

Atom in chemical combination are alloys, *etc.* of a crystal like nature. Molecules in combination would be compound or alloys of lesser refinement. One is reminded of the great controversy surrounding superconductivity now raging throughout the scientific community. Seems some of the phenomena of superconductivity is involved with exotic combinations of ceramics and metals (near crystal forms). Yet the scientists can't explain these phenomena using their current excepted theories. Perhaps through these laws we might get a glimpse of what may be taking place.

We all know that atomic substances, say a crystal, will expand when heated. We aren't concerned with reiterations of common knowledge. Yet within this law Keely is telling us something else. He is telling us *why* the crystal expands. It expands because it absorbs *higher harmonics* which in turn reduces the component pitches.

As for the second part of the law he is disclosing something altogether new - "harmonic combination." He is telling us of a method of deducing atomic combination or allowing of atomic substances. This combining of elements takes place, in this law, as a function of harmonic relations of frequency. When the fundamental lines of the spectra bear harmonic ratio (see back issues) the atomic substances readily combine and maintain their new state of mixture. Likewise, we can assume they will separate when these lines are brought into non-harmonic ratios.

In a few of the past issues we indicated that there may be marvelous revelations awaiting us. This is one of them. If atomic frequency is behind the merging of elemental combinations instead of ion-exchange, we may be able to create new and novel substances of extraordinary utility.

NOTE: When considering ion-exchange from the quantum mechanical viewpoint Keely is exactly right. Ions are bundles of vibrating energy and not particles. Therefore one would have to work with their vibration frequencies instead of their "charges." Said charge is considered a function of velocity, mass, frequency, *etc.*, *i.e.* mathematical derivative of same. These modern mathematical derivatives are so complex we need supercomputers to calculate them. Yet here Keely is explaining something so simple as to seem preposterous. The Ancient Egyptians created alloys (electrum - which we can't yet duplicate) thousands of years ago. Did they have more advanced computers than we or did they simply understand the nature of chemical combinations better? Did Keely *pre* -discover the entire field of quantum mechanics or quantum acoustics and then went ahead and found how to apply it in a practical sense 100 years ago? Did he have a supercomputer or did he have a better understanding than we ourselves possess? Will this understanding prove simpler than we can even imagine? Stay tuned to this publication for the rest of the story.

Keely's Secrets

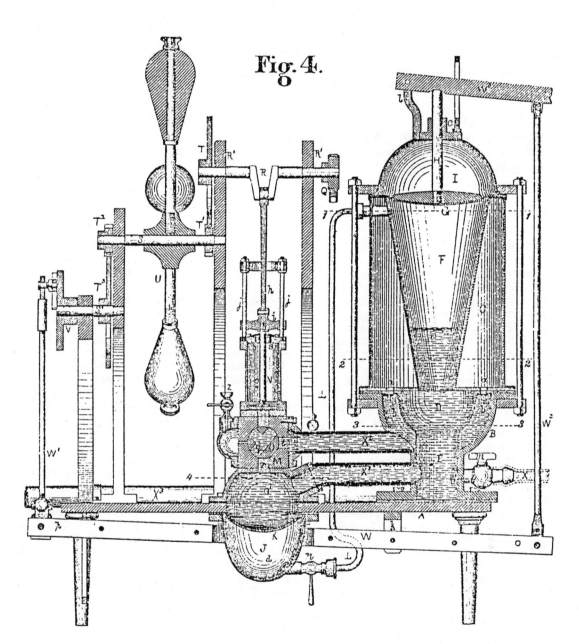

Fig. 4.

Witnesses.

J. Snowden Bell.

J. W. Schuckers.

Inventor.

John W. Keely
by Francis D. Pastorius
his Atty in fact

Law of Pitch of Atomic Oscillation

"Atoms not isolated and in a state of tension between forces that oppose and increase the equilibrium oscillate bodily at a pitch that is a resultant of the atomic weight, atomic volume, and tension."

Keely, 1894

Commentary July, 1987

If an atom is part of an aggregate and it is caught between the two forces as Keely defined and used them, *i.e.,* the *harmonic* which tends to stabilize or equates forces and the *enharmonic* which tends to de-stabilize or create dis-equilibrium, it will oscillate as a resultant computed from the atomic weight, atomic volume and tension acting upon it.

What we are beginning to see here is Keely's system of atomic physics. In this law and the next few we will see a totally new system laid out before us. One that is *natural, whole* and very simple when compared to the current system now in use which has a tendency to separate the various aspects of atomic physics into distinct and unrelated forms. His various tables, charts and monitoring devices were all synchronized or related in such a fashion as one reading on a given chart would bear direct and meaning relations to other readings of other charts, measurements, *etc.*. In other words, his system was *complete, relative and whole.*

In order to get a better understanding of what Keely meant by volume and weight of the atom let us quote how he determined these characteristics:

MATHEMATICAL DEMONSTRATION OF THE SIZE OF AN ATOM ITS WEIGHT AND VOLUME

by *John Keely*

"A rectangular, or preferably, a circular, disk is suspended from the ceiling of a room in such a manner that vibrations cannot be communicated to it from the vibrating walls of the room. It is the experimentally determined to what fundamental note the metal plate sympathetically vibrates. Then, according to the law of linear dimensions, which is equally applicable to solids, liquids, or gases, it is mathematically determined what size of plate will produce successive oc-

taves above that pitch, until a size of plate is obtained capable of producing a period-frequency corresponding to that of dark radiant heat, which we know is produced by the oscillations of atoms, and is termed therma. The vibrating atomic substance of the plate is capable of producing the transmissive force called sound and sono-thermism, which is propagated through atomic media by wave-motion, but which cannot be propagated through space devoid of atomic substance. But when the plate has been reduced theoretically to a size sufficiently infinitesimal to correspond to the maximum or minimum size of an atom, as determined by the atomic researches of Professors Tait & Clerk Maxwell, we reach vibration frequency so high that it can be propagated through a vacuum devoid of atomic substance, as a transmissive force called rad-energy, beginning with dark radiant heat. And be it carefully observed that period-frequency corresponds with that of dark rad-energy. The law of linear dimensions may be thus stated: *The vibration-periods of two similarly circumstanced homologous bodies are to each other as their cubical contents, and therefore the vibration-frequencies of homologous metal plates are to each other as the inverse ratio of their linear dimensions.* The octave of a given plate will be a homologous plate having 1/8 of its volume. A circular disk twenty inches in diameter and one inch thick vibrates, *e.g.,* 1024 times per second. The ten octaves from unity successively reducing the size of the disk by $\frac{1}{8}$, we get at each reduction the octave of the previous pitch, and at any given octave we have the volume, weight, and vibration-frequency of the vibrating atomic substance.

Ten octave 1024 vibrations per second; metal disk, twenty inches in diameter, one inch thick. To get the cubical contents of this vibrating aggregate it is necessary to square the diameter; we multiply by 0.7854, which is equal to 314.16 inches in volume. Starting from this point, we progress through successive octaves upward increasing in pitch and diminishing in size."

Keely's Secrets

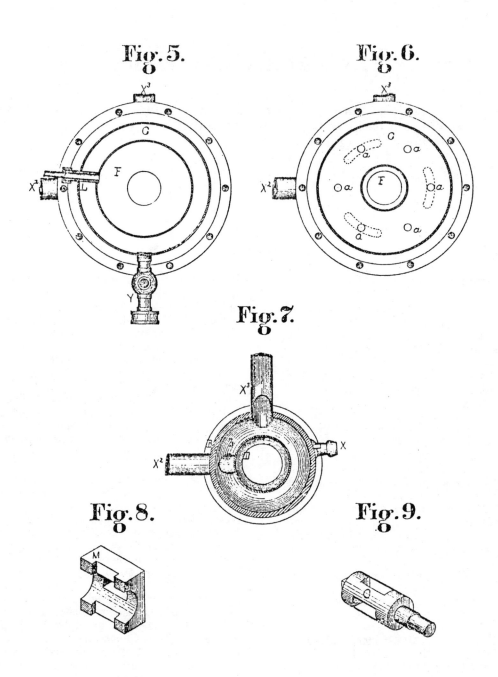

Fig. 5.

Fig. 6.

Fig. 7.

Fig. 8.

Fig. 9.

Witnesses.

J. Snowden Bell

J. W. Schuckers

Inventor.

John W. Keely

by Francis D. Pastorius

his Atty in fact

Law of Variation of Pitch of Atomic Oscillation by Pressure

"The frequency of atomic oscillation increases and diminishes inversely as the square of the pressure."

Keely, 1894

Commentary August, 1987

Here is a neat and simple law. All it says is that as we increase pressure on an atomic substance the *internal oscillations* of the atoms increases as the square of the pressure. Likewise when the pressure is decreased the oscillations also decrease but *always proportionate to the amount of pressure.* Small wonder then that matter "heats up" when pressure is applied and cools down when pressure is lessened.

We can then see the difference between Keely's ideas and orthodox science. He equates heat and cold to *atomic oscillation* (an internal activity) and pressure has a *direct relationship to the frequency* of that oscillation. Modern science recognizes heat as a "friction" caused by particles rubbing against each other whereas Keely doesn't believe that these particles actually come in contact. IN fact he claims that no force on earth can cause molecules to actually come in contact with each other. He maintained that even though particles never actually touched they had effects on each other. The manner of transmitting these effects was through *sympathetic vibrations.* In fact, it is beginning to appear that it is *only through sympathetic vibrations that action at a distance can take place simply because any and all actions take place at a distance.* Each particle maintains its individuality yet is part of whatever aggregate it is associated with. Yet for an effect to pass from one to another or many to one there must be some degree of sympathy between them. Without this sympathetic attunement no action whatever would be transmitted or felt or experienced through whatever degree of association. Before two or more individual particles or people can have a harmonious association (form an aggregate or association of ONE) this degree of sympathy (attunement) must exist.

The same process takes place in social activities. Because these laws are deemed universe, *i.e.,* universally applicable, they also apply every where else. Human beings are individuals (with their own ideas, graces and habits) yet *through association* they *may* partake of whatever social ideas, graces, mores or traditions their respective communities possesses. They may only take up these outside attributes (become harmonious with or one with) if they are so inclined *from within themselves* (resonant) to them or may be induce (modulated) to become inclined (resonant) to them. Here again the sympathetic attunement must exist or be induced to exist before individuals can associate or aggregate into groups of whatever size be it one on one in a marriage or as an integral part of a community. Only through harmonious thought and action can individuals ever hope to have peaceful co-existence. Thoughts of self or negative actions contribute to dis-harmony and hence separation resulting in aloneness of the individual.

This is where Man is greater (much greater) than the rest of materiality - he can *chose* to be in harmony with something other than his individual self or he can chose to be apart and separate.

These laws can be applied to human functions when one associates atoms as though they were individuals who may aggregate into groups (molecules). The laws which apply to molecules apply similarly to groups. The atoms (individuals) are composed of three fundamental segments or parts, *i.e.,* physical, mental and spiritual or the enharmonic, harmonic and dominant. But here we are leaving our main topic and this would be better pursued in another article.

Keely's Secrets

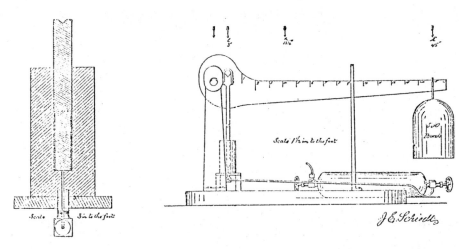

The undersigned, at the request of Mr John W Keely, have carefully examined his structure termed a Liberator, and also his Lever by means of which the energy of the force generated by the Liberator is measured: both of said structures having been wholly dismantled for the purpose of such examination.

As the result of our examination we would state as follows:—

1st The construction and organization of the Liberator is such that it is incapable of containing or concealing any stored power.

2nd The respective arms of the Lever are about Sixteen (16) to one (1), that is to say, the length of the longer arm is forty-eight (48) inches, and the shorter arm is three (3) inches from the fulcrum; the diameter of the piston upon which the uplifting force impinges to raise the lever is seven-eighths (7/8) of an inch, and its area in cross section is accordingly six tenths (6/10) of an inch.

This being the case, and adding the weight of the lever, it follows that when a weight of Five hundred and fifty (550) pounds is suspended on the end of the longer arm, it requires a force of Fifteen thousand seven hundred and fifty one (15,751) pounds per square inch impinging on the lower end of the piston to raise the lever.

The accompanying sectional drawing signed by J. E. Schiedt, correctly represents the construction of the piston and the cylinder in which it works.

There were present at such examination, in connection with ourselves, the following named gentlemen; Dr Henry P. Hudson, of New York, T. F. Weeds M.D. and Mr Chas B Collier

J. H. Livolles
W. Barnet Le Van

Philadelphia, Oct. 22nd 1886.

Law of Variation of Atomic Oscillation by Temperature

"The force of cohesion diminishes inversely as the square of the distance the atoms are apart, and the force of the chemical affinity diminishes in the same ratio. Heat increases the amplitude of the oscillations in a direct ratio to the temperature of the natural scale.

Scholium: New thermometers and accurate thermometric tables, on the natural bases, wherein doubling the temperature doubles the pitch of the transmissive energy, are required. Such a table of temperature will bear natural relation to atomic weights, pitches, specific heats, chemical affinities, fusions, solubilities, etc., and will disclose new laws. One table for each must be constructed."

Keely, 1894

Commentary September, 1987

This is perhaps one of the most important of the laws discussed to date. It is important because we can readily relate to what Keely is saying. Everyone knows that as a substance is heated the atoms are caused to be spread further apart. Likewise, when the substance is cooled the atoms tend to contract. The major difference between the orthodox viewpoint and the one given above is what causes the repulsion and contraction. Keely maintains that it is the discords between the vibrations of the atoms which cause the repulsion and heat is a form of vibration that adds to this discord. Contraction he maintains is the opposite where more harmony in the atomic frequencies causes cohesiveness.

That these opposite actions are related as simply as he states remains to be explored and verified. I suppose some of the readers having access to proper facilities could perform this verification fairly easily.

The second part of this law, the scholium, is nothing short of a gift for someone with the proper facilities and support. What would a properly related system of calibration be worth? If what he says is true about the relative values of an integrated system of temperature and frequencies imagine what such a simplistic system would mean to today's research and development operations. It looks like it might be worth someone's time and expense to check this out. I haven't had the time nor opportunity to do anything with this though I plan on it. If I get the time, I'll publish whatever I find out.

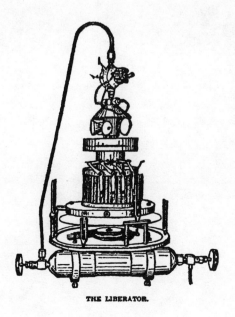

THE LIBERATOR.

The disk on the bottom of the resonator may be the hydrogen impregnated disk
mentioned by Dr. Plum

Law of Variation of Atomic Oscillation by Electricity

"The electric current destroys cohesion and chemical tension directly as square of current in amperes, inversely as the resistance in ohms, inversely as the chemical equivalent, and conversely as the coefficient of the difference between the freezing and volatizing temperature of mass acted upon."

Keely, 1894

Commentary October, 1987

This law tells us what we already know about electrical currents operating within a chemical substance such as a length of copper wire. I don't believe I've seen this phenomenon described in any other literature as a *law* though.

A conductor "melts" or breakdown as we call it in the manner described above. The cohesion between atoms of a given atomic mass (chemical substance or alloy) is disrupted if there is too much amperage or too great a resistance and this breakdown is related to the chemical composition and temperature limits of the material. What is unique in Keely's approach is that this atomic breakdown of the substance can be calculated from a table of the mass' properties and that this calculated atomic structural breakdown is *directly proportional* to these same quantities.

If tables were created according to the law given in the previous September, 1987 issue and calculations were run based on the above law we should be able to tell at a glance how differing elements and alloys would behave given any parameters of applied vibratory currents.

This should apply to commonly used materials such as copper, aluminium, etc., but should also help in deciphering the resultant activities of so-called superconductive materials as well. In other words, if what Keely is describing is accurate, we should be able to accurately predict behavior of exotic blends of materials before they are incorporated into current carrying circuits. Not only that, once such tables were created one should be able to specify a current and its parameters and have a computer tailor design an alloy which would carry it and we would known how the material would react beforehand.

The latter part of this law says that the cohesion breakdown occurs *"as the coefficient of the difference between the freezing and volatizing temperature of mass acted upon."* Temperature limits of ceramic materials is generally very broad. Take this law and **The Law of Vibrating Atomic Substances** dis-

cussed in the December, 1986 issue and perhaps we have an explanation for the phenomenon of superconductivity wherein resistance is caused by the expansion and twisting of the atomic structure (lattice structure?). This expansion and twisting we commonly call cohesion breakdown. In short, as the atomic mass expands and twists the crystalline structure is gradually disrupted until a point is reached where the material is "melted" or dissociated. As this expansion and twisting increases so too does the resistance, *etc.*. When the mass is "frozen" as is commonly done in superconductor research, the tendency to expand or twist is reduced thus allowing the transmission and inductance of the vibrating electrical current without interference (modulation). Modulation of the primary vibrating current , in this case electricity, causes the creation of secondary and tertiary frequencies - heat, light, *etc.*. The ability to expand or twist is directly related to the atomic structural parameters, *i.e.*, density, crystalline configuration, *etc.*. But what governs the density, structure, *etc*? See **Law of Oscillating Atomic Substances** discussed in September, 1986 issue.

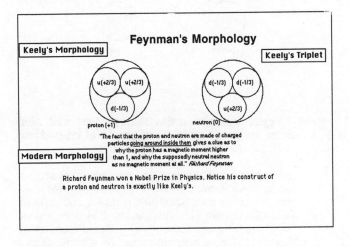

164

Keely's Secrets

Keely's Discoveries Vindicated?

Some of you are familiar with my logo of the three circles enclosed tightly by another circle. It is reproduced below:

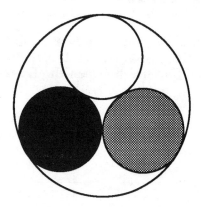

This configuration was developed by John Keely circa 1880 and was his depiction of positive, negative and neutrally charged particles making up molecules and atoms. He maintained that all molecular, atomic particles has this configuration. In his completed chart (dated 1894 and reprinted in this journal in the December, 1985 and again in the January, 1986 issues) he showed the complex structure as he saw it derived from his researches.

A recent book by Richard Feyman, titled **QED, The Strange Theory of Light and Matter,** has a similar drawing on page 134. It is reproduced below:

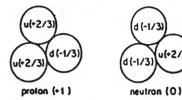

Feyman demonstrates that protons and neutrons are made up of three quarks of types *d* and *u*. Ratio of *d* to *u* determines polarity.

Feyman is the foremost quantum physicist according to some sources. Most of his book describes current efforts to understand this complex and difficult field of quantum electrodynamics. It is a very good book, readable and entertaining. I would recommend this work for anyone interested in natural science (what makes things tick and why).

Comparing Feyman's chart to Keely's we see that the black circle in Keely's chart corresponds to Feyman's proton. The grey circle applies to the neutron and the white would correspond to the electron if Feyman had included one. Thus the black is the negative charged "particle," the white is positive and the grey of course as the neutral charged "particle."

Today the electron is considered having a negative charge, this is unfortunate. Since this charge state is actually a label placed by somebody years ago we must accept it as it is. However one should consider an electron as a particle of *positive* energy because it is ACTIVE. In other words, it has an expressive energy whereas the proton is in a receptive or negative state even though we call it positive. Common sense would reverse these polarities in conversation and application. Then again some orthodox quantum physicists maintain the position that if the physics makes sense then it is wrong! You can make up your own mind on what makes sense or not.

The rest of the book is quite interesting but I will not go into it here. The most interesting thoughts come to mind when we think that Keely did this original and accurate research over 100 years ago and it has taken orthodox science all this time and money to only begin to see the same result. Small wonder then, that Keely wasn't understood by his "peers," he was ahead of them by more than a century.

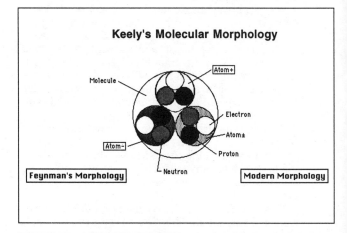

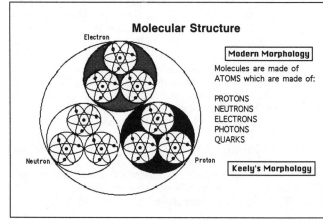

Law of Variation of Atomic Oscillation by Sono-thermism

"Diminishes the tensions directly as the quantity of heat developed, and in antithetical proportion to the harmonics absolved."

Keely, 1894

Commentary November, 1987

We identified and discussed the nature of thermism in the August, 1987 issue. *Sono-thermism* may be defined as "heat produced from this frequency sound waves or phonons." This definition is made after the McGraw-Hill definition of sono-luminescence which they define as *"Luminescence produced by high frequency sound waves of phonons."* Ultrasonic transducers do produce a goodly of heat and I believe it is this particular heat Keely is referring to in this law.

So we might say that as this heat is developed within the atomic substance and acts upon the tension between the atoms which is reduced in proportion to the quantity of heat. The second half of this law says that as the harmonics are absolved or done-away-with or dampened out of the material the tension between the atoms *increases*. In other words, if you refer back to the October, 1987 issue, we will see that the state of the atomic structure is a result of the fundamental frequency and the harmonics or partials present in the material. The greater the coincidence (harmony) of all the associated frequencies, the greater is the tension between the atomic particles. In other words, there is a greater tendency to develop and retain crystalline form when the *coincidence of frequencies is greater*. *Harmony* (female form of the energy manifesting as vibrations) *creates attraction or rigidity.* When the reverse is true, when there are a great number of harmonics or partials, the tension lessens and there is then experienced "melt-down" or breakdown of the crystalline structure. If this discordant tendency is allowed to run unchecked or unbalanced, complete volatization of the material takes place. The particles, being discordant to each other, repulse each other. *Discord* (the male from of the energy manifesting as vibrations) *creates repulsion or expansion.* Please see the **Laws of Attraction and Repulsion** given in the May, 1986 issue.

The above tells us a lot about the inner nature of gases and crystals. Crystals are a demonstration of atomic particles vibrating in unison and expansive gases are particles vibrating in a discordant fashion. We can also surmise that cold absolves harmonics and brings about concordance of vibrations whereas heat creates harmonics and discord. Actually heat is discord because it is the addition of non-concordant frequencies. Heat, then, is not something other than a vibration. Inversely we can say that cold, then, is not something other than a **lack** of vibrations.

To summarize in a graphic fashion - ice is an aggregate of water molecules vibrating in unison and steam is a collection of water molecules vibrating discordant to one another. Please keep in mind that there are also lattice patterns apparent in gaseous states as well. This is because there are concordant frequencies within and between the particles even though they have this discordant quality. A water molecule is always a water molecule and they will always retain some degree of harmonic attraction. Steam can be greater or lesser dense such as is the case with low pressure steam and super-heated steam or atmospheric air for that matter. This greater or lesser degree of density in gaseous substances explains the difference of velocity of sound in the air when considering the **Law of Vibrating Atomic Substances** (September, 1986 issue). *The degree of discordance is also the cause of pressure just as harmony is the cause of the density of aggregation.*

One more graphic illustration -*uranium or any other potentially radioactive substance demonstrates the very same idea of concord and discord discussed above. If radioactivity is caused by a discordance among the alpha and gamma particles may not radioactivity be reversed by bringing these same particles into a state of concordance? Is not this discordance the cause of radioactivity.*

166

Photograph of the final Hydro-Vacuo Motor. This motor was donated to The Franklin Institute by Mr. Howson, Keely's lawyer. Its story is on page 84.

Law of Chemical Affinity

"Atoms whose atomic pitches are in either unison, harmonic or concordant ratios, unite to form molecules.

Corollary: When two atoms are indifferent, they may be made to unite by varying the pitch of either, or both.

Scholium: This necessitates the construction of tables representing variations of atomic pitches by temperature, pressure, etc.

Scholium: Tables of all harmonics and concords, and harmonics founded upon a normal harmonic scale, are equally essential.

Scholium: Optical instruments may be made to measure pitches of energy."

Keely 1894

Commentary December, 1987

This law is fundamental to the basic concept of sympathetic vibratory physics. Concord or harmony causes unition of elements while discord causes separation or dissociation. One must always keep in mind that he is not referring to a single vibration but to a chord of vibrations. In today's parlance we would call this a vibration signature. However, in my estimation a vibration signature is a passive measurement of a group of associated vibrations whereas a chord of vibration is a properly determined set of specific frequencies one would use as a tool. In other words, a signature is passive and a chord is causative.

The corollary above says that indifferent elements may be united by changing the rate of either element. An element not in harmony made be rendered into a concordant condition (matching frequencies) by increasing or decreasing its vibrations. A simple way of doing this, as everyone knows or should know, is by simply heating one or both of the elements. Heat is a vibration and when applied to a mixture will bring about a commonalty of frequencies such that the two previously unrelatable elements will relate and merge (unify themselves) into a common substance. Another great source of vibratory motion is water. The molecular vibrations of water have the same effect (in the final analysis) as heat.

Table of atomic pitches can easily be prepared and then matched with computers. The various possible positions of frequencies can be related from element to element similar to what I've done with the previously mentioned Music Interval Spreadsheet (see SVP March, 1987 page 5). By matching the various frequencies the points of harmony and discords are readily discernible and this data may be used to predict the mixability and conditions of mixability of various elements or compounds, etc..

The last part of the scholiums indicates instruments can be made to measure frequencies. Remember this law was published in 1894 and what we have today was simply unknown. Today we have electron microscopes which operate via UV, X-Ray and electron frequencies. We also have a device called a spectrometer which uses band-pass filters and also measures frequencies. I don't know when these and other similar devices were invented but their existence demonstrated once again that Keely was a few years ahead of his time.

DIAGRAM 6.

Photograph of the final Hydro-Vacuo Motor. This motor was donated to The Franklin Institute by Mr. Howson, Keely's lawyer. Its story is on page 84.

Law of Chemical Dissociation

"If the pitch of either atom, in a molecule, be raised or lowered; or, if they both be unequally raised or lowered in pitch until the mutual ratio be that of a discord; or, if the oscillation amplitude be augmented by heat until the atoms are with the concentric waves of attraction, - the atoms will separate."

Keely, 1894

Commentary January, 1988

Last month there was mentioned some rather startling statements about Keely disintegrating quartz. That ultrasonic vibrations can break stones or other hard materials should be of no surprise to readers of this publication. Kidney stones breaker are in many hospitals throughout the land and many dentists now have an ultrasonic device operating at 25 kHz which literally explodes tartar from teeth. What is surprising in the article is that Keely claims to have been able to disintegrate *a ton of quartz in 15 seconds* - and this was in 1887! The other surprise (to me) was the wording in this particular law. Keely used the word amplitude - no big deal but in last month's article he used the word intensify - as in intensifying vibrations. I had supposed intensify was his intended word for amplify - but now I see that it was not. He intensified vibrations but amplified oscillations. These are two distinct and different things. His own definition of oscillation by his own hand is: *OSCILLATION is a rhythmical motion of a body within itself.* A good analogy of this type of motion is a water balloon we used to play with when I was young and wilder. When the balloon was launched it oscillated within the confines of its elastic membrane kind of like jello on a plate. Amplifying a vibration is an increase in the force or degree of polarity as measured from the zero or neutral state. In other words to amplify a vibration we are increasing its state of either positive or negative or both states of polarization.

Another curiosity of this law is the phrase "the atoms are with the *concentric waves* of attraction." Now immediately what comes to mind are the orbital paths of particles within a molecule or atom. These paths (and their distance from the center) have been quantified using Planck's Constant. Under current theory a particle will maintain its orbit until a certain quantity of energy has been applied thus causing it to "jump" to the next orbital path. These orbital paths are what Keely refers to as *concentric waves of at-*

traction. For it is only at and on these rings that a particle is stable. Therefore they must possess this quality of attraction for if they didn't the particle would not be attracted to them and be held these. This action is not unlike particles on a Chladni plate. The nodal lines or areas are places of "least activity" or quiet when compared to the intervening spaces which have comparatively greater activity or motion. Just as has been indicated in past issues - the male energy is active and the female is quiescent. It is the female or negative part of vibrations that possesses this quality of attraction. A very universal principle as we can see this even in human psychology.

It is like the attractive energy says "thus far and no further you can go." Small wonder then that nuclei "capture" wandering particles just as suns capture planets or asteroids and women capture loose males!! I could go on and on with this subject of positive/ negative or male/female interactivity - I find it a fascinating subject - however I'd rather progress on to the next subject.

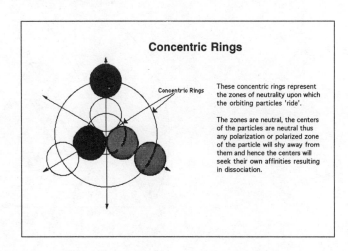

Concentric Rings

Concentric Rings

These concentric rings represent the zones of neutrality upon which the orbiting particles 'ride'.

The zones are neutral, the centers of the particles are neutral thus any polarization or polarized zone of the particle will shy away from them and hence the centers will seek their own affinities resulting in dissociation.

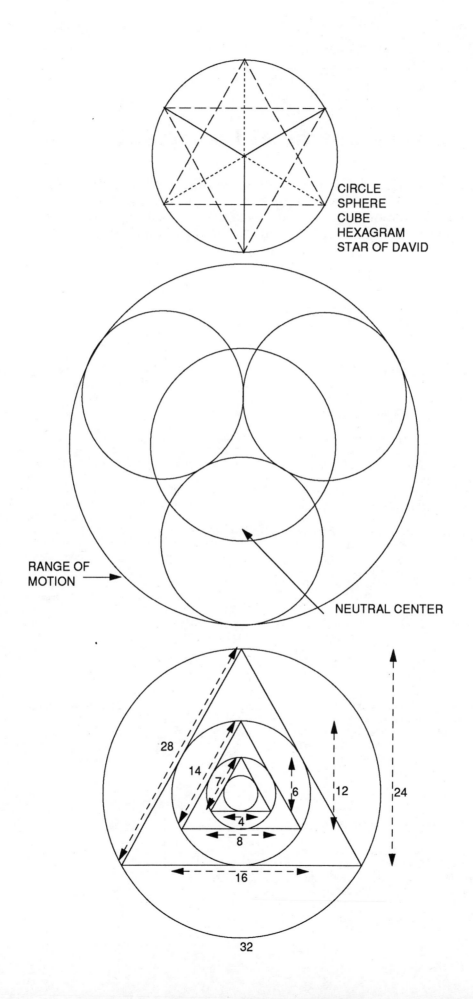

CIRCLE
SPHERE
CUBE
HEXAGRAM
STAR OF DAVID

RANGE OF
MOTION

NEUTRAL CENTER

28

14

7

6

12

24

4

8

16

32

Law of Chemical Transposition

"New molecules must be harmonics of the fundamental pitch."

Keely, 1894

Commentary February, 1988

If anything can be said about Keely's physical philosophy it is that of consistency. Over and over the same idea is conveyed. *For vibrating bodies to associate they must be of a harmonic relationship.* Remember that this harmonic relationship is not restricted to numbers of octaves as 2, 4, 8, *etc.*. It also applies to the other intervals as are demonstrated in music notation. Greater number intervals simply implies less aggregative power by degrees. In other words a molecule may be very in dense when the numbers are octaves or even fourths or fifths but may be much less dense if the interval is a ninth or twelfth.

The vibrations of a molecule may be said to be its signature. The signature, together with the fundamental, is synonymous with Keely's term "mass chord."

Conversely if the intervals be rendered into discords and amplified we may expect dissociation. This is one of the aspects of gases. The molecules are discordant one to another and repulse the other bodies around themselves. This repulsion is also by degrees of discordance. The greater the discord and amplitude the greater the pressure developed by the gas.

Thus perhaps we can see where or how Keely took plain water (a partially discordant collection of molecules) and increased their particular frequency amplitude until it simply "exploded" itself into a vapor. By knowing the frequencies of the vapor he could simply repeat the process using higher and higher frequencies until he had a confined plasma gas under incredible pressure. This we hope to demonstrate in the next subsequent issues and articles, it was this plasmic gas he apparently used to power his cannon and motors.

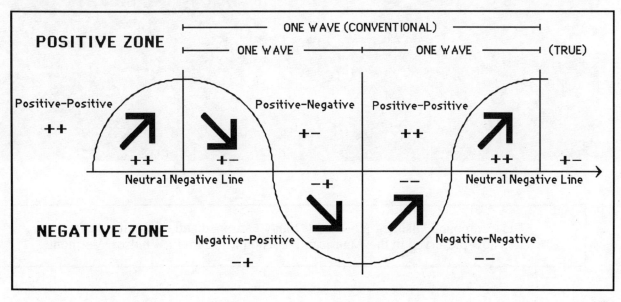

The Compound Disintegrator as it is today - stripped and canabalized of parts.
It is now preserved in the American Precision Museum in Windsor, Vermont.

Law of Chemical Substitution

"(Too complex for brief statement)"

Keely, 1894

Commentary March, 1988

The first law mentioned above has not an explanation with it. As you see it written above is the way it has come to me. There is no more written on this law by John Keely in the material I have in my possession. Some persons have accused me of withholding this information - but it is not available to me. This is more evidence that somewhere, in someone's care

there is more of Keely's writings. I hope that one day this person will come forward and allow these materials to become public for the benefit of us all.

ETHER OR ÆTHER

"The luminiferous ether - the compound interetheric element - in other words, *celestial mind force* - is the substance of which all visible and invisible things are composed." Keely circa 1888

"Æther is an atomolic liquid 986,000 times the density of steel." Keely

"The fundamental mode of vibration changes as we reach the fifth subdivision [of matter], to the dominant, the diatonic third of the mass chord, which controls the vibratory states of both the etheron and interetheron. The awful might concealed in the depths of the etheric and interetheric subdivisions utterly transcends anything Science has ever known. Even the theoretical energy value of radium now accepted by Science, pales into insignificance in comparison to the energy value of an equal amount of water subdivided to the etheric or interetheric state." Keely

According to Rudolph Steiner there are four different typse of ether:

Life Ether
Light Ether
Chemical or Tone Ether
Warmth Ether

KEELY'S PROVISIONAL ENGINE

The globe and the drum revolve in opposite directions through the action of etheric force which is transmitted to them by a wire of platinum and silver.

Universal Laws Never Before Revealed: Keely's Secrets

Law of Catalysis

The presence of harmonics and discords.

Keely, 1894

Commentary March, 1988 (together with previous law)

This law appears to be a simple reiteration of what has been so often mentioned in previous laws. The actions of chemical dissolution and formation are governed by the harmonics and discords present in the active and passive elements under discussion. So much has already been written about this process I fear it would be redundant to rewrite what has already been presented in past issues.

Over Unity is Recognized in Conventional Science

CAVITATION: "The collapse of the smaller vapor filled cavities [during cavitation] causes many extreme results as the *intensity of the resulting shock wave may be considerably greater than the originating action.*" [1]

"Cavitation is mainly known for its harmful effects, namely, loss of performance, erosion, and noise.[2] However, attempts to induce and harness cavitation for useful purposes have been increasingly successful. [For instance] In high-pressure jets, cavitation has for some time now been purposely induced in order to increase their drilling, cutting, and cleaning capabilities."[3]

"... *pressure of thousands of atmospheres* may be developed at the moment when the cavity collapses to a small fraction of the original diameter. Such collapses are, therefore, bound to cause *enormous effects, as high kinetic energies* are being concentrated at very small spots."[4]

"To give an idea of the amazing effects of cavitation, it may be pointed out that after a destroyer had rushed for several hours at maximum speed, the armor plates above the propeller were pierced by a hole of the dimension of about one square foot."[5]

"If the cavities are larger than about 10^{-4} cm in diameter the pressure at the solid [boundary] is about 1000 atmospheres (14,000 psi), while smaller bubbles give rise to increasingly higher pressures."[6]

"While denucleated liquids may have a number of practical applications such as their use for a transmission medium in high intensity ultrasonic equipment, the use of enhanced nucleation in liquids could have far reaching possibilities. If it were possible materially to reduce the power necessary for active cavitation many of the actions utilizing the phenomenon of cavitation would become more economic and practical from the point of view of commercial exploitation."[6]

(1)Crawford, Alan E.,*Ultrasonic Engineering with particular reference to high power applications;* Butterworths Scientific Publications, 1955, London. pg 26.
(2)Hammitt, F. G., *Cavitation and Multipahse Flow Phenomena*, McGraw-Hill International Company, 1980.
(3)Johnson, V. E., Jr., Chahine, G. L., Lindemuth, W. T., Conn, A. F., Frederick, G. S., and Giacchino, G. J. Jr., *Cavitating and Structured Jets for Mechanical Bits to Increase Drilling Rates.* ASME Journal of Energy Resources Technology, Vol. 106, 1984, pp. 282-294.
(4)Prakash, Satya, and Ghosh, Ashim K., *Ultrasonics and Colloids*, Scientific Research Committee, Allahabad, India, 1961.
(5)Prakash, Satya, and Ghosh, Ashim K., *Ultrasonics and Colloids*, Scientific Research Committee, Allahabad, India, 1961.
(6)Crawford, Alan E.,*Ultrasonic Engineering with Particular Reference to High Power Applications;* Butterworths Scientific Publications, 1955, London. pg

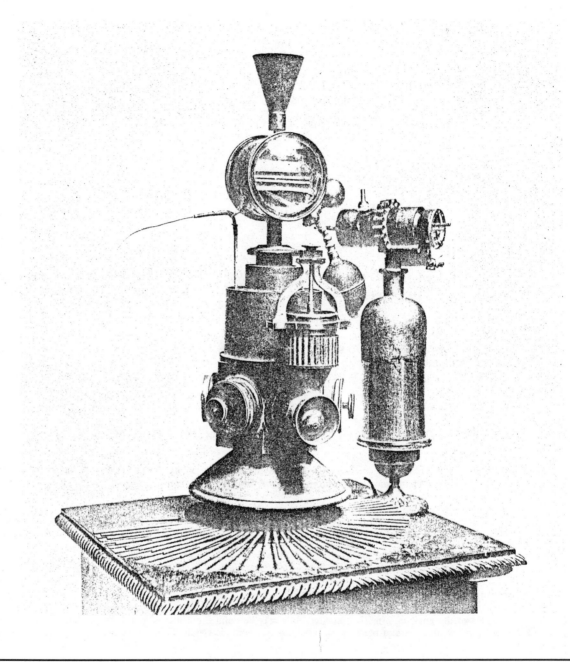

Liberator (improved form.)

Law of Molecular Synthesis and Combination

"The molecular pitch must be a derived harmony of the radicals.
Scholium: Reconstruction of electric units to represent pitches and amplitudes."

Keely, 1894

Commentary April, 1988

This law is another example of what appears to be the fundamental principle conveyed throughout Keely's work. That all frequencies being dealt with must always be a harmonic relationship if the intention is to maintain integrity. When seeking to create molecules from atoms the end frequency must be in harmonic relation to the frequencies of the combining frequencies of the atoms. (If the hypotenuse A is the fundamental: the sum of the squares of the height b and base a demonstrates this.) If the atoms (b and a) have a frequency of 2 or 3 then the resulting molecule A must have a frequency relative to 2 or 3 for the molecule to be stable.

The scholium evidently refers back to what was said in the Law of Chemical Affinity (SVP December, 1987), *i.e.,* recalibrating tables that they will reflect the vibratory state of the elements of calculation used as a basis of mathematical notation in these processes.

Once all these modes of measurement have been brought into a true and meaningful relationship one to another much more will become apparent in physics and the final result will be a *true whole view of science and nature.* Just as music has all of its components relative to one another so to should science restructure its mathematical components such that we aren't burdened with overly complex formulae and methods while attempting to decipher nature's art.

Relativity of Circles and Triangles

by *Dale Pond*

It is a marvel of nature how simply She works. The elegance of matching triangles with circles can be extended to encompass squares and cubes. Nature works with whole numbers as can be witnessed in every egg eaten at breakfast. *Even seen 9/10 of an egg*

in its natural state?

The drawing below shows very easily how these shapes merge one with another - each equating the other - without a fraction of excess of difference. It is sometimes helpful and more relevant to visualize these shapes as 3-dimensional entities. Thus we can see a hexahedron inside a cube inside a sphere. All the points or apexes meeting on common points and the center pivot point is likewise shared.

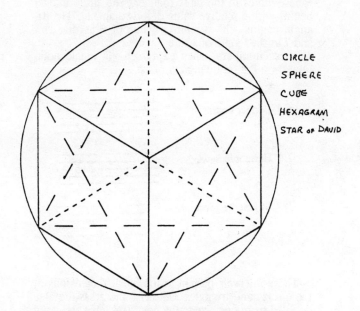

CIRCLE
SPHERE
CUBE
HEXAGRAM
STAR OF DAVID

The next drawing shows equilateral triangles circumscribed by circles which are in turn circumscribed by triangles. The relative values of each dimensions is given.

Keely's Secrets

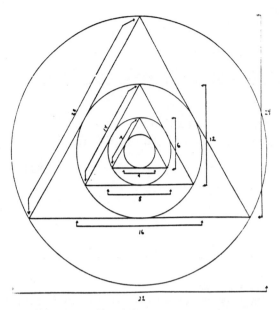

Notice that each increase from one size to the next larger size is a doubling of values, always equally. This is synonymous with the increase of a single value in music (middle C for instance) which becomes its octave - each dimension doubles in value. In the diagram we can see three distinct series of numbers. Each begins with a different integer yet each doubles in the same manner. The circle integer begins with a relative value of 4 as diameter. The triangle begins with a relative value of 6 as diameter and 7 as the length of a side.

These numbers, when expressed via music notation, form the following intervals:

6:4 Perfect Fourth

7:4 Harmonic Seventh

7:6 Augmented Second

These intervals pertain to the linear dimensions of the circles and triangles. Likewise the areas are also doubled from one size to the next. But what about the volume? According to Buckminster Fuller: *"Every time we double the diameter of a spherical structure, we increase its contained atmosphere eight-fold and its enclosing surface only fourfold."* Therefore we can express this doubling as follows:

Double any dimension:	2x
Double area:	2x
Perimeter of circle:	2x
Perimeter of triangle:	2x

Simultaneously:

Volume of sphere is increased:	8x
Surface of circle is increased:	4x
Volume of hexahedron is increased:	8x
Surface of hexahedron is increased:	4x

These relationship are all octaves or double octaves. Therefore they all remain in sync or harmony no matter to what degree of expansion. In other words, the 3-dimensional solid maintains its integrity at all times. We've been told by Keely that harmonic (octave) relationship are the strongest and most stable - perhaps these numbers demonstrate that assertion.

Neutral Center Defined
by *Dale Pond*

Keely says the neutral center is that area contained in a sphere as one-third of its total volume. Looking at his three-body molecule design below the confines of the neutral center can be seen as a circle (visualize this as 3-dimensional sphere) with its perimeter running just beyond the centers of each of the three revolving bodies. This neutral center perimeter coincides with a one-half radius perimeter of each revolving body. Furthermore, this one-half perimeter intersection point, happens to coincide with the center points of the **next** smaller enclosed triplet of bodies. Geometrically this circumscribed area defines one-third of a sphere's volume.

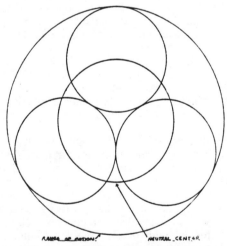

Since the term neutral implies neither negative nor positive charge or state we can see why he called this area of volume *neutral*. The three bodies each possess a charge - negative, positive and one is neutral. The point at which they each meet cancels out the charge of the other and hence we have a state of mutual charge or one that may be called neutral when considered relative to the charge on the opposite or outermost hemisphere of each body. One is reminded of the well known phenomenon in electricity that a hollow cannot contain a positive charge but which charge always travels to the points or outer rims of any containing shape.

Therefore the inner one-third volume is neutral while the outer three points of the three bodies maintain their respective positive, negative and neutral states.

Law of Chemical Morphology

"The angle of crystallization is determined by the relation between the molecular pitch of the crystallizing substance to the vibration-density of the liquid depositing it."

Keely, 1894

Commentary May, 1988

This law is very interesting especially with the faddish beliefs surrounding crystals reportedly possessing mystical properties that is so prevalent now days. To this day I have found no concrete or verifiable arguments explaining why crystal do what so many profess them to do - perform miraculous healing or establish some sort of high level communication with other life forms.

One of the few properties of crystals I've been able to uncover (the subsequent meaning of which is pure conjecture at this point) is the fact that crystals possess a vector quality or *directional valency*. Meaning a crystalline substance has different values depending on the direction in which such values are measured. This vector quality extends to heat transfer, light refraction and reflection and *cohesion* (1). Directional valency is no small factor as each of these functions is based on frequency count and form - according to what we have been learning from Keely's work.

By way of illustration the formation of a hexagonal and flat shaped snowflake from a spherical droplet of water may be useful. This illustration is, by necessity, an over simplification of the issue. The actions of subatomic particles are, for the most part, shrouded in great mystery. The effort here is to push back the veil just a little. It may be years before we may have a complete and accurate revelation concerning these matters.

Taking Keely's premise that cohesive forces act according to harmonic vibrations (synchronized according to number) then we might assume that the spherical droplet of water possesses a vector pattern of frequencies, emphasized along a triple plane configuration which planes vibrate similarly to a Chladni plate only in three-dimensions - or equidistant areas of intense vibration (relatively speaking) which combine along six equidistant node lines. It is an assumption to imagine one of these vectors becoming dampened (the heat vector) thus rendering the spherical form into a flattened pattern along two-dimensions and emphasizing the six nodal lines along which the micro-crystals of ice (directionally vectored and aggregated water molecules) aggregate. The third vector (heat and cold vector), at right angles to the two-plane configuration, has little coincidence (numeric synchrony) with those of the six-directional vector frequencies (thus resisting amplifying resonance) of the biplane hence little aggregation takes place on this plane of vector.

For this symmetrical aggregation to take place water must possess this vibration pattern or better the hydrogen-oxygen association must possess this pattern. The question then is, "Does the hydrogen-oxygen molecule possess a chord of frequencies that would manifest as Keely's law predicts it should?" His diagram of a molecule shows this configuration if we assume his diagram is one of the water molecule. What does modern science say of this?

"As we know, the molecules of any substance are in constant motion, this motion being of an oscillatory nature in solid substances. When we place a solid in a liquid which can dissolve it, individual molecules are gradually torn away from its surface as a result of interaction with the molecules of the solvent. The separation of the molecules from the surface of the solid is caused by their own oscillatory motion on the one hand, and by attraction on the part of the solvent molecules on the other. This process would continue until all the solute present dissolved, were it not for the reverse process, namely, crystallization, proceeding simultaneously. When the molecules which have passed into solution collide with the surface of the substance not yet Dissolved, they are attracted back to it and form part of its crystals. Obviously, *the higher the concentration of the solution, the faster the solute molecules will deposit from it.* And since the concentration keeps increasing as the substance dissolves, there comes a moment at length when the rate of solution becomes equal to the rate of crystallization and dynamic equilibrium is established, it is then said to be saturated." (2)

180

Keely's Secrets

"When a solid dissolves, its *crystal lattice* is broken down and its molecules (or irons) distributed through the bulk of the solvent."

"Indeed, by various methods of investigation it has been proved that when dissolved the molecules of many substances unite with the molecules of the solvent to form a special type of compound called solvates." [3]

"The formation of solvates is due to the *polarity* of the solute molecules, owing to which the latter attract the polar molecules of the solvent. It is obvious that the more polar both types of molecules are, the more stable the solvates. And since water molecules have the highest polarity of all ordinary solvents, we have to deal mostly with hydrates in practice." [3]

"The idea of the existence of hydrates in aqueous solutions was suggested and grounded in the 1880s by Mendeleyev. Confirmation of the chemism of solution is that many substances crystallize out of their aqueous solutions in a form containing what is known as **water of crystallization,** a definite number of water molecules combining with each molecule of solute. *"This,"* wrote Mendeleyev, *"leads us to believe that there are such or similar compounds between the solute and the solvent in the solutions themselves, though in liquid (and partly decomposed) form."* [4]

"The solubility of most substances decreases as the temperature falls and therefore if hot saturated solutions are cooled,the excess of solute usually crystalizes out. However, if these solutions are cooled carefully and slowly, care being taken not to let any solid particles of the solute into the solution, *the crystals may not fall out (form).* In this case the resulting solution contains considerably more solute than is required to saturate the solution at that temperature. This solution is then said to be **supersaturated.** If left undisturbed they may remain unchanged for years. But if only a tiny crystal of the solute is introduced into the solution, other crystals immediately begin to grow around it and in a short time the entire excess of solute will have crystallized out. Sometimes crystallization may be initiated by simply shaking the solution or by rubbing a glass against the walls of the vessel containing the solution.

From the above it follows that supersaturated solutions are unstable systems capable of existing only of there are no solid particles of the solute present in the solution. The possibility of these solutions existing for a long time is due to the difficulty of the initial formation of minute "germ" crystals, called crystallization centers, from which crystallization spreads through the bulk of the solution.

Since the crystals of each substance are characterized by a quite definite arrangement of the particles forming them, the appearance of a crystallization center evidently requires that the particles, which are in a state of continuous disorderly movement in the solution, be grouped at some point of the solution precisely in the order characteristic of the crystals of the substance in question." [5]

All of this tells us that the atoms and molecules tend to arrange themselves according to their polar forces of attraction and repulsion and this polarity

takes place on the ionic level. When electrolytes are dissolved in water their molecules break up to a greater or lesser degree into ions, *i.e.*, electrically charged particles: which may be "simple" or "elementary," a single atom or even several atoms together. Since the particles are vibrating the vectors evidently possess a frequency chord of their own and set up a resonance along certain axis. The water molecules, which possess these same chords, will align themselves along a resonant path and establish themselves as parts of this "stream" or "current" of resonating frequencies. Thus creating straight lines and angles which are so prevalent in crystal formation.

It appears that it was Jacobus Hendricus Van't Hoff (1852-1911) who was the first *recognized* scientist to put forth this idea of directional valency in atoms and molecules.

Directional valency is pictured below where a molecule of water (shown as an ionic crystal) on the left possessing six poles (Keely's original configuration) is attracted to the ends of the polar molecule stretching the latter, moving the poles apart, resulting in dissociation into separate ions. This polar attraction and formation or arrangement of polarized particles becomes the lattice structure of the resultant compound that if solidified becomes a crystal exactly reflecting this polar alignment. Not forgetting that particles are in actually something similar to "bundles of vibrating energies" and not hard billiard ball like objects and that each of these vibrating bundles of energy possess a certain frequency or chord of frequencies and that an electron (electronic or electrical ener-

Dissociation of polar molecules in solution

gy) is also fundamentally vibratory in nature then we might possible find ourselves in a position of admitting that Keely's law, as stated above, is accurate.

Keely's Chords and Synthesized Wave Forms

By *Dale Pond*

Perhaps one of the more puzzling aspects of Keely's legacy is his constant reference to chords - all kinds of chords. He even goes as far as alleging that *certain chords possess or perform certain and specific actions.* This part of the of the puzzle can now be answered at least in part. With the solution of this problem we will see that Keely knew what he was doing and some of **the ever nagging question on his character can forevermore be put to rest.** It goes without saying that just because we don't understand him doesn't mean be didn't understand his own work.

Keely's Secrets

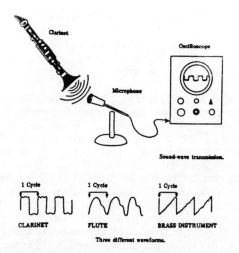

Sound-wave transmission.

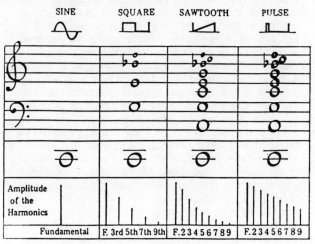

Three different waveforms.

It is commonly and scientifically known that wave forms, as used throughout electronic music synthesis, utilizes different shapes of waves. The sine wave which is the most widely known as an undulation curve much like an ocean wave. Another wave form is the square wave and yet another is sometimes called a saw-tooth wave or triangle wave. These three forms of waves are depicted below.

Harmonic series.

What is really interesting about wave forms is that each one of them is made up of several notes or frequencies. Therefore each wave form is not just a single note but a *chord of notes or group of frequencies.* 1 And what is more - each chord of notes is different. The notes (relative frequencies) which make up each of these wave form patterns are shown below.

A similar wave form may be created using different chords of frequencies. This process is called Frequency Modulation or FM. When the frequencies of the chord are similar the modifying difference is introduced by changing the relative amplitudes of the individual notes. This is called Amplitude Modulation or AM.

The term chord therefore may be seen as a very generic term and in actually these chords may be quite

different from each other. Is it too difficult to see that they may have varying effects on resonant bodies? They have varying effects on the ear, the pulse wave sounds brighter than a sine wave because there is more amplitude in its higher harmonics, relatively speaking. This is shown in the next diagram where the sounds of different instruments are shown to be due to different wave patterns which in turn has just been shown to be due to a different chord composed of the fundamental and varying harmonics and relative differences in amplitude of the separate frequencies.

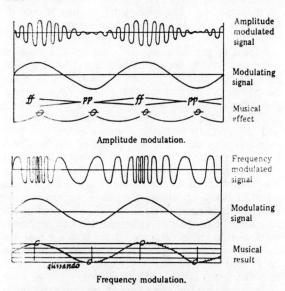

Amplitude modulation.

Frequency modulation.

When asked how be was able to generate his forces Keely replied: *The different conditions include the change of the mediums for disturbing equilibrium under different mediums for intensifying vibration as associated with them progressively from the molecular to the inter-electric:*

First: Percussion;
Second: Undulation;
Third: Vibratory undulation;
Fourth: Vibratory percussion:
Fifth: Water and air;
Sixth: Air alone."

It is my belief that this phrase is Keely's description of four different types of wave patterns. *Percussion,* as if hitting something sharply, creates a wave form giving great amplitude to the higher harmonics which is characterized by a pulse wave. The striking of a hammer on a hard surface can be analyzed and its spectrum of frequencies demonstrates percussive forms or pulse wave patterns. *Undulation* may be the sine wave form we are most accustomed to. The vibrating pattern of a rod set in vibration is a good example of this type of wave pattern. The *vibratory undulation* may be the saw-toothed wave of a frequency modulated pattern. The *vibratory percussion* may be akin to some type of pulse-like wave form. The fifth and sixth steps above are in reference to his use of these wave forms within differing "mediums." A

Universal Laws Never Before Revealed: Keely's Secrets

"medium" of course refers to the vibrating environment - whether atmospheric, water, gas or types and forms of material such as his famous platinum, gold and silver wires. But whatever the wave may be called the name is unimportant. What is important is its *shape* which is caused by the fundamental and its harmonics each with their own amplitude. We can change the different harmonics and get a new wave form or we can change the amplitude of any one or several of the harmonics and likewise change the wave form.

Keely's *"disturbance of equilibrium"* is the actual creation of the sound (perceptible vibrations). When his mediums were in equilibrium they may be considered to be in a state of quietness, neither creating, transmitting or receiving vibratory impulses. As was indicated in previous articles - the natural state of things is harmony between vibrations - a state of mutual balance. It is only when a disturbance is introduced into his harmonium that action (force or energy) is perceived by Man.

Thus the idea of the Void, as mentioned in Genesis and John, can be pictured as a state of *Perfect Harmonium*. This quietness was disturbed by the Creative Force extant throughout itself when it desired companionship - as the story goes. [2] Thus we can see that sound (or that which causes sound) has three states of being - positive or creative, negative or assimilative and neutral (equilibrium). The Void therefore must be considered as neutral and this argument lends considerable credence to the concept that the universe is a vast "sea of neutrinos" from which can be evoked (precipitated) any form of material manifestation one is capable of calling forth.

This idea of *infinite potentiality* coincides with concepts put forth by mystics, magi, spiritual organization and other systems of belief which may be based on ancient knowledge. This idea of infinite potentiality is not admitted to by the doctrine of materialism or those systems of belief built upon such narrowly derived understandings. Various systems of belief that tend to enslave thought and action such as totalitarianism, socialism, fascism and communism are all founded upon the idea that *"resources are finite"* and must be controlled by a few "for the benefit of the many." It is seen that Truth, assuming these ideas as put forth are near the truth, can indeed set Mankind free. To paraphrase Buckminster Fuller on the fuel shortage of the 1970s: *"There is no fuel shortage - only a shortage of technology (applied knowledge)."*

1. A musical note is a frequency relative to another frequency. The degree of relativity between notes is called an interval. A simple frequency is an unrelative number of cycles.

2. According to this Philosophy of Sympathy - first there is a creative vibratory force which by natural necessity must have an assimilative opposite force to which it is attracted and adheres to and continues activity with. This idea is presented in Genesis as the story of Adam and Eve, the dance of Shiva of Hindu origins and countless other ancient depictions.

Mr. Keely's New Philosophy

by **Clara Jessup Bloomfield-Moore**
Scientific Arena
December, 1886

In reading, quite recently, Macvicar's "Sketch of a Philosophy," I have been frequently struck by the similarity of the views between himself and the discoverer of etheric force, whose inventions you have noticed in your column. How long it may be before men of science will think it worth their while to master the details given in the writings of these men remains to be seen. The late Dr. Macvicar said that, when he considered how difficult he had found it to believe that such insight into nature as his views imply is possible to be attained, he was not so unreasonable as to expect that others would, in his time, regard them even as probable, much less as proved. He expressed himself as content with the private enjoyment which these views imparted to himself, "especially as that enjoyment is not merely the gratification of a chemical curiosity, but attaches to a much larger field of thought." One of the points to which he refers, as possessing great value to his own mind, is the place which his investigations assigns to material nature in the universe of being. He says that it is much the fashion in the present day to regard matter and force, more shortly matter, as all in all. But, according to the view of things which has presented itself to both of these men, "matter comes out rather as a precipitate in the universal ether, determined by a mathematical necessity; a grand and beautiful cloudwork in the realm of light, bounded on both sides by a world of spirits, on the upper and anterior side, by the great Creator himself, and the hierarchy of spirits to which he awarded immediate existence; and on the lower and posterior side, by that world of spirits of which the material body is the mother and nurse." Macvicar says the hypothesis that there are no beings in the universe but those who possess a molecular structure, and that sensibility and intelligence take their first beginnings in such structures, is one of the most inadequate conceptions that was ever proposed for scientific belief, and posterior side, by that world of spirits of which the material body is the mother and nurse." Macvicar says the hypothesis that there are no beings in the universe but those who possess a molecular structure, and that sensibility and intelligence take their first beginnings in such structures, is one of the most inadequate conceptions that was ever proposed for scientific belief. Science is not only very blind, but glorifies in her blindness. She gropes among the dead seeking the origin of life, instead of going to the Fountain of all life, the Ever Living, as these philosophers have done.

The theorizing on the philosophy of planetary suspension Mr. Keely says: "As regards planetary volume, we would ask in a scientific point of view: How can the immense difference of volume in the planets exist without disorganizing the harmonious action that has always characterized them? I can only answer this question properly by entering into a progressive analysis, starting on the rotating etheric cen-

Universal Laws Never Before Revealed: Keely's Secrets

ters that were fixed by the Creator with their attractive or accumulative power. If you ask what power it is that gives to each etheric atom its inconceivable velocity of rotation (or introductory impulse), I must answer that no finite mind will ever be able to conceive what it is. The philosophy of accumulation" (assimilation, Macvicar calls it) "is the only proof that such a power has been given. The area, if we can so speak of such an atom, presents to the attractive or magnetic, the elective or propulsive, all the receptive force and all the antagonistic force that characterizes a planet of the largest magnitude; consequently, as the accumulation goes on, the perfect equation remains the same. When this minute center has been fixed, the power to rend it from its position would necessarily have to be as great as to displace the most immense planet that exists. When this atomic neutral center is displaced, the planet must go with it. The neutral center carries the full load of any accumulation from the start, and remains the same, forever balanced in the eternal space."

Mr. Keely illustrates his idea of "a neutral center" in this way: *"We will imagine that, After an accumulation of a a planet of any diameter - say, 20,000 miles, more or less, for the size has nothing to do with the problem - there should be a displacement of all the material, with the exception of a crust 5000 miles thick, leaving an intervening void between this crust and a center of the size of an ordinary billiard-ball, it would then require a force as great to move this small central mass as it would to move the shell of 5000 miles thickness. Moreover, this small central mass would carry the load of this crust forever, keeping it equi-distant; and there could be no opposing power, however great, that could bring them together. The imagination staggers in contemplating the immense load which bears upon this point of center, where weight ceases. This is what we understand by the neutral center."*

Again, Mr. Keely, in explanation of the working of his engine, says: *"In the conception of any machine heretofore constructed, the medium for inducing a neutral center has never been found. If it had, the difficulties of perpetual-motion seekers would have ended, and this problem would have become an established and operating fact. It would only require an introductory impulse of a few pounds, on such a device, to cause it to run for centuries. In the conception of my vibratory engine, I did not seek to attain perpetual motion; but a circuit is formed that actually has a neutral center, which is in a condition to be vivified by my vibratory ether, and while under operation, by said substance, is really a machine that is virtually independent of the mass (or globe), and it is the wonderful velocity of the vibratory circuit which makes it so. Still, with all its perfection, it requires to be fed with the vibratory ether to make it an independent motor..."*

Alluding to his illustration of a neutral center, Mr. Keely says: "The man who can, even in a simple way, appreciate this vast problem has been endowed by the Creator with one of the greatest gifts which He can bestow upon a mortal...All structures require a foundation in strength according to the weight of the mass they have to carry, but the foundations of the universe rest on a vacuous point far more minute than a molecule; in fact, to express this truth properly, on an inter-etheric point, which requires an infinite mind to understand. To look down into the depths of an etheric center is precisely the same as it would be to search into the broad space of heaven's ether to find the end; with this difference, that one is the positive field, while the other is the negative field..."

Again Mr. Keely gives some suggestive thoughts as follows: *"In seeking to solve the great problems which have baffled me, from time to time, in my progressive researches, I have often been struck by the fact that I have, to all seeming, accidentally tripped over their solution. The mind of man is not infinite, and it requires an infinite brain to evolve infinite positions. My highest power of concentration failed to attain the results which, at last, seeming accident revealed. God moves in a mysterious way his wonders to perform; and if he has chosen me as the tool to carve out certain positions, what credit have I? None; and, though it is an exalting thought that he has singled me out for specific work, I know that the finest tool is of no value without a manipulator. It is the artist who handles it that makes ti what it is. Indifference to the marvels which surround us is a deep reproach. If we have neither leisure nor inclination to strive to unravel some of the mysteries of nature, which task to the utmost the highest order of human intelligence, we can at least exercise and improve our intellectual faculties by making ourselves acquainted with the operation of agencies already revealed to man; learning, by the experience of the past, to be tolerant of all truth; remembering that one of Nature's agencies, known once as of use only in awakening men's minds to an awful sense of the Creator's power, has now become a patient slave of man's will, rushing upon his errands with the speed of light around the inhabited globe..."*

In comparing the tenuity of the atmosphere with that of the etheric flows obtained by Mr. Keely from his invention for breaking up the molecules of air by vibrations, he says, "it is as platinum to hydrogen gas. Molecular separation of air brings us to the first subdivision only; inter-molecular, to the second; atomic, to the third; inter-atomic, to the fourth; etheric, to the fifth; and inter-etheric, to the sixth subdivision, or positive association with luminiferous ether. In my introductory argument I have contended that this is the vibratory envelope of all atoms. In my definition of atom I do not confine myself to the sixth subdivision, where this luminiferous ether is developed in it's crude form, as far as my research prove. I think this idea will be pronounced, by the physicists of the present day, a wild freak of the imagination. Possibly, in time, a light may fall upon this theory that will bring its simplicity forward for scientific research. At present I can only compare it to some planet in a dark space, where the light of the sun of science has not yet reached it..."

It seems particularly fitting that *The Scientific Arena* should be the first to make known to the reading public Mr. Keely's marvelous researches and still

Universal Laws Never Before Revealed: Keely's Secrets

more marvelous inventions, inasmuch as the view of its editor on some subjects are identical with those held by Mr. Keely. Take, for example, the following quotation from one of Mr. Keely's papers: *"I assume that sound, like odor, is a real substance of unknown and wonderful tenuity, emanating from a body where it has been induced by percussion, and throwing out absolute corpuscles of matter - inter-atomic particles - with a velocity of 1120 feet per second, in vacuo 20,000.* [1] *The substance which is thus disseminated is a part and parcel of the mass agitated, and if kept under this agitation continuously would, in the course of a certain cycle of time, become thoroughly absorbed by the atmosphere; or, more truly, would pass through the atmosphere to an elevated point of tenuity corresponding to the condition of sub-division that governs its liberation from its parent body."* [Here comes in Dr. Macvicar's Cosmical Law of Assimilation.] Mr. Keely continues: *"The sounds from vibratory forks, set so as to produce etheric chords, while disseminating their tones (compound) permeate most thoroughly all substances that come under the range of their atomic bombardment. The clapping of a bell in vacuo liberates these atoms with the same velocity and volume as one in the open air; and were the agitation of the bell kept up continuously for a few million centuries it would thoroughly return to its primitive element; and, if the chamber were hermetically sealed, and strong enough, the vacuous volume surrounding the bell would be brought to a pressure of many thousands of pounds to the square inch, by the tenuous substance evolved. In my estimation, sound truly defined is the disturbance of atomic equilibrium, rupturing actual atomic corpuscles; and the substance thus liberated must certainly be a certain order of etheric flow. Under these conditions is it unreasonable to suppose that, if this flow were kept up, and the body thus robbed of its element, it would in time disappear entirely? All bodies are formed primitively from this high tenuous ether, animal, vegetable, and mineral, and they only return to their high gaseous condition when brought under a state of differential equilibrium."*

Thus Mr. Keely teaches, with Dr. Macvicar, that ether is the true protoplasm.

"As regards odor," continues Mr. Keely, *"we can only get some definite idea of its extreme and wondrous tenuity by taking into consideration that a large area of atmosphere can be impregnated for a long series of years from a single grain of musk; which, if weighed after that long interval, will be found to be not appreciably diminished. The great paradox attending the flow of odorous particles is that they can be held under confinement in a glass vessel! Here is a substance of much higher tenuity than the glass that holds it, and yet it cannot escape. It is as a sieve with its meshes large enough to pass marbles, and yet holding fine sand which cannot pass through; in fact, a molecular vessel holding an atomic substance. This is a problem that would confound those who stop to recognize it. But infinitely tenuous as odor is, it holds a very crude relation to the substance of subdivision that governs a magnetic flow (a flow of sympathy, if you please to call it so). This sub-*

division comes next to sound, but is above sound. The action of the flow of a magnetic coincides somewhat to the receiving and distributing portion of the human brain, giving off at times a depreciating ratio of the amount received. It is a grand illustration of the control of mind over matter, which gradually depreciates the physical till dissolution takes place. The magnet on the same ratio gradually loses its power and becomes inert. If the relations that exist between mind and matter could be equated, and so held, we would live on in our physical state eternally, as there would be no physical depreciation. But this physical depreciation leads, at its terminus, to the source of a much higher development - viz., the liberation of the pure ether from the crude molecular; which, in my estimation, is to be much desired. Thus God moves in a simply way his wonders to perform..."

Again, Mr. Keely writes as follows: *"I shall not forestall an unproved conclusion, but fight step by step on the dark paths I am exploring; knowing that, should I succeed in proving one simple fact in science heretofore unknown, I shall in so doing be rewarded in the highest degree. In whatever direction the human mind travels, it comes quickly to a boundary line which it cannot pass. There is a knowable field of research, bordered by an unknown tract. My experience teaches me how narrow is the strip of territory which belongs to the knowable, how very small the portion which has been traversed and taken possession of. In this our century of widely diffused knowledge how ignorant is the vast majority! The father we traverse the unknowable, the stronger will become our faith in the immovable order of the world; for, at each advancing step, we find fresh proofs of the immutable laws that reign over all things - from the falling apple up to the thoughts, the words, the deeds, the will of man; and we find these laws irreversible and eternal, order and method reigning throughout the universe. Some details of this universal method have been worked up, and we know them by the names of "gravitation," "chemical affinity," "nerve power," etc. These material certainties are as sacred as moral certainties... The nearest approach to a certainty is made, through Harmony with Nature's laws. The surest mediums are those which Nature has laid out in her wonderful workings. The man who deviates from these paths is sure to suffer the penalty of a defeat, as is seen in the records of "perpetual-motion" seekers. I have been classed with such dreamers; but I find consolation in the thought that it is only by those men who are utterly ignorant of the great and marvelous truths which I have devoted my life to demonstrate and to bring within reach of all. I believe the time is near at hand when the principles of etheric evolution will be established, and when the world will be eager to recognize and accept a system that will certainly create a revolution for the highest benefits of mankind, and inaugurate an era undreamed of by those who are now ignorant of the existence of etheric force."*

(1) Keely is saying the *sound particles* possess this velocity, he *is not* referring to the velocity of compression waves as they propagate through the molecular medium of the atmosphere which is ordinarily considered as the speed of

sound. If we consider sound as a causative force then it would be better to say that *compression waves propagate through the atmosphere at 1204 fps* and recognize the distinction of terms as Keely does. The atmosphere is a molecular medium whereas, in his nomenclature, a vacuum is an inter-atomic medium, *i.e.,* space filled with subatomic particles - just what we now know it to be. These sound particles, being themselves subatomic or what we now call *phonons (quantized sound vibrations),* apparently are able to travel through this rarefied medium of a vacuum without *interference to coincidental action.* Such interference being caused by the "slow" vibrations of molecules.

Notes & Scales

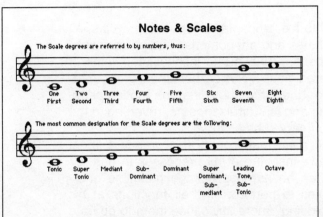

Octaves

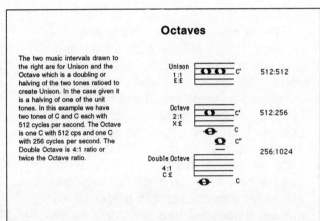

Perfect Interval

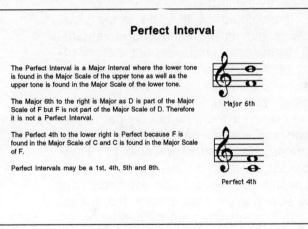

Power of Beat Harmonics

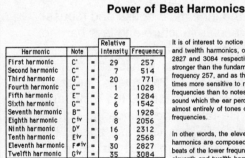

Properties of Light

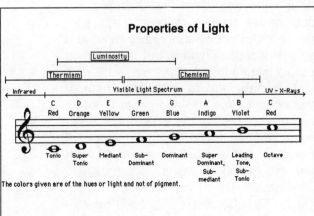

Ratios - Quantizing to One

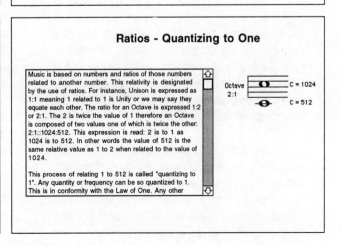

MAN'S GREATEST ACHIEVEMENT

Nikola Tesla

There manifests itself in the fully developed being - MAN - a desire mysterious, inscrutable and irresistible: to imitate nature, to create, to work himself the wonders he perceives. Inspired to this task he searches, discovers and invents, designs and constructs, and covers with monuments of beauty, grandeur and awe, the star of his birth. He descends into the bowels of the globe to bring forth its hidden treasures and to unlock its immense imprisoned energies for his use. He invades the dark depths of the ocean and the azure regions of the sky. He peers in the innermost nooks and recesses of molecular structure and lays bare to his gaze worlds infinitely remote. He subdues and puts to his service the fierce, devastating spark of Prometeus, the titantic forces of the waterfall, the wind and the tide. He tames the thundering bolt of Jove and annihilates time and space. He makes the great Sun itself his obedient toiling slave. Such is his power and might that the heavens reverberate and the whole earth trembles by the mere sound of his voice.

What has the future in store for this strange being, born of a breath, of perishable tissue, yet immortal, with his powers fearful and divine? What magic will be wrought by him in the end? What is to be his greatest deed, his crowning achievement?

Long ago he recognized that all perceptible matter comes from a primary substance, or a tenuity beyond conception, filling all space, the Akasa or luminiferous ether, which is acted upon by the lifegiving Prana or creative force, calling into existence, in never ending cycles, all things and phenomena. The primary substance, thrown into infinitesimal whirls of prodigious velocity, becomes gross matter; the force subsiding, the motion ceases and matter disappears, reverting to the primary substance.

Can man control this grandest, most awe-inspiring of all processes in nature? Can he harness her inexhaustible energies to perform all their functions at his bidding? more still cause them to operate simply by the force of his will?

If he could do this, he would have powers almost unlimited and supernatural. At his command, with but a slight effort on his part, old worlds would disappear and new ones of his planning would spring into being. He could fix, solidify and preserve the ethereal shapes of his imagining, the fleeting visions of his dreams. He could express all the creations of his mind on any scale, in forms concrete and imperishable. He could alter the size of this planet, control its seasons, guide it along any path he might choose through the depths of the Universe. He could cause planets to collide and produce his suns and stars, his heat and light. He could originate and develop life in all its infinite forms.

To create and to annihilate material substance, cause it to aggregate in forms according to his desire, would be the supreme manifestation of the power of Man's mind, his most complete triumph over the physical world, his crowning achievement, which would place him beside his Creator, make him fulfill his ultimate destiny.

Law of Atomic Dissociation

"Overtones of high rad-energy pitches produce separation of the atomoles and recombinations among the atomic molecules of the atoms."

Keely, 1894

Commentary June, 1988

This law has a number of new and seemingly contradictory (from previous statements) meanings and concepts. Therefore, I'm going to step aside and let Keely explain his concepts of molecular morphology.

"Each molecule has three envelopes. In the first diagram this is illustrated as a sphere upon which has been traced a number of meridian lines. The next diagram shows the three envelopes. The outer hemisphere of one of the envelopes is removed to show the under envelope, the outer hemisphere of which is removed in still another part of the diagram to show the inmost envelope. The third diagram shows the position of the atoms which the rotating envelopes enclose. The fourth diagram shows the lines of interference of the rotating envelopes. There being three perfect envelopes, these of necessity must have six poles, to which add the neutral center of the sphere itself, comprising the origin of the septenary of mysticism which is universal in nature. The fifth diagram shows the subdivision of matter into atomic, atomolic, and atomolinic. A black disk representing a sphere shows the negative atom; two while disks also representing spheres illustrate the two positive atoms in the triad, completing the tertiary aggregation forming the molecule. Each atom is in turn composed of three atomoles; in the negative atom are three positive atomoles, positive in the sense of activity; in the positive atom are also three atomoles, two of which are negative, i.e., passive, and one positive. The negative is always that which seeks the neutral center; the positive represents the active radiating energy: for instance the sun is a medium for transmitting radiant energy of positive order, which all the planets receive negatively, i.e., it focalizes upon their neutral centers. This order extends to infinity. The final diagram intends to further illustrate the compressing force of the rotating spheral and the protection of the neutral poles. In the rotating envelopes force acts in the opposite direction to its action in the revolution of the earth, where the centrifugal action is greatest at the equator; and the greater the speed of rotation, the greater the center-fleeing force.

In the case of the etheric envelope, however, the greater the speed of rotation, the more powerful is the centripetal (center-seeking) force which compresses the atoms within; the pressure, therefore, is greatest at the equator and gradually lessens toward the poles. If there were only one envelope, the tendency would be for the atoms to be oblate, to fly out at the poles, where the pressure is least. A beautiful provision of nature obviates this, by providing three envelopes, rotating one within the other, like three shells; the line of greatest internal pressure in each one of which being protected by the equatorial lines, the line of greatest pressure covering the line of least pressure on the others. Each of the three atoms is placed directly under one pole of each of the three envelopes.

If the rotating envelope of the molecule were in any way checked in its motion, the enclosed matter would immediately burst forth, producing the phenomenon of disintegration, releasing from its previously pent-up condition a volume of matter many times as great as that before disintegration took place. Sound-force moving at certain rates of vibration negatizes the action of the rotating envelopes, producing conditions which result in their breaking up, followed by the separation of the atoms contained in those envelopes, and also of inter-molecular substance occupying space not taken up by the atoms. By successive orders of vibrations the atoms, atomoles, and atomolini are disintegrated, and so on to the luminous order, where all control ceases."

Keely's Molecular Morphology

Keely's diagram of molecular and atomic morphology exploded to reveal relative relationships of the "particles". It can be seen that Keely's triune inner particles are very similar to the modern concept of triple Quarks occulted within protons.

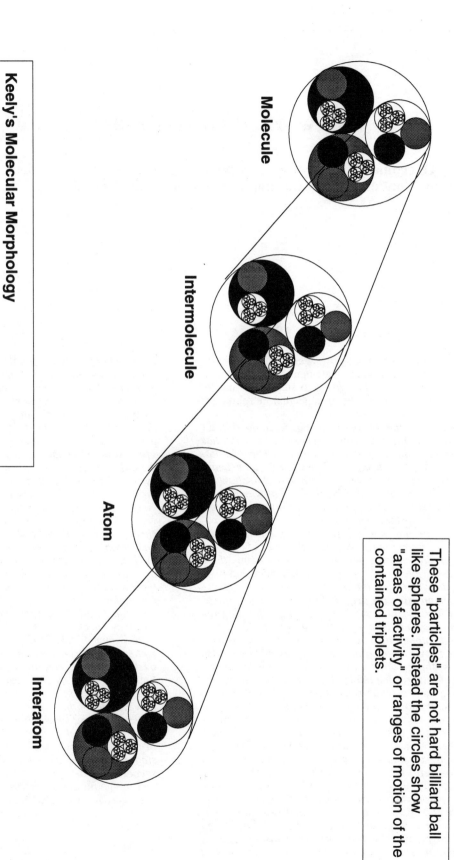

Molecule

Intermolecule

Atom

Interatom

These "particles" are not hard billiard ball like spheres. Instead the circles show "areas of activity" or ranges of motion of the contained triplets.

Law of Atomolic Synthesis of Chemical Elements

"Harmonic pitches of atomolity produce association of etheric atomolic particles to form atoms: the kind of atom is determinable by the pitches employed."

Keely, 1894

Commentary July, 1988

Atomolity begins at the 87th octave of frequencies or above 14524 Hz. The extent of this range is not known at this time. This is a frequency range far far in excess of that of gamma rays. How Keely was able to attain such a formidable range of vibrations and control is beyond comprehension and known science. One thing is evident - if he did do this work with these frequency ranges - it can't be that difficult to figure it out as he worked with mechanical means before the turn on the century. In other words if he discovered how to do this 100 years ago it should be rediscoverable especially with our advantage of 100 years of advancing technology.

It has been stated by myself and others that Keely developed some form of nuclear or sub atomic power in his devices but this law indicates he may have exceeded that attainment and went beyond it. It looks like he is attempting to explain the actual formation of atoms themselves from a higher for of elemental particle. The formation of which is governed by the relative frequencies employed. Not being personally familiar with high energy physics I cannot equate what he is saying with modern achievements. It is assumed that energy forms of this magnitude have been witnessed in accelerators (atom smashers) and other state of the art devices. One description of accelerator performance sticks in my mind though: "Accelerator devices are really giant resonators." I don't remember where I read this - in an article describing accelerators work no doubt.

Higher forms of sub atomic particles are numerous and have been the subject of avid research for many years. The theoretical physicists working with quantum mechanics and quantum physics have been theorizing with colors, quarks and flavors in their attempt to bring their research data to some form of equation. Perhaps this is why there has been so much comparative writing of their work to John Keely's. An item that has bothered me and still gives me difficulty is that a great many physicists still speak of these parti-cles as though they are solids. Even the simplest book on quantum phenomena never fails to mention at some point that these particles are in actuality something akin to "bundles of vibrating energy" yet the persistence is there to equate said "aggregated energy patterns" as hard particles. It seems clear to me that as Keely persists in equating these phenomena with frequency that he has a steadier command of the subject than some of the popular writers on the subject. There really isn't any *thing* there, it is not a hard particle like a billiard ball. This is a difficult thing to explain and see in one's mind's eye.

An analogy I like to use in explaining this phenomena of "bundles of vibrating energy" is that of a bicycle wheel. A bicycle wheel at rest (the part between the hub and rim) is mostly air or in our case no *thing* can be seen between the spokes and it is an easy matter to insert a rod or screwdriver between the spokes. However, if the wheel is caused to spin at an infinite velocity it would be impossible to insert anything between the spokes. The "empty" space between the hub and rim would possess such energy that it would repel any attempt at penetration.

Now suppose we had no knowledge of what this wheel looked like at rest. Suppose all the knowledge we had was of this wheel as it spun at its infinite velocity. Could anyone accurately describe its spokes? Of course not. At best we could only derive theories concerning its construction and components. We can only know that it does possess tremendous velocity and that from all experiments done on it we would have to conclude that it was solid! Since no known mechanism could penetrate between the hub and rim we would be forced to conclude that it was solid and hard, when in actuality the spoked area is anything but solid and hard.

However, there is a tremendous amount of research data available that demonstrates and proves that an outside vibratory force does have an effect on this periodic revolving phenomena. The only conclusion reasonable to adapt is that the makeup of the spinning atom somehow corresponds to the imping-

Universal Laws Never Before Revealed: Keely's Secrets

ing vibratory energy because of its susceptibility to these vibrations (sound). The inevitable conclusion is all atoms and sub atomic particles are nothing but bundles of vibrating energy and we must therefore admit these vibrations must relate as vibrations do, one to another, and not as solid particles or billiard ball-like entities. Since vibrations relate according to their frequency relative to each other we can surmise that Keely's description of their behavior is correct.

Unfortunately science has not yet caught up with Keely in the generation and control of these super high frequencies. Until it does we can only conjecture as to the demonstrative validity of his assertions.

Mastery of Self is Mastery of Science

by *Dale Pond*

In the past and indeed all throughout the publication of this column I have made many statements, some believable and acceptable, some not so believable and acceptable and others from "left field." It is the intent and scope of this column to uncover what John Ernst Worrell Keely discovered as well as make sense of the discoveries of others such as Nikola Tesla, Newman and the like. As one digs deeper into the ether world of such mental giants it becomes essential and necessary to make statements that may be questionable from the point of view of what is currently good and acceptable. How can the scope of any scientific field be expanded if one doesn't tread on untrodden ground? It can't be. Daring, boldness and a willingness to open one's eyes and mind are absolutely a must.

When using the scientific method one is obliged to seek up or down whatever investigative corridor presents the likeliest path to success. If such a path is blocked by facts and indomitable obstacles, then one simply moves on to the next likely path. Edison pursued 599 paths before he got a good light bulb. To his peers and other researches, the idea of creating such a device to illumine the darkness was unthinkable. Edison dared to think the unthinkable and he believed in his vision. Keely strove mightily 1200 times before he succeeded in making his "deep blue light" by shining a sunbeam through hydrogen gas held in a soap bubble. *Tenacity* is the word to describe such relentless effort. Building his 129th motor after the first 128 failed is an accomplishment few of us will ever dream of replicating in terms of perseverance. The Wright brothers built and crashed several prototype flying mechanisms before the "impossible dream" became a reality.

These great men of scientific accomplishment are an excellent example to those of us desiring to join them along the hard and rocky roads of scientific discovery. Through their work and lives they have shown us how to conceive, hold and believe in an idea and then with determination and hard work render it a real and substantial thing.

Discoverers on the path to the future *must* be bold enough to think new and revolutionary thoughts regardless of the stick-in-the-muds who refuse to let go of old ideas and embrace new ones and dogmatism

which claims or infers we can only do what we already know to do. Flying was "crazy" or "crackpot" until it was actually done. Traveling faster than 29 mph was impossible until the first person went 30 mph. The list goes on and on of "impossible" and "crank" devices which worked.

The very same idea applies to our approach to Keely's strange jargon. It is impossible to read his words explaining whatever the subject is and at the same time say with absolute certainly that this word or phrase means this or that. The words he uses are correct English to a high degree and his command of the language is phenomenal. The words can even be looked up in a good dictionary (I have over 30 dictionaries and dozens of technical reference books) and a semblance of a meaning can be found. Anyone with enough patience and perseverance can fathom his meanings simply by allowing that he knew and meant something and pursuing it until his meanings are perceived. *It is not so much what he is saying that may be wrong but it is more likely that what we think he is saying that may be in err.* It is an understanding of his meaning we are after and this meaning can be and has been, to a small degree, transposed into modern terms. These modern terms are such that Keely would have thought them as strange as we find his.

I have found the greatest hindrance in this study is my already implanted ideas and concepts about such and such a word, phrase or idea. Modern scientific ideas are somewhat parallel to Keely's and Tesla's viewpoints on the subjects. To grasp their meanings behind their words is a mind-expanding experience. One must reach for new concepts and ideas to see if they match what is being described. There are many holes in the available writings of these men but with deductive reasoning and imagination some can be filled in. The difficulty lies not in their words, for they are valid words and come together in a vast and novel explanation of wondrous paradigms. The difficulty lies in that these are unfamiliar terms, phrases and concepts to most of us and seldom to they parallel good and accepted physics. Our tendency is to panic because what we are being told does not substantiate what we think we already know. The basis of our own training and what we have come to rely on is becoming threatened (we think). When fear for our beliefs comes in the first reaction it to cry "It cannot be so! The man *must* be a crank." Alas, human nature being what it is.

We can marvel at these men and their accomplishments - so many patents and world shaking devices but few of us realize what they struggled with and overcame in order for their work to succeed and be accepted. Galileo was excommunicated and imprisoned, Tesla was ostracized and condemned by his "peers," Keely was effectively slandered, buried and forgotten, Moray was shot twice, Reich, Drown and Bacon were imprisoned - the list is as long as history itself. It took a blinding vision, courage few of us will ever experience or understand and tremendous strength to withstand the condemnations, calumnies and harassments heaped upon them from "the experts" and know-it-alls. The overcoming of the physical engineering and scientific limitations of the era

Universal Laws Never Before Revealed: Keely's Secrets

was only a part of their victories.

It takes even more of the "right stuff" to overcome personal handicaps or shortcomings than it does to invent a device from existing technologies. This mastering of self is what matures a simple inquisitive investigator into a masterful discoverer of scientific or Universal Truths. For a discoverer challenges every idea, "scientific fact," dogmatic belief and the fears and doubts within himself with an unshakeable courage and faith in himself and what he is about. The fears of not being accepted, of making mistakes and of failure must all be overcome before he finds success. ***The conquering of self then is the conquering of worldly matters.***

Daring to think new thoughts and courage to act upon them is the challenge to those who seek a newer and better science or a better understanding of himself and his relationship to the Universe. Perseverance, courage, vision, and dog-work will allow anyone so inclined to travel the rocky road and scale the heights to true mastership.

Dangers of Ultrasonic Energy

By *Dale Pond*

Ultrasonic usage in medical treatments has been gaining more acceptance everyday. Frightening as it may be there is more and more evidence that sonograms (fetal examinations in the womb) and other applications of this energy are destructive to cellular structures. Even more disconcerting is that damage to these cells may be latent and not reveal itself for years. A 134-page booklet titled "An Overview of Ultrasound: Theory Measurement, Medical Applications, and Biological Effects" put out by the U. S. Department of Health and Human Services, July 1982 draws information from hundreds of citations of published studies. This book casts serious doubts on the safe use of ultrasound as a diagnostic instrument.

Ultrasound is very destructive to cellular structures. The following pages lists various biological effects of this energy. If you are exposed to ultrasound you might want to heed some sort of precautionary measures. If you are working with ultrasound experimentally using high energy levels it is strongly suggested you adapt safety measures until such time as the truth of this matter can be rightfully investigated. One is reminded of the time when Keely exposed himself to a burst of high frequency radiation and wound up in bed for three weeks. As a precautionary measure he henceforth did his work in water instead of exposed to the air. The destructive nature of ultrasound can be either heat, radiation force or cavitation or a combination of these.

To quote from Dr. Mendelsohn's article "Ultrasound Dangers Revealed - Part II" from the Dynamic Chiropractor (May 1, 1988): *"Ultrasound is the latest example of an unproven technology being sold to the public as being "perfectly safe." It falls in the same class as painting radium on watches, fluoroscoping children's feet in shoe stores, routine mammography, routine chest X-rays, radiation therapy for tonsils, exposing army personnel to atomic bomb tests - in each case, the medical profession failed to take the necessary steps to protect people against a malignant technology whose risks were already well understood."*

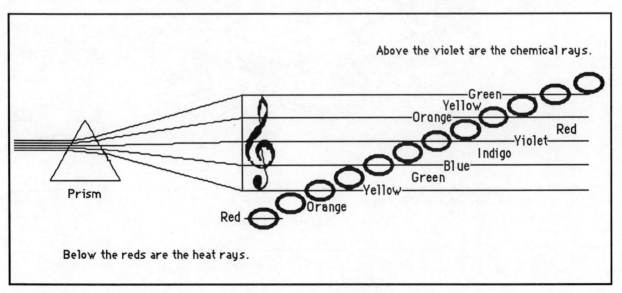

Above the violet are the chemical rays.

Below the reds are the heat rays.

Prism

192

Sympathetic Negative Transmitter

Law of Heat

"Atoms under the tension of chemical combination oscillate with an amplitude directly as the temperature, inversely as the pressure, and as the square of the specific heat. Diminishing the pitch of oscillation inversely as the square of the distance of the atoms apart, and simultaneously increasing the vibrating pitch of the atoms by absorption of overtones and higher harmonics."

John Keely, 1894

Commentary August, 1988

Heat is a fascinating subject. Fascinating because the modern theory is quite different from the one Keely had in mind. His perspective was developed from and with the continual work in vibratory phenomena. The modern theory is developed from the concepts of gross materialism employed up to this day. The notable exception is the work being done by quantum physicists who are rapidly developing a philosophy emerged in vibrations.

While it is sometimes difficult to mentally view atoms or molecules not as hard particles but as "vibrating bundles of energy" this is how sympathetic vibratory physics views them and not as hard billiard ball-like mini-spheres. When considered as such it becomes impossible to consider that they actually come in contact with one another thus causing friction which in turn is the alleged source of heat. A key to understanding Keely's meaning may be found in his definition of oscillation and vibration.

"Oscillation is a rhythmically recurring translatory movement." (Keely)

Oscillation: "Any effect that varies periodically back and forth between two values." (McGraw-Hill Dictionary of Scientific and Technical Terms)

"Vibration is the rhythmical motion of a body within itself." (Keely)

Vibration: "A continuing periodic change in a displacement with respect to a fixed reference." (McGraw-Hill Dictionary of Scientific and Technical Terms)

We see that the modern terminology has very little distinction between what is considered as a vibration and an oscillation. Whereas Keely makes a definite distinction between the two types of motion.

The pitch of oscillation refers to the relative oscillation rates of the individual atoms. Each atom is vibrating at a certain and definite rate and each atom is oscillating at a given rate. The atom vibrates within itself and at the same time is oscillating back and forth. A following article describes some of the different modes of vibration and will cast some light on this subject.

This back and forth oscillation also diminishes inversely as the square of the distance the atoms are apart referring to the Square Law as it applies to propagating wave energies.

The latter part of this law gives us an insight into superconductivity. If the vibratory forces acting within the aggregate under study are all of a harmonious nature, heat will not be developed. According to Keely, it is the absorption of overtones and harmonics into the vibrating atom as it separates from the other atoms. This follows along with the idea that harmony of pitch causes aggregation and discord of pitch causes repulsion or separation.

Universal Laws Never Before Revealed: Keely's Secrets

Vibratory Indicator. Attractive Disks. Musical Globe. Medium for testing centripetal force.

Law of Electro-Chemical Equivalents

"An atom vibrates sympathetically under the influence of electric energy, such undertones of which are absorbed as are a harmonic or harmony of the electric pitch; the amount of energy absorbed being directly as the arithmetical ratio of the undertone of the fundamental electric pitch.

Scholium: A table of electro-chemical equivalents on the normal basis will indicate the electrical conditions and amount of chemical change."

Keely 1894

Commentary September, 1988

Keely is emersing us deep into his philosophy with this law. It appears the entire premise of the above description comes from his ideas and understandings concerning the vibratory nature of atomic and subatomic structures and their respective energy flow patterns and characteristics.

He considered electric current or electricity as a flow of oscillating atomoles held within the atoms. He considered this energy a *creative* energy and is conveyed from atom to atom provided the size and weight are uniform. (This was explained in the 12/86 and 1/87 issues of SVP.)

It is assumed from the above that when the atoms are of varying sizes and weights interference to coincidental action is the result. *Interference to coincidental action is akin to what we now call resistance or impedence.*

Speaking strictly of electro-chemical equivalents, we are concerned here with the electrical state of the atoms. McGraw-Hill defines electro-chemical equivalency as:

"The weight in grams of a substance produced or consumed by electrolysis with 100% current efficiency during the flow of a quantity of electricity equal to 1 faraday (96,487.0 + - 1.6 coulombs).

Then he goes on to say that a table of these values will indicate the atoms' relative state. Again McGraw-Hill defines an electro-chemical series as:

"A series in which the metals and other substances are listed in the order of their chemical activity or electrode potentials, the most reactive at the top and the less reactive at the bottom. Also known as electromotive series."

Keely's law then gives us an explanation of how and why the elements have the potential they have and hints at what it wouild take to bring a change in their respective states. Which ability to render change would prove of enormous value to the one able to master such a technique.

Basically he says that atoms are oscillating within themselves (an interior particle?) at the same rate and mode of the electric pitch. The electric pitch, we have already seen, is the rate of oscillation of the atomole (electron?) found within the atom. He has already stated that the atomoles are of uniform size and weight therefore we can assume that the rate and mode of vibration is consistent whether propagated in solids, liquids or gases.

This whole idea of electro-chemical equivalents brings to mind a series of objects each having absorbed a deferring quantity of water. Since water is common to each and every object one has the latent ability of changing the state of each object simply by injecting into or taking away water from each of them. Keely's law says that each object will absorb energy according to an undertone of the object or atom's vibration rate which forms a harmonic or harmonizes with a component of the electrical pitch. This relationship is directly dependent on an undertone of the fundamental of the electric pitch and can be expressed as a simple arithmetical value. Thus getting us back to arithmetic here and away from complex mathematics as is commonly found in today's quantum physics.

This very clearly demonstrates the value in studying music construction techniques. The manners and methods of relating vibration rates one to another is simple arithmetic and not the overpowering complexity of using unrelated values forced into compliance by over-complicated rules of so-called higher mathematics. This also illustrates the meaning behind Cayce's often overlooked references to the effect that *"Music is the connecting link between God and Man or the spiritual and material realms."* (paraphased).

This particular phrase is easily grasped when one considers energy (higher states of manifestation) as belonging to the spiritual realm and gross matter such as atoms or molecules representing the material realm. Keely even goes so far as to classify electricity as a *creative* force. God or the God-force is always considered as a creative force especially in Genesis which is the story of the creative process bringing a spiritual realm into materiality or how pure energy

Universal Laws Never Before Revealed: Keely's Secrets

becomes pure matter - they are one and the same save for rate and manner of vibratory actions.

This is the beauty of Keely's philosophy - it ties these two seemingly separate and different realms of activity into ONE. *Nowhere else and in no other system of science or philosophy is this so dramatically demonstrated.* Here is a dramatic departure from the innane materialist's viewpoint that things are separate and unrelated. Here is a departure from the religionist's concept that all is spiritual giving little or no value to material things. The connecting link is that which governs music development. Here, at long last, is a middle ground from which the Darwinists and Creationists can meet and finally reconcile their bitter battle by uniting around that which bridges the two opposing ideas granting equal value to each -**sympathetic vibrations.** Vibrations being the material manifestation and sympathy being the connecting force or energy - undulating together in a coordinated and cooperative Cosmic dance of action and reaction.

Harmonic Scale

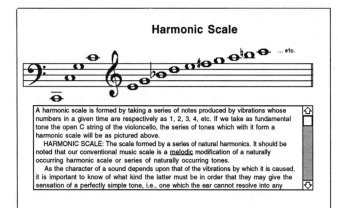

A harmonic scale is formed by taking a series of notes produced by vibrations whose numbers in a given time are respectively as 1, 2, 3, 4, etc. If we take as fundamental tone the open C string of the violoncello, the series of tones which with it form a harmonic scale will be as pictured above.

HARMONIC SCALE: The scale formed by a series of natural harmonics. It should be noted that our conventional music scale is a melodic modification of a naturally occurring harmonic scale or series of naturally occurring tones.

As the character of a sound depends upon that of the vibrations by which it is caused, it is important to know of what kind the latter must be in order that they may give the sensation of a perfectly simple tone, i.e., one which the ear cannot resolve into any

Intervals

An interval in music is distance (between the notes) expressed in terms of difference in pitch. Sound the two tones to the right. The ear immediately detects that one tone is higher than the other. The eye detects the interval which is represented graphically by two signs (notes), one of which is higher on the staff than the other. This audible and visible highness is, in music, distance or interval. This distance can be measured. To measure an interval we must have a definite and unchangeable unit of measure.

Major 6th

In expressing intervals by name several technical terms are employed. For example: this interval is a Major Sixth because there are six steps (inclusive) between the two tones. We infer from the word Major that there are other kinds of sixths, and from the word sixth we infer that in naming intervals, something is counted, something which in this example contains six distinct units.

Major Interval

To determine the number name of an interval we must be able to count from one to nine, and to say the first seven letters of the alphabet. To determine the specific name of an interval we must know the Major Scale of the lower tone of the given interval. This will inform us if the upper tone of the given interveal be in the Major Scale of the lower tone, or if it be above the Major Scale tone, or if it be below it.

RULE: An interval is Major when the upper tone is found in the Major Scale of the lower tone.

D (in the diagram) is the sixth degree or step or tone in the Major Scale of F. Numerically F to D is a Sixth. Hence the interval is accurately described when we say it is a Major Sixth. Major Intervals are the 2nd, 3rd, 6th, 7th and 9th.

Major 6th

Minor Interval

The Minor Interval is a Major Interval where the upper tone is not found in the Major Scale of the lower and the interval is slightly less distance than a Major Interval.

Just as we have the Major 2nd, 3rd, 6th, 7th and 9th so we also have the Minor 2nd, 3rd, 6th, 7th and 9th.

The Major interval above and right is six steps between the C and A. The Minor Interval to the lower right is marked slightly less or smaller than six steps with the flat sign indicating the A is flattened or slightly lowered in pitch from its natural pitch when found in the Major Scale of C.

Major Sixth

Minor Sixth

Intervals of Triangle

Music Intervals of the triangle

Go to next card to see more on Quantum Arithmetic and Musical Intervals.

Unison	1:1
Octave	2:1
Perfect Fifth	3:2
Major Third	5:4
Perfect Fourth	4:3
Major Tenth	5:2
Perfect Twelfth	3:1
Major Sixth	5:3
Double Octave	4:1

The ratios above are taken directly from a plot of a right triangle created using the rules of QA. It is interesting to note that of the nine ratios six are Perfect Intervals (1, 2, and 3 par numbers) the remaining three are all Major Intervals (5 par numbers). This demonstrates that the triangle is indeed a unit of strength.

Intervals

The various symbols used in Quantum Arithmetic are interchangeable with music notes and form Music Intervals when related one to another. The Music Intervals given to the right are derived from the primary symbols of QA which are found to be involved with a right triangle. (Below the interval name are given the numeric ratio of that interval and below that are given the QA symbol ratios.)

Perfect Fifth
3:2
F:X

Major Third
5:4
G:D

Perfect Fourth
4:3
D:F

Major Tenth
5:2
G:X

Perfect Twelfth
3:1
F:E

Major Sixth
5:3
G:F

Law of Cohesion

"The cohesion between atoms diminishes directly as the square root of the pressure and temperature, and as the square of electric intensity."

Keely, 1894

Commentary October, 1988

Cohesion is often equated with electron valency. The greater the valence - the greater the cohesion. The actual accepted definition of cohesion is: "The tendency of parts of a body of like composition to hold together, as a result of intermolecular attractive forces."[1] Upon further investigation, the definition of molecular attraction is: "A force which pulls molecules towards each other."[1] What we have here, when all is said and done, is a nebulously undefined term called "force" which is alledgedly responsible for causing this pulling together. Again modern science doesn't or is hesitant in giving a clear definition of that which it deals. Keely, on the other hand, doesn't shy away from such a task.

He says cohesion is *caused* by the interaction of pressure, temperature and elecrticity and goes on to say just how they relate to cause varying degrees of cohesion. In other words, cohesion is a function of vibratory energies. Heat is a vibration, the electrical current is a vibration and pressure has a direct effect on frequency and amplitude of vibrations.

Cohesion is very important to SVP because it is the dissolution of inter-molecular cohesion which Keely used to create his awesome pressures from the disintegration of water. By breaking the cohesiveness between those particles which go to makeup the water molecule he was able to release their subatomic energies which, as we know from our experiences with nuclear energies, can be enormous.

Here is a place where a table defining these values would be helpful. A table of each element in its neutral or natural state and comparative tables of it as it is subjected to pressure and temperature and then the table discussed last month of electrical equivalents. Remember, Keely is speaking of *intensity* of the electrical current. He considered the electrical current as a stream of atomoles of extremely high frequencies. He also spoke often of his *intensifying* the current as opposed to *amplifying* it. In electrical ter-

minology I believe the equivalent would be *amperage* of the current. I am not sure but that he meant he was increasing the frequency of the current when he intensified it. More thought is needed here.

The previously discussed Law of Chemical Dissociation (SVP 1/88) gives a little insight here as dissociation may be considered opposite to cohesion. He disusses the attraction of cohesion as being between atoms and not molecules whereas the quotes given earlier both speak of molecular attraction. What is the difference? There aren't any definitions of atomic attraction in my reference books. I would think that Keely is correct in his assertions. After all a molecule is composed of or is actually the sum total of the atomic interactions making up that molecule. Therefore a modulation of those atomic forces would have an effect on the molecule whereas modulating the molecule itself would be difficult. An analogy would be not unlike the dismantling of a brick wall. We can use a large hammer and strike the wall's surface, in which case, the energy would soon dissipate throughout the wall's surface. However, if we dealt with each individual brick, less energy is needed and less energy is dissipated throughout the structure. Dissolve a few bricks and the whole wall falls apart. In like manner, one could find a way to dissolve just the cement between the bricks and get dissociation of the structure leaving the bricks whole. Striking the wall with a huge wrecking ball would destroy some of the bricks thus releasing smaller particles (radioactivity). I think I like Keely's method and way of thinking much better.

Pneumatic Gun

Law of Refractive Indices

"A table of the refractive indices of substances indicates their molecular pitch; and in connection with crystalline form the phase of molecular oscillation."

Keely, 1894

Commentary November, 1988

The August 1988 issue detailed the certain properties of how an angled sound beam can refract from longitudinal wave forms into shear waves, plate waves and other wave forms of differing undulatory characteristics.

It is not known at this time if certain materials refract sound differently than do others as indicated by this law. There doesn't appear to be any study confirming or refuting this indication. It is likely that differing substances have different refractory characteristics. Perhaps Keely is suggesting that this is so and tables of these refractive indices can be built and indeed should be built if one were to delve deeply into the science of Sympathetic Vibratory Physics. Some readers may be familiar with these things and can enlighten the rest of us thus absolving the need for a lengthy period of research to establish these refractory properties of materials.

Crystalline substances are formed by this very nature of vectorial alignment along axis of the molecules forming the crystals. Based on the past laws we have discussed, this vectorial alignment is dictated by the frequencies associated with the various angles clearly illustrated by crystal formation. Further, different substances which become part of the crystal substance form different geometric patterns as they aggregate into the various crystal shapes. This is further evidenced by the different ways in which different crystal substances refract light. Light being a phenomenon common to each of them.

Therefore what Keely is saying here about forming tables of these refractive indices is very valid and may lead to some revolutionary insights of molecular behavior. That these tables could indicate molecular pitch (relative frequency) is not as obviously correct. It seems that if one could determine molecular pitch from an angle of refraction then the ideas inherent here are somewhat different than one would expect if considering the matter from a standpoint of numbers of vibrations.

There is an incongruity in all this: When a longitudinal vibration is converted into a shear wave simply by varying the angle of incidence the frequency remains the same (we are told) but the velocity changes. It seems that wave length, time and frequency are solidly locked together not unlike the simple formula used in electrical calculations for figuring resistance, voltage and amperage. By varying one the others change yet always maintaining a rigid arithmetical relationship to each other.

Keely stated in another article(1) that the angle and velocity were more important than the frequency and wave length. The idea that "God geometricizes" and that vibration is a big part of the picture seems to jive very well together. Another strong argument is the simple formation of a rainbow. This little phenomenon is due entirely due to light waves being refracted by water vapor spheres. Why a rainbow creates and maintains a fixed color pattern never changing even though one changes location and angle while viewing it is also a mystery. One we can find a reasonable solution to eventually.

Much work and thought needs to applied to this promising area of research. As we go along more and more will undoubtedly be made clear.

(1) Universal Truths Never Before Revealed: Keely's Secrets, Delta Spectrum Research P. O. Box 316 Valentine, Nebraska 69201.

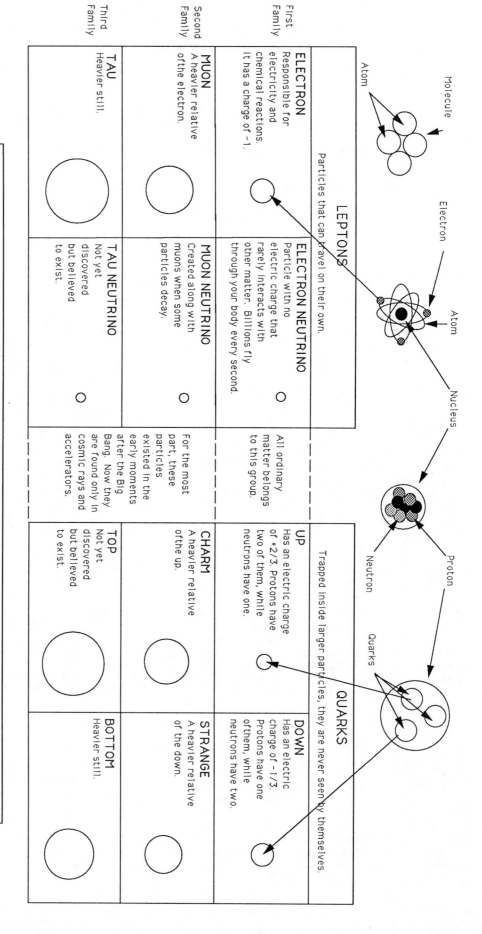

Molecule

Atom

Electron

Atom

Nucleus

Neutron

Proton

Quarks

LEPTONS

Particles that can travel on their own.

First Family

ELECTRON
Responsible for electricity and chemical reactions. It has a charge of -1.

ELECTRON NEUTRINO
Particle with no electric charge that rarely interacts with other matter. Billions fly through your body every second.

All ordinary matter belongs to this group.

Second Family

MUON
A heavier relative of the electron.

MUON NEUTRINO
Created along with muons when some particles decay.

Third Family

TAU
Heavier still.

TAU NEUTRINO
Not yet discovered but believed to exist.

For the most part, these particles existed in the early moments after the Big Bang. Now they are found only in cosmic rays and accelerators.

QUARKS

Trapped inside larger particles, they are never seen by themselves.

UP
Has an electric charge of +2/3. Protons have two of them, while neutrons have one.

DOWN
Has an electric charge of -1/3. Protons have one of them, while neutrons have two.

CHARM
A heavier relative of the up.

STRANGE
A heavier relative of the down.

TOP
Not yet discovered but believed to exist.

BOTTOM
Heavier still.

BOSONS

Particles that transmit the fundamental forces of nature.

PHOTONS
The particles that make up light, they carry the electro-magnetic force.

GLUONS
Carriers of the strong force between quarks.

INTERMEDIATE-VECTOR BOSONS
Heavy carriers of the weak force, which is responsible for some forms of radioactive decay.

GRAVITONS
Not yet discovered but believed to carry the force of gravity.

Law of Electric Conductivity

"Electric energy is transmitted through homogenous bodies with a completeness in direct proportion as the atoms are more or less perfect harmonics of the electric pitch, but not at all through substances whose atoms are discordant to the electric pitch; also through molecular substances, when their resultant notes are harmonics of the electric pitch, - the transmissions being inversely as the temperature, directly as the density diminished in proportion to the amount of crystallization, and *inversely* as the cube of the dyne, also *directly* as the reciprocal of the local magnetic intensity."

Keely, 1894

Commentary December, 1988

Is this law the key to superconductivity? Sounds like it may just be that.

According to the idea presented in this law - if the particles of a conductor are of a harmonically related frequency to the electric frequency then the conductor will transmit the current without any resistance. Is this not the idea behind superconductivity?

Keely called this superconductivity - perfect *concordant transmission* or *coincidental action* - which is what is really taking place in the conductor when viewed from the quantum level. Resistance he would call interference to coincidental action. Depending on the degree of attunement between the electric current and the frequency of the conductor particles resistance is created to the passage of the electric current through the substance. Conversely, if there are discordant frequencies between them - the resistance can be so high as to prohibit transmission and the substance would be called an insulator.

He goes on to give the laws governing the mathematics of such a phenomenon. Those who have the required physics and engineering backgrounds might want to build the required mathematical formulas represented by this law. The potential of such a formula may well be worth the effort to work it out. It is hoped that credit be given where it is due.

His law states that the *lower the temperature the higher the rate of transmission.* This has been proven with the work done recently by and with superconductivity experiments.

Looking at a Periodic Table of the Elements (one of your choice as there is a difference between charts) we can see that copper, silver and gold are all in the same group. The periodic tables are supposedly arranged according to like properties of the elements. Since vibration determines these properties then we know that elements occupying the same group or period possess similar vibration rates. The electrical conductivity of an element is a function of its atomic vibratory rate therefore those that vibrate harmonically towards each other possess similar traits such as the ability to conduct electrical currents.

Likewise we can see those elements which are poor conductors of the electrical current such as oxygen and nitrogen grouped close together. We can then know that the atomic frequencies of these elements are not harmonics of the electrical current. It is a well established fact that neither of these two elements conduct electricity very well just as copper, silver and gold do transmit this current very well.

Gravity also has an effect on electrical conductivity. As the dyne (accelerating force on a mass) is increased the lower the conductivity. Conversely the lower the dyne the greater the conductivity. Hence it may be assumed that conductivity, in the absence of gravity would increase. This may point to some discovery about why and how there is more electrical potential the higher one gets from the ground. And may even give us an insight into how Tesla was going to trnsmit electrical current through the upper atmosphere.

This law also gives us an insight into what is called *resistance*. Resistance is a term used in electrical work to give measure to the inability of a substance to transmit electrical current. Very little is given in electrical texts that explains why and how resistance is caused. Keely gives us a perfectly good explanation. Once tables have been created giving the vibratory rates of the elements correlated with temperature, gravity, etc. we can then predict exactly how electrical current will behave in a substance. It will not require as much trial-by-error methods to find superconductive substances and circuits. Knowing this law and the prerequisites of this function it should be relatively easy to custom design materials exhibiting rather novel and useful practicalities.

On the "negative" side, this law is the nemesis of the so-called electron theory and blows all kinds of holes in the "hole" theory of micro-chip function theories. The dragon of ignorance is slain again! Knowledge based on a materialistic paradigm cannot withstand a higher revelation that the spiritual essence of force(polarity) is more important in the physical function of matter than matter itself.

Speaking of polarity, it is the female polarity or negative attractive that causes densification and then crystallization. As density increases transmission increases and as crystalization increases transmission decreases. It is the male polarity or positive propulsive that lessens density - as density decreases trans-

mission decreases. Positive polarity also increases temperature thus lowering transmissions as well.

Beat Frequencies Dissonance

Dissonance or discord arises from beat frequencies generated from two or more tones.

These may occur in any of the following types:

1) Beat Dissonance Between Fundamentals;
2) Between one Fundamental and partial of the other;
3) Between Overtones;
4) From the occurrence of Differentials;
5) From the occurrence of Summation Tones.

Beat Dissonance Between Fundamentals

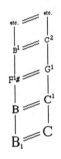

When beats arise between the fundamentals of two compound tones, the dissonance will in general be harsherthan between two simple tones of the same pitch, for in the former case each pair of overtones may beat also. Supposing for example, the two fundamentals to be B1 and C, the diagram shows the dissonant overtones. The harshness of the beats between each pair of overtones in the diagram, must be estimated in the case of simple tones, for these overtones are simple tones; but in estimating the total harshness of the whole combination, it should be remembered that for ordinary qualities of tone, the intensity of the partials becomes less and less as we go farther from the Fundamentals (a fact roughly indicated in the diagram by the use of smaler type for the upper partials).

Beat Dissonance Between Tonic and Overtone

Beats arising from the Fundamental of one tone and an overtone of the other. As an example we may take the common dissonance between F and G1.

This interval, when sounded between simple tones, is quite free from harshness,

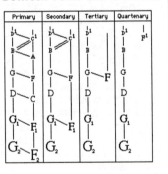

Beat Dissonance Between Overtones

Partials of C	= 256,	512, 768, 1024, 1280
Partials of G#	= 200, 400, 600, 800, 1000, 1200
Beats formed:	156	112 32 24 80

Partials of G#	= 200, 400, 600 800
Partials of C1	= 128, 256, 384, 512, 640, 768
Beats formed:	56 16 40 32

To complicate matters even more, these beat tones will also become generators themselves and create secondary, tertiary, etc. orders of beats. This is taken to be Jacob's Ladder of the Bible and also demonstrates "as above - so below" and that all things are connected.

Beats arising from the overtones of Compound Tones. In music it is considered a beat when the resultant numbers are small. The 156 and 112 of the first series is not considered a beat frequency as is the 56 in the lower series. However, these tones are generated and constitute a new tone resulting from the generator tones.

Only the first six partials are shown. The actual number of partials are infinite and consequently there are many more beats present even though they are not heard or measured.

Beat Frequencies Between Differentials

Simple Tones and Harmonics			
	200	400	600
	Difference Tones		
304	104	96	296
608	408	208	8

104	208	304	408	400	600
96	200	296	400	304	608
8	8	8	8	96	8

According to musical theory beats of 8, 96 and higher numbers are beyond the range of beats which are normally heard. But in hard numbers these secondary tones are present and should be accounted for even though they are not heard or measured.

Beat Frequencies due to Summation Tones

	Compute			
200				
Interval	Ratio	Rate : Rate	Calculate Summation	Summation Tone
Octave	2 : 1	400 : 200	200 + 400 = 600 = 3	G
Fifth	3 : 2	600 : 400	600 + 400 = 1000 = 5	E'
Fourth	4 : 3	800 : 600	800 + 600 = 1400 = 7	A#'''
Major Third	5 : 4	1000 : 800	1000 + 800 = 1800 = 9	D''''
Minor Third	6 : 5	1200 : 1000	1200 + 1000 = 2200 = 11	F'''
Major Sixth	5 : 3	1000 : 600	1000 + 600 = 1600 = 8	C'''
Minor Sixth	8 : 5	1600 : 1000	1600 + 1000 = 2600 = 13	Ab''''
Major Second	9 : 8	1800 : 1600	1800 + 1600 = 3400 = 17	B''''
Diatonic Semitone	16 : 15	3200 : 3000	3200 + 3000 = 6200 = 31	A#'''''

From the above table we can see that the fundamentals of the Octave generate the Summation Tone of C which coincides with the 3rd partial of the lower tone, so in the case of the Octave no new element is introduced however the Summation Tone is present.

Music: A Vibration Analysis Shortcut

by Dale Pond

Attempting to isolate an experiment from influential factors is for the greater part a waste of time and leads to false findings. For instance, is a hard vacuum really empty? It is empty of molecules and atoms but what about photons and electrons and other subtler particles? Because we can see through a vacuum indicates it is full of photons and because we can send and receive radio waves to and from interplanetary probes indicates it is also full of electrons. It is this type of unrealistic and incomplete data that hinders modern science and technology. Another false truth or incomplete paradigm based on incomplete analysis is that aspect of wave or vibration analysis based on isolating frequencies from a complex waveform. Nothing, absolutely nothing, can exist of and by itself anywhere in the universe. How then can a vibration be separated from its fellow vibrations and be taken to be meaningful? As Einstein pointed out the obvious in his Law of Relativity: everything relates to something else and it is this relationship that gives value to each of them.

This principle of relativity is perhaps the single most important discovery Keely[1] left us. His laws use this principle as a given fact and not something viewed extraordinarily. If you get no other thought from this article you should get this one: RELATIVITY. Not as Einstein stated: $E=MC^2$ but simply that everything is dependent on everything else and all things can only have value when considered relative to another thing. This principle is embodied in music intervals found throughout Keely's charts and writings. A musical note sounded by itself is simply another vibration. But when a number of perfectly tuned musical notes are sounded together concordant chords, motions up and down, and a whole meaningful host of acoustic phenomena begin to manifest. Musical renditions can play upon human emotions demonstrating a connecting link to human psychology and physiology[2]. Music can cause inert concert hall walls to vibrate in resonance, armies to march, babies to sleep and lovers to react. Vibrations when set to fixed intervals of frequency and time are indeed powerful forces in our world.

There appeared in the November 1989 issue of Sound & Vibration[3] a very interesting article on Chladni wave plate modes. The capable author used the latest and best technology in his effort to decipher this intriguing phenomenon. He set out to find the various frequencies and modes of a vibrating square plate.

Approaching his study with an idea of finding the interrelationships in the vibratory activities he found, I have prepared a table below of the actual frequencies and modes as he found them in these plates. I then determined the musical intervals[4] of the various modes and frequencies. It is very interesting to see that the frequencies compared one to another all fall very close to known musical intervals (boldface items).

Taking just two modes, "Mode 3" and "Mode 2," we see the difference between these two numbers is only 19/100ths greater than a Minor Third. The differences of some of the other numbers are even closer to the comparative musical interval. What this could mean to us as practicing technologists is that if we had 1207 vibrations per second in the Mode 2 pattern and desired to achieve the Mode 3 pattern at 1472 cps

Universal Laws Never Before Revealed: Keely's Secrets

all we'd need to know and do is to increase the 1207 cps by a musical third . There would not need to be a complicated mathematical derivation of this new frequency. The art of music would win out in its simplicity. In other words, the right brain simplicity would succeed easily over the left brain complications. Even more significant is the grasp we would weld over a complicated subject. We should know the results even before we complete the experiment. Thus instead of finding a series of unrelated numbers we find a highly relative and organized phenomenon taking place before our very eyes.

This study is very significant in our effort to understand Keely's work and his devices. He used a variety of wave plates in his work most notably circular disks to which are made many references in the literature[5]. The diagram above shows the square wave plate Mr. Lang used in his experiment. The nodal lines and their relative motions are clearly shown of each mode as are the resultant frequencies. It is assumed the progressive mode generation would be different for circular plates as would be the frequencies.

It must be kept in mind that these musical intervals are the distances between the associated frequencies. An interval is the amount of change (Delta) between the measured frequencies. The frequencies can be set up as algebraic variables set to a given difference between them. It would then be easy to determine the resultant secondary frequencies and modes from this fundamental number by using the decimal values given above. In other words: when given a vibrating plate of these dimensions and characteristics it would be a simply matter to "predict" its vibrational behavior using these musical intervals. An in-depth, time-consuming and expensive analysis would not be required.

RATIO1: RATIO2	MUSICAL INTERVAL	DECIMAL
Mode 3: Mode 2		
6: 5	Minor Third	= 1.2
1472: 1207		= 1.219...
5: 4	Major Third	= 1.25
Mode 4: Mode 3		
64: 45	Diminished 5th	= 1.4222
2105: 1472		= 1.430...
36: 25	Diminished 5th	= 1.44
Mode 2: Mode 1		
36: 25	Diminished 5th	= 1.44
1207: 817		= 1.477...
3: 2	Perfect 5th	= 1.5
Mode 4: Mode 2		
125: 71	Augmented 6th	= 1.736...
2105: 1207		= 1.743...
7: 4	Harmonic 7th	= 1.75
Mode 3: Mode 1		
9: 5	Tonic 7th	= 1.8
1472: 817		= 1.801...
15: 8	Major 7th	= 1.875
Mode 4: Mode 1		
5: 2	Major 10th	= 2.5
2105: 817		= 2.576...
8: 3	Perfect 11th	= 2.666...

and modes from this fundamental number by using the decimal values given above. In other words: when given a vibrating plate of these dimensions and characteristics it would be a simply matter to "predict" its vibrational behavior using these musical intervals. An in-depth, time-consuming and expensive analysis would not be required.

Thus we can see that this premise is accurate in its execution and accurate in the information it gives us. As near as I can tell this process has not been used since Keely developed the process 100 years ago. At this point it is not well understood and the insights gained not yet fully appreciated. I have applied this method to several frequency analysis projects all resulting in formidable insight into that studied. This method may also be considered as a very accurate check on your work. The process is simple and because of its simplicity easily verifiable. It is hoped that those of you now doing scientific investigations will employ this method in your work that it may become more fully developed and comprehended.

It should be noted that this above related process can be successfully applied to any accurately derived series of numbers. A good example is the Fibonnacci number series revealing the reproduction rate of breeding rabbits. This number series is obtained by taking 1 adding it to the next number to derive the third number: 1:1:2:3:5:8:13:... An analysis of these numbers reveals them to be: Unison, Octave, Perfect Fifth, Major Sixth, Minor Sixth ...[6]

A difficulty exists in using this process however. That is the fact that the empirical musical numbers of the intervals is subject to evaluation at this point. There are as many systems of computing these intervals as there are musical systems. All the books touching on this subject are different from each other in one way or another. The numbers we now have are accurate enough for this type of projection but more work needs to be done in sorting them out.

Bibliography

1 *Keely and His Discoveries*
   Clara Jessup Bloomfield-Moore
   Delta Spectrum Research
   P. O. Box 316
   Valentine, Nebraska 69201
   (402) 376-1523

2 *The Science of Musical Sounds*
   Dayton Clarence Miller, D.Sc.
   The Macmillan Company
   New York, 1926

3 Sound & Vibration magazine
   Acoustical Publications, Inc.
   27101 E. Oviatt Rd.
   P.O. Box 40416
   Bay Village, OH 44140
   (216) 835-0101

4 Complete list of these intervals can be found in:
   The Journal of Sympathetic Vibratory Physics
   Volume V, Issue 2, page 16
   Delta Spectrum Research
   P. O. Box 316
   Valentine, Nebraska 69201
   (402) 376-1523

5 A complete catalog can be ordered from:
   Delta Spectrum Research
   P. O. Box 316
   Valentine, Nebraska 69201
   (402) 376-1523

6 *The Journal of Sympathetic Vibratory Physics*
   Volume II, Issue 6, page 4, March, 1987
   Delta Spectrum Research
   P. O. Box 316
   Valentine, Nebraska 69201
   (402) 376-1523

Keely, much older in this photo, seated at his final motor. This machine operates via amplified gluonic bonding/repulsing forces as near as we can understand Keely's explanations. See other photo on page 145.

Scale Of The Forces In Octaves

by John Ernst Worrell Keely

"First octave (unity of sound) is approximately the lowest frequency capable of producing waves of rarefaction and condensation in the air. The atomic aggregate oscillating at this pitch can be experimentally determined, and the aggregate vibrating at a pitch one octave higher will have a mass lying between $1/_8$ and the cube root of the mass of the first mentioned aggregate; the exact relation under varying conditions of gravity, magnetic saturation, and pressure, can be determined only by accurate measurements. But assuming a body of a size represented by x, with a pitch represented by 1024 per second, then a pitch of 2048 per second will be produced by a body having a volume of some mean between $1/_8$ of x and the cube root of x. By accurately determining the pitch of a volume of any metallic sphere capable of oscillating at the pitch of, *e.g.*, the eleventh octave of sonity (1024 per second), under normal conditions of gravity, pressure, magnetism, and then successively diminishing its size by $1/_8$ of itself, we get the successive octaves of pitches higher and higher in period-frequency until we pass the domain of sonity and enter the domain of sono-thermity. The point where the one form of energy merges into the other lies approxiimately at the twenty-first octave, and this pitch also marks the point where the air is no longer capable of vibrating at that pitch in waves of transverse form. The first gamut of 21 $1/_2$ octaves consists of three forms; *viz.* sonity, sound, and sonism. The following is a tabulation of the pitches of sonity in octaves from one vibration per second to where the next form of energy commences."

Fraunhofer Lines

"The Fraunhofer lines represent the silences, or the places of invisible pitches between the luminous pitches of rad-energy. They cannot therefore be conveniently used as data from which to measure the fundamental pitches of the atoms undergoing examination. When a series of sound-pencils are projected upon a screen, they undergo a combination of overtones and under-tones at the point of contact producing tones of a pitch either too low to be recognized by the human ear or too high to be called sound. The Fraunhofer lines are not therefore simply silences, but may be the higher invisible ultra-actinic rays. The fact is that some of the Fraunhofer lines are capable of producing a variety of chemical actions, when reflected and focalized. Observation thus far shows that these lines do not bear any definite ascertainable relation to the pitches producing them, but that they do bear some uniform relation from which the fundamental pitch could be determined cannot be doubted. The relation of the Fraunhofer lines to the luminous spectra are undoubtedly such as would enable one to compute the creative pitches producing them; but as yet no such determinations have been made. The accurate method of determining them is from the mutual relation of the harmonic pitches of the luminous spectra.

A table representing the harmonic overtones and undertones of simple vibrations, and the resultant harmonics of associate vibrations, will be of great convenience in making these determinations.

The natural unity of sonity lies above 1 per second, and below 2 per second, and for this reason the numbering of the octaves is accomplished by calling the end of the first octave No. 1 instead of No. 2. At the end of the twenty-first octave sono-thermity commences, and the bodies oscillating at this pitch are either correspondingly smaller by $1/8$ than the preceding sonitic aggregates; or larger aggregates undergo vibration in submultiple portions of themselves. In either case the originating oscillation of sono-thermic pitch is that of an isolated or localized aggregation. This first class of forces, or first double gamut, is included within the range of about forty-three octaves. The bodies of the translatory pendulous motion and produce waves of the transverse form, while the bodies of the second gamut undergo internal nodal vibration and produce waves of a longitudinal form. Beyond the upper limit of the forty-third octave we reach bodies of a size (determined by the same method as in sonity) which we know to be about the size of an atom as approximately determined by various physicists to lie between eleven and twelve micromillimeters (hydrogen molecules), which gives the highest pitch of the known atoms, and from which can be roughly estimated the pitch of the heavier atoms. Starting with the approximate pitch of hydrogen as determined from its associate spectrum with oxygen, and working back to the size of the largest atoms, we again reach a pitch corresponding to the highest sono-thermic vibrations. Starting with the known temperature and pitch of a heated body, emitting definite rays of light, and working back to absolute zero, we again reach the pitch of the sono-thermic limit."

FIRST CLASS
Scale of Forces in Octaves
Sonity, Sound, and Sonism begins

1st Octave	2
2nd	4
3rd	8
4th	16
5th	32
6th	64
7th	128
8th	256
9th	512 Keynote Molecular Chord
	620 First Octave Keynote Atomic Chord
	630 Second Octave
10th	1,024
11th	2,048

12th	4,096
13th	8,192 Keynote Etheric Chord
	12,000 Third Octave Heat (highest rate of)
	14,000 Vibro-Atomic
14th	16,384 Lowest Molecular Vibration
	20,000 Harmonic Thirds
15th	32,768 Disintegration of Water
	42,800
16th	65,536
17th	131,072 Trans. of Odor in Molecules
	220,000 Sympathetic Negative
18th	262,144 First Inter-Atomic Lowest
	300,000 Full Harmonic Chord
19th	524,288 First Inter-Atomic Highest
	780,000 Full Harmonic Chord
20th	1,048,576
	1,620,000 Major 5th
21st	2,097,152
Major 5th	3,145,728 Ninths

Sono-thermity, Sono-therm, Sono-thermism

22nd	4,194,304
23rd	8,388,606
24th	16,777,216
25th	33,554,432
26th	67,108,864 Highest Molecular Vibration
	100,000,000 Harmonic 3rds
27th	134,217,728
28th	268,435,456 Highest Inter-Molecular
	300,000,000 Enharmonic 6ths Atmospheric
	519,655,633 Highest made in air
29th	536,870,912 Atomic Vibration
	900,000,000 Diatonic 9ths
30th	1,073,741,824
31st	2,147,483,648
32nd	4,294,967,296 Highest Etheric
	8,100,000,000 Dominant Etheric 6ths
33rd	8,589,934,592
34th	17,179,869,184 Highest Inter-Etheric
	24,300,000,000 Inter-Etheric 9ths
35th	34,359,738,368
36th	68,719,476,736
37th	137,438,953,472
38th	274,877,906,944
39th	549,755,813,888
40th	1,099,511,627,776
41st	2,199,023,255,552
42nd	4,398,046,511,104

SECOND CLASS
Thermism, Rad-energy, Chemism

43rd	8,796,093,022,208 Dark heat begins
44th	17,592,186,044,416
45th	35,184,372,088,832
46th	70,368,744,177,664 Chemism begins
47th	140,737,488,355,328 Infrared (Light begins)
48th	281,474,976,710,656 Major 4th (above)
49th	562,949,953,421,312 Below Major 4th
50th	1,125,899,906,842,624 (Light ends)
51st	2,251,799,813,685,248
52nd	4,503,599,627,370,496 Limit Actinic Rays
53rd	9,007,199,254,740,992
54th	10,814,398,509,481,984
55th	36,028,797,018,963,968 Chemism ends
56th	72,057,594,037,927,936
57th	144,115,188,075,855,872 Full Ninths
	156,057,552,198,220,000
58th	288,230,376,151,711,744
59th	576,460,752,303,423,488
60th	1,152,921,504,606,846,976
61st	2,305,843,009,213,693,952
62nd	4,611,686,018,427,387,904
63rd	9,223,372,036,854,775,808
64th	18,446,744,073,709,551,616 Major 5th
Major 5th	27,670,116,110,564,327,424 Limit of thermism

Electricity, Induction, Magnetism

65th	36,893,488,147,419,103,232
66th	73,786,976,295,838,206,464
67th	147,573,952,591,676,413,928
68th	295,147,905,183,352,827,856 Copper-zinc couple
69th	590,295,810,366,705,655,712

70th	1,180,591,620,733,411,311,424
71st	2,361,183,241,466,822,622,848 50,000 volts
72nd	4,722,366,482,933,645,245,696
73rd	9,444,732,965,867,290,491,392
74th	18,889,465,931,745,580,982,784
75th	37,778,931,863,469,161,965,568
76th	75,557,863,726,938,323,931,136
77th	151,115,727,453,875,647,862,772
78th	302,231,454,907,753,295,724,544
79th	604,462,909,815,506,591,449,088
80th	1,208,925,819,631,013,182,898,176
81st	2,417,851,639,762,026,365,796,352
82nd	4,825,703,278,524,052,731,592,702
83rd	9,671,406,557,048,105,463,185,408
84th	19,342,813,114,096,210,926,370,816
85th	38,685,626,228,192,421,852,741,632
86th	77,361,252,456,384,843,705,483,204

The limit of electricity and the beginning of atomolity.

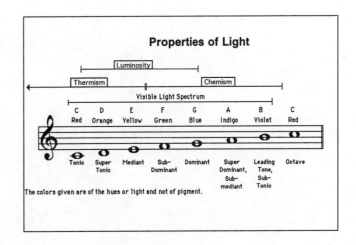

The colors given are of the hues or light and not of pigment.

GUN WITH WHICH KEELY EXPERIMENTED AT SANDY HOOK, AND OTHER APPLIANCES.

Sympathetic Negative Transmitter.

Induction, Sympathy & Resonance

by Dale Pond

Throughout electrical and electronic terminology there is constant reference to the function and use of *induction* as a means of attaining certain effects in electrical circuit applications. Induction is a curious thing: It is *"The act or process of causing."*[1] When it is desired to cause or to induce a certain effect or to convey what is found in one object or system into another this process of induction used. It has occured to this author that induction and sympathetic vibrations are sometimes confused with one another as well as that other concept known as *resonance*. Perhaps we can explore these three concepts thereby gaining a new and more accurate perspective.

Beginning with two systems (molecules, people or metallic objects) in rhythmic motion(vibration) and separated by a discrete distance it can be said they each possesses certain vibration characteristics exclusively their own, independent of each other. They each possess a natural mode of motion and it has been declared that no two objects, however carefully engineered, can be vibrating with precisely the same modal pattern or vibration signature. In terms of this discussion, we are not going to split hairs that fine - suffice the objects to be engineered close enough such that they are in a fair state of coincident motion or we may say they are of the same fundamental mode of vibration and thus are tuned to each other.

The frequency at which these two objects are tuned is called their resonant frequency possessing a fundamental number of vibrations per second. This state of affairs is called "being in tune" or "being in sympathy" one to the other. When the eigenfrequencies (composite vibrations) of one object are modulated by an electrical or mechanical oscilla-

tion the vibrations of the other responds accordingly. This method of energy transference is done through and by way of *sympathetic vibrations* which have been defined as follows:

sympathetic vibration: [PHYS] *"The driving of a mechanical or acoustical system at its resonant frequency by energy from an adjacent system vibrating at the same frequency."*[1]

Once the two objects are in rhythmical motion, caused by sympathy of vibration, they are said to be in resonance or resonating together. In other words, they vibrate **as one**. From the above we can safely say that resonance is brought about through and by way of sympathy. The New World Dictionary defines sympathy *as used in physics::* *"The relation between two bodies whereby vibrations in one produce responsive vibrations in the other."*[2]

On the other hand induction is considered somewhat different. The word is used almost exclusively in electrical jargon and is defined as: *"The process by which a body having electrical or magnetic properties calls forth similar properties in a neighboring body without direct contact."*[2]

To this author's way of thinking the above scenario may be simplified by stating that the two objects, having been tuned, may be said to be in a state of sympathy or harmony of vibration frequencies and modes. When one object is modulated by either mechanical (striking one with a physical blow) or electrical or any other means, then, because they are tuned or are in a state of sympathy, the energy is transferred to the other. This process of transfer we sometimes call induction. Because they are *in tune* the energy pattern raised in the first object is caused, through sympathetic vibrations, to induce a similar

212

Universal Laws Never Before Revealed: Keely's Secrets

action in the second object. It thereby begins to resonate to those frequencies and is then said to be in a state of resonance.

What we have here is a very nifty state of affairs. On the one hand we are in a situation where we must *induce* an effect from one object to the other. In other words, if we want to induce this effect we must *put out work* or *expend energy* to some degree. However, if we at first, engineer the two objects such that they are in a high state of sympathy, or attunement, very little work is required to complete this process of causing an effect other than what is needed to modulate or change the first body. Being in tune means being in harmony or concordance such that the two bodies are *as one body*. Work to overcome resistance is required when the two bodies are not in agreement or are slightly out of tune and it then requires considerably more energy to override the inertia of discord (degree of non-attunement) between them.

This is not unlike a highly trained football team. When all the players are of one accord (in harmony of purpose, training and physical condition) they can act *as one* and are a formidable force on the field. When a new player is taken into their midst special time, attention and work are required to get the new team member to resonate as the others such that he eventually becomes a harmonious component of the *one team* and is not wasting energy working at odds with them. He must be brought into sympathy with the team spirit. One may say that this team spirit must be *induced* in him such that he absorbs and resonates to it. This inducement is usually accompanied by a great expediture of time and/or energy. Until this new member becomes an integral part of the whole there will be *resistance to coincidental action* (team work) - the parts won't flow with each other in a harmonious pattern.

Just so in electrical and mechanical systems. If only the fundamental frequency is engineered to be in tune there is only a partial *sympathetic coincidence* (everything working together towards a single purpose) established. If a perfectly tuned circuit is desired then attention must be paid to have all vibration components sympathetic to all others for there to be complete harmony of vibration (motion). Tuning just the fundamental and its harmonics leaves all the other partials to do as they please thus creating discords and resistances to integrated harmonious action. The whole will not function as smoothly as it might if all vibration components were put in a state of sympathy. When all are in sympathy or agreement a resistance-free circuit or system (marriage, team) may be engineered and constructed.

References:

(1) McGraw-Hill Dictionary of Scientific and Technical Terms, 3rd edition.
(2) The New World Dictionary, 1948, Appleton-Century-Crofts, Inc.

Negative Attraction

Negative Attraction behaves very much like magnetism but is not magnetism. Negative Attraction is the causative agent from which magnetism is brought into being.

Negative Attraction is the Enharmonic Third of the Triune Stream of vibratory forces constituting the particle's structure.

Negative Attraction has been called NAVAZ or NIGHT-SIDE or FEMALE or ISIS in ancient times.

Neutral Center

Positive Propulsive

Negative Attractive

Neutral Center

The Neutral Center is the point to which all the attractive forces of the unit are attracted and from which they re-radiate.

The Neutral Center is therefore the center of attraction and radiation.

The Neutral Center is not polar but is neutral and may be polarized with either positive, negative or no polarization.

The Neutral Center is a virtual center and no thing actually exists at this infinitely small focal point.

Sometimes refered to as the Zero-Point.

Neutral Center

Neutral Center

The entire particle structure is built and maintained around and by virtue of the Neutral Center.

Gravity

John Ernst Worrell Keely
Edgar Cayce

"Gravity is the mutual attraction of at-omoles." (Keely)

Gravity is an eternal existing condition in etheric space, from which all visible forms are condensed. It is inherent in all forms of matter, visible and invisible. It is not subject to time or space. It is an established connective link between all forms of matter from their aggregation. Time is annihilated by it, as it has already traversed space when the neutral centers of the molecules were established. It is nothing more than an attractive, sympathetic stream, flowing towards the neutral center of the earth, emanating from molecular centers of neutrality, concordant with the earth's center of neutrality and seeking its medium of affinity with a power corresponding to the character of the molecular mass. (2)

"Gravity is transmittive inter-etheric force under immense etheric vibration." Keely (1)

"Gravity acting through space on everything has no action on space itself." (195-57)(4)

"The Amount of Aggregation reached by any system of bodies at any point in time depends upon the relative proportions of its Forces and its Energies at that moment." (3)

"Gravity may be considered a negative force, for it tends to balance the positive forces. Gravitational forces are vibratory forces and might be defined as the centralization of vibratory forces ready to change into power by non-activity." [(195-70) (4)]

"Gravity is nothing more than an attractive, sympathetic stream, flowing towards the neutral center of the earth, emanating from molecular centers of neutrality; concordant with the earth's center of neutrality, and seeking its medium of affinity with a power corresponding to the character of the molecular mass. Gravity, he defines as transmittive inter-etheric force under immense etheric vibration. He continues: - The action of the mind itself is a vibratory etheric evolution, controlling the physical, its negative power being depreciatory in its effects, and its positive influence elevating." (1)

"The force of gravity may be considered to have elements in octave of density, and these in relativity to same force of the object being acted upon. See, as to how the octave of forces - Now let this apply not only to what is commonly considered as octave(meaning vibration thrown off as sound), but as an octave or a vibration as would be set in motion by this very activity of the gravitation in its activity - as pushes up as well as pushes down. Not until you have overcome gravitation. Now you are beginning to understand the law of gravitation. So as the raising power, there must be the opposite power, understand these, then we begin to see how the vibratory forces is the active principle all radiates from.
What is gravitation? The centralization of vibratory force, ready to be changed in power by non-activity, see?" [(195-54) (4)]

"Molecular terrestrial masses, composed of the "ultimate ether" bound latent in substance, are sympathetically drawn to the earth's neutral center according to the density of their molecular

Universal Laws Never Before Revealed: Keely's Secrets

aggregation, from which must be deducted their celestial sympathetic outreach. In other words, molecular weight consists in the difference between these forces. Either one can be intensified by polar or antipolar vibrations, giving either one predominance. If the celestial (repulsive) predominates, the mass will rise, its velocity proportionate to the concentration of the dominant or the "negative thirds of its mass chords" inducing high neutral radiation together with "celestial attraction." The "terrestrial propulsive" and "celestial attractive" cause ascension and the *celestial propulsive* and *terrestrial attractive* cause descension or increased weight." [2]

Beyond disintegration lies dispersion, and Keely can just as easily disperse atoms of matter as disintegrate its molecules, dispersing them into ether. The law of gravity appears in the light of Keely's experiments but one manifestation of a law which provides for the reversion of the process of attraction in the shape of a process of repulsion. Keely, by means of a belt and certain appliances which he wore upon his person moved single-handed, a 500 horsepower vibratory engine from one part of his shop to another, without a scratch on the floor, and astounded engineers declared it could not have been moved without a derrick, to use which would have required the removal of the roof.

Demonstrating the overcoming of gravity, Keely used an air-ship model weighing about 8 lbs., which, when the differentiated wire of silver and platinum was attached to it, communicating with the sympathetic transmitter, rose, descended, or remained stationery midway, the motion as gentle as that of thistledown floating in the air.

The experiment illustrating "chord of mass" sympathy was repeated, using a glass chamber, 40 inches in height, filled with water, standing on a slab of glass. Three metal spheres, weighing about 6 ounces each, rested on the glass floor. The chord of mass of these spheres was B flat first octave, E flat second octave and B flat third octave. Upon sounding the note B flat on the sympathetic transmitter, the sphere

having that chord of mass rose slowly to the top of the chamber, the positive end of the wire having been attached, which connected the covered jar with the transmitter. The same result followed the sound of the other spheres, all of which descended as gently as they rose, upon changing the positive to the negative. J.M. Wilcox, who was present remarked: "This experiment proves the truth of a fundamental law in scholastic philosophy, that when one body attracts or seeks another body, it is not that the effect is the sum of the effects produced by parts of one body upon parts of another, one aggregate of effects, but the result of the operation of one whole upon another whole."

The vibrations induced by this experiments reached over 700,000,000 per second, unshipping the apparatus, thus making it insecure for a repetition of the experiments. The decarbonized steel compressors of said apparatus moved as if composed of putty. Volume of sphere 15 cubic in weight of surrounding metal, 316 lbs."

"Gravity is not subject to time or space. It pervades the Universe without reference to time or space, instantaneously and without intermission. It is, however, a sympathetic flow, proceeding from the molecular or mass neutral centers to the earth's neutral center with a power corresponding to the character of each individual molecular mass." He believed gravity dependent on the medium of the polar stream, for he says "If the sympathetic negative polar stream were cut off from the earth the molecular neutral centers would float away into space like a swarm of bees."

"Under my system the gravital flow comes under the order of the "sympathetic concordant of the 9ths" and is that third of the triune combination called the "polar propulsive." Gravity is polar propulsion while magnetism is polar attraction. Both magnetism and gravity can be accelerated by proper vibrations."

He believed gravity to be the result of a law which provides for a reversion of attraction in repulsion, and which acts by transmission of force under immense etheric vibration through the "interetheric subdivision." He also showed that gravitation acts "as a lever." MacVicar states "Every individualized object assimilates itself to itself in successive moments of its existence and all objects tend to assimilate one another." Keely says "Gravity is an ever existing eternal force, coexistent with the compound etheric or high luminous(seventh subdivision) since it entered into, and is an inherent property of, all forms of aggregated matter from their birth. It is the source from which all matter originated and each substance-unit or neutral center is a concordant link, attractive and dispersive, to all other neutral centers. Each neutral center is the nucleus of what we recognize as substance and is potentially the nucleus of a planet."

"The sympathetic concordants (planetary vibrations) established by the Infinite One from the birth of the planetary neutral centers, are simply the operation of the laws of gravity. The inaudible atomic, etheric and interetheric vibrations, which control and direct the movements of the Universe, must of necessity from the magnitude of their result, be the most powerful of all sounds." These vibrations collectively constitute the "Music of the Spheres" discovered by Pythagoras of old and so long considered merely a poetic fancy. This is now proved experimentally in Keely's workshop to be an actual fact.

He calls all planetary masses "terrestrial" and says the "celestial concordant sympathetic vibrations between the spheres govern their motions in their orbits, that at their maximum distance the attractive forces assume supremacy, bringing them toward each other, and at the minimum distance, the repulsive forces assume control causing them to again recede from each other.

Molecular terrestrial masses, composed of the "ultimate ether" bound latent in substance, are sympathetically drawn to the earth's neutral center according to the density of their molecular aggregation, from which must be deducted their celestial sympathetic outreach. In other words, molecular weight consists in the difference between these forces. Either one can be intensified by polar or antipolar vibrations, giving ei-

ther one predominance. If the celestial (repulsive) predominates, the mass will rise, its velocity proportionate to the concentration of the dominant or the "negative thirds of its mass chords" inducing high neutral radiation together with "celestial attraction." The "terrestrial propulsive" and "celestial attractive" cause ascension and the "celestial propulsive" and terrestrial attractive cause descension or increased weight. [2]

"Any visible molecular mass of metal can be so impregnated by triple orders of sympathetic vibration as to give it the same sympathetic transmittive qualities that exist in the mental forces, which make such mass subservient to either the attractive or repulsive conditions of terrestrial sympathy.

"Gravity is nothing more than a concordant attractive sympathetic stream flowing towards the neutral center of the earth. This force is inherent in all visible and invisible aggregated forms of matter, from the very birth of a planet, around whose center the molecules cluster by the sympathetic affinity which is thus induced. If these conditions had always maintained a neutral position in etheric space, no planet would ever have been evolved. These conditions have been fixed by the Infinite. These rotating neutral centers, set in celestial space, have been endowed with the power of rotation to become their own accumulators. It is through the action of these sympathetic forces of the Infinite etheric realm that planets are born, and their volume of matter augmented.

"If we pick up an object we feel a resisting power in it which physicists call gravity; but they do not explain what gravity is. It is simply a sympathetic flow, proceeding from the molecular centers of neutrality; which flow is concordant with the earth's neutral center of same, seeking this medium of its affinity with a power corresponding to the character of its molecular mass. There is no actual weight in the molecules of the mass of which the earth is composed. If the sympathetic negative polar stream that flows towards the neutral center of the earth were cut off from

Universal Laws Never Before Revealed: Keely's Secrets

it, the earth's molecular mass would become independent, and would float away into space as would a soap bubble filled with warm air.

"The gravital flow comes, in this system, under the order of the sympathetic concordant of the 9ths, and belongs to that third of the triune combinations called polar propulsive.

"Magnetism is polar attraction."
"Gravity is polar propulsion."

"Both magnetism and gravity can be accelerated by the proper medium of sympathetic vibratory influences." Keely, [1].

References

1) Bloomfield-Moore, Clara Jessup; "Keely and His Discoveries." Delta Spectrum Research P. O. Box 316 Valentine, Nebraska 69201 (402) 376-1523

2) Snell, C.W.; "Snell Manuscript." Delta Spectrum Research P. O. Box 316 Valentine, Nebraska 69201 (402) 376-1523

3) Allen, Grant; Force & Energy, The Theory of Dynamics. Delta Spectrum Research P. O. Box 316 Valentine, Nebraska 69201 (402) 376-1523

4) The Edgar Cayce readings. The Edgar Cayce Foundation. 67th & Atlantic Ave., Virginia Beach, VA 23451

GLOBE MOTOR AND PROVISIONAL ENGINE.

Music of the Molecule

by Dale Pond

Perfectly equated (balanced) vibrations within a molecule may be pictured as the circle below. All three major axis of rotation are equal as well as range and angle of motion. Each orbit is at right angles to the other two and the range of extension is the same in each case.

In the second drawing the range of motion has increased from 1 to 2 in one axis and 1 to 1.25 in the third. Correspondence to musical intervals we would have Perfect Unison (harmony) in the circular drawing and three intervals of Unison, Major Third and an Octave in the second drawing. The angle has not changed therefore the modes have remained the same indicating discords from differing partials are not present.

If we assign a numeric value to the numbers the fundamental being C or 512 vibrations per second (in the circular drawing) the other two would be 640 cps and 1024 cps respectively in the elliptical drawing (facing page).

These numbers pertain to the radius, diameter and circumference of orbit. The line of circumference would be the center of the orbiting body. The enclosed space represents (in this case) the area of the neutral center. It is believed that the volumetric areas of the orbiting

1:1:1 ratio

bodies extending beyond this circumference would possess a "positive" charge or state and may at times be of an odd shape wholly originating within the orbiting body itself and not a part of the configuration of the neutral center's domain. The question remains: can the neutral center maintain perfect harmony if and when the outer peripheral activities are not? It is further believed that this can and is a possibility. This disord within harmony is in fact sub-atomic activity which may be the electrical or photonic states of matter.

According to Keely the molecule will maintain its integrity until the ratio of width to length exceeds 1:4 at which point the molecule disrupts or comes apart forming a dipole and a monopole particles. Implying that the molecule can not separate into three distinct particles at one time. Because to do so would mean that as they got further and further apart approaching the 1:4 ratio its confines of ratio would be held in strict relativity - *i.e.*, as the molecule stretched the ratios would remain relative to one another. This scenario is interesting in that a molecule could be made to stretch in all three directions artificially. Once it reached a point where all three diameters exceeded the original 1:4 ratio two

Universal Laws Never Before Revealed: Keely's Secrets

frequencies could be quickly demodulated such that they instantly revert to the original rates thus leaving one of them at the 4+ ratio. The molecule would instantly disrupt with little apparent energy input. In other words, the molecule could be stimulated until it was in a state of maximum instability and then "nudged" into dissociation with a small tickle of force.

The Quantum Leap of science can be easily seen in the two drawings. When the ratios increase from one steady state (state of relative harmony) to the other we can perceive the quantum energy level increase by a fixed value usually known as Planck's Constant. Planck's Constant is a fixed amount of energy being the difference of energy quantities as measured from orbital shell to orbital shell or from one energy state to another. As stated above: Planck's Constant is the *difference* between the energy levels. This *difference* is the same as the *interval* as spoken of in music.

It is assumed the natural progression of discord follows the following pattern of ratios from perfect harmony or equation of forces to the least harmonious or the point of disruption:

Harmony
1:1:1
1:1:2
1:2:2
1:2:3
1:3:5
Disruption

This projection has not yet been verified by experimental means but is deemed to be accurate. The above figures are the natural progression of the Fibonnaci spiral and all other life activities resulting from a natural progression of events.

Of course the above discourse is theoretical but so are the abundant theories concerning electrons orbiting around a "heavy" nucleus. Until recently this centralized theory was eagerly accepted without much question. Then Richard Feynman (Nobel Prize winner for his work with quantum electrodynamics) voiced his theory which very much resembled Keely's work. It may be a long time before the dust is settled over the disputed configuration of molecules and that which it contains. At any rate, Keely's theory appears to hold when quantum mechanics are looked at from his viewpoint. There are a few things known with certainty about quantum mechanics and these things can be fitted into either theory:

1) Planck's Constant is real and verifiable.

2) Photons, electrons, *etc.* do originate from within these minute structures. Just how they do this is at the root of the dispute.

3) Direct observation does have an effect on these phenomena. What is the mechanism of such effects is also disputed.

4) Keely's theory worked for him. Modern science's theory works for them.

5) Quantum particles vibrate and oscillate.

6) Matter is composed of tiny particles.

2.000"

2

1.250"

1

1.000"

1:1.25:2 ratio

Much Ado About Nothing

by Dale Pond

Whenever one reads about electrical phenomena, especially theoretical works, one constantly runs into the subject of vacuums. Rarely ever does one find much thought given to the subject - after all what is there to write about when discussing nothing?

Funny how so important and basic a subject as vacuums are to electronics that seldom is hear or read a single thing on the matter or lack of matter as it were. There are some things that can be said for vacuums. And these things play a vital role in whatever takes place in such a rareified medium.

The first and probably the most important thing to know about a vacuum is that it is nothing other than the lack of something else. In other words there is *no thing* present in a vacuum (ideally speaking). However this ideal state is never the case. Even the scientist hard at work creating more and more of nothing - harder and harder vacuums - admit there is always something left in his chamber. We are speaking of one or two elusive molecules of air or atoms of whatever element may be present. This proposition can easily be seen by anyone with at least one eyeball. If the vacuum chamber in question is glass(transparent) we can see right through it after it has been exhausted to the highest possible degree. This indicates to us that at least photons are going through the chamber walls and contained space. So we must therefore admit that this so-called nothingness is at least *full* of photons. Of no less a noticable trait of our little vacuum (especially to electronic engineers) is that radio waves also permeate this "empty" space. So we must therefore also admit that this "empty" space is also *full* of electrons (if

we accept the idea that radio waves are conveyed by electrons). No doubt this "empty" space is also full of all kinds and genres of other sub-atomic "particles" as well. However the point has been made and need not be labored.

This brings us to a really interesting sylloquism derived from common high school level physics. We were all told by our highly educated teachers and professors that heat does not travel through a vacuum. They backed up this "fact" with countless demonstrations and validated reports from other authorities. We believed them because they were educated and we weren't.

The same idea was voiced concerning electrical wave propagation. How could radio waves travel through interplanetary space (vacuum) if there are no electrons to carry them?

This was the foundation argument for the ever elusive ether.

Some postulated there had to be *some thing* that propagated the electrical waves. Since no one could isolate this "thing" they simply called it "ether" being (in this context) something named but not understood much like gravity is today.

The great question which has appeared on the scene is:

If heat cannot travel through a vacuum and they tell us the Sun heats the Earth and all other material bodies in our Solar System, then how can this take place?

POINT: Heat cannot travel through a vacuum.

220

Keely's Secrets

POINT: The space between the Earth and the Sun is a vacuum.

POINT: It is said that the Sun heats the Earth.

What is going on?

Now, modern physics recognizes three kinds of heat: convection, radiant and conduction. These are the three ways in which heat is propagated to adjacent objects from a source, so they tell us.

Convection and conduction both activate through physical contact, these must be eliminated from our discussion. Therefore the heat from the Sun reaches the Earth through the process known as radiant heat. But what is radiant heat? What is there in the vacuum of space that is the means of conveyance of this heat (vibratory) energy? If vacuum of space is "empty" then there is *no thing* acting as a means of transmission. So we wind up with the ether (unproven) or is there something else we haven't considered?

Believe it or not - there is another theory that just may lay all this debate to rest. That is the theory put forth by John Keely over 100 years ago. It is the theory of Triple Concordant Flows. It goes like this:

Radiant energy is a composite form of energy that does not manifest itself to our senses until it strikes a molecule or atom.

Heat and light are vibrating forms of energy. Therefore we can assume that radiant energy (as used in heat) is a form of vibration we cannot perceive. Light poses the same dilema because interplanetary space is full of darkness (the absence of light) so we can assume that light does not manifest to our senses until it also strikes a molecule or atom. This is actually the process of modulation or demodulation from a higher or lower frequency to another, newer form or rate of vibration.

What is happening, really happening, between the Sun and the Earth which is full of heat and light yet these two powerful forces are not noticeable until this radiant solar energy strikes molecules or atoms?

First we know several things: that this solar energy has a frequency and that the molecules and atoms have their respective frequencies. We also know that vibrations are not simple sine wave-like entities. We know this because we can create and transmit a longitudinal wave which also possesses transverse, vortex and a whole series of other dissimilar wave patterns and forms. These newer derivatives are dependent on direction and medium of transmission. Might we not say that there is no such thing as a simple vibration? May we also say that any vibration is in truth a composite made up of all these inherently different wave forms? What is it that liberates these newer forms of vibration? Isn't it the direction of propagation alone?

The concept is now clear - the radiant solar energy begins its lengthy trip from the Sun as *undifferentiated vibration*. This matrixed vibration has within itself all the known forms of manifesting energy: heat, light, sound, *etc*. These lesser forms of energy are liberated from the greater when the greater strikes a molecule or atom which results in a *change of direction* and frequency and hence *manner of association* with other composite vibrations.

Keely maintained that this greater stream of energy was made up of three major components. He called this stream a Triple Concordant Flow. He further maintained that this stream of energy manifested as electricity, magnetism and gravity when it struck the Earth or was assimilated to the Earth. These became what he termed "terrestrial polar currents" and were easily proven (he said) by the manifestations we see in the far north known as the aureos borealis. It has been noted elsewhere that Tesla took great interest in this light phenomenon. If he did determine this process as outlined above he would have been able to find a manner to differentiate this terrestrial polar current into both electrical forces and magnetic forces. It is theorized that it is through this undifferentiated state he meant to transmit electrical energy to any place on the Earth's surface. If he could have tapped into this unlimited supply he could most easily have illuminated the world for next to nothing. The energy is already there, cozy in its undifferentiated state, waiting to obey the man who could fathom its secret key and liberate it into manifestation.

One more thought on the subject of electricity.

The electrical spark so often seen is simply the differentiated electrical stream seeking to get back into this cozy existence with its brother forces magnetism and gravity.

Thus reunited as one force ever present to spring forth when equilibrium is again disturbed.

If one looks closely it may be perceived that this method of disturbing the triune equilibrium of a single force by directional or frequency demodulation is what happens in the ordinary light bulb, the doped micro circuit and in the ideas as expounded by Henry Moray. This is what happens in flourescent gases and molecules of the atmosphere. This may also be the solution to superconductive transmissions whether through a wire or through the atmosphere.

But this is only a hint at the total process under discussion - how *no thing* holds all things. Differentiating the forces held latent in a seemingly innocent piece of uranium, plutonium or carbon mixed with sulfur and potassium nitrate liberates tremendous heat, light and pressure. From whence come they these beasts of burden? How are these forces held there unseen and unperceived until disturbed from their timeless sleep? What is the condition or state of this unseen but extraordinarily powerful force that can hold all this heat, light and pressure in total obeyance as though they didn't exist? What is it that can hold back a lightening bolt until its time is ripe? Who dares open this door to nlimited power? *Tesla and Keely dared and did.*

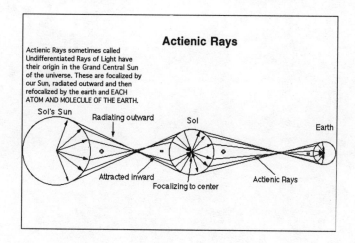

Actienic Rays

Actienic Rays sometimes called Undifferentiated Rays of Light have their origin in the Grand Central Sun of the universe. These are focalized by our Sun, radiated outward and then refocalized by the earth and EACH ATOM AND MOLECULE OF THE EARTH.

Sol's Sun
Radiating outward
Sol
Earth
Attracted inward
Focalizing to center
Actienic Rays

GLOBE MOTOR AND PROVISIONAL ENGINE.

Keely's Globe Motor and Provisional Engine.

Music - The Realm of Activity

by Dale Pond

"Remember that music is the one element which may span the difference between the sublime and the ridiculous. It may arouse violent passion, yet it may soothe the beast of passion. It may bring up thoughts of home, of heaven, of loved ones; of the laugh of a baby, or the tears of a beautiful woman, or the arms of a loved one, or the jeers of a crowd." (7053-1) also (5253-1)

How is it that music has these or other powers? What is the cause of these effects on the human beingness? Is it possible to learn about these things and then use them in a more sane and rational manner? Can music be used as a tool for healing or other constructive purposes? This is the premise of this subject - that we can learn enough about the hidden power of music such that we can heal a disturbed physical or mental condition or we can add constructive power to life's experiences such that a positive and more profitable life is assured.

The principles of music evolution and the general theory of music contain all of the fundamental metaphysical and scientific principles required to understand the Universal Creative Forces.

"Music! History of it, activity in it -- all such varied forms. If you learn music, you learn history. If you learn music, you'll learn mathematics. If you learn music, you'll learn almost all there is to learn -- unless something bad!" (3053-1)

Music is an organized system of vibrations. Sound is a vibration and when the principles of sound are properly understood and applied much can be done with it. Within music the Law of Relativity is held absolute in the concept of the interval. Music can therefore be a strong guide-post for an exploration of these principles.

Modern physics, especially quantum physics and quantum mechanics, acknowledges that all things in the universe *vibrate*. That is each and every organized thing is in a state of perpetual motion constantly moving in a rhythmic pattern to and fro or inwardly and outwardly. This motion is manifest in many different ways or types of activity. The most preponderant motion is from a positive state of energy to a negative state of energy. *This is what a vibration is.* Just as in the 24 hour day - we have 12 hours of daylight where most things and beasts of the earth have plenty of energy and are active for the most part - this is the positive half of the day. The other half of the day is really night where all things and even most beast of the earth are quiescent and are usually asleep with their consciousness focused inward - this is the negative time of day.

Positive here does not mean "good" and negative does not mean "bad."

When an object, in vibratory motion (going from a positive to a negative state and back again), is positive it is said to be expansive or outgoing or expressive. When an object, in vibratory motion, is said to be negative it is in a receptive, inward seeking, aggregating, coalescing or crystallizing activity. These two forces are opposite to one another in their activity.

The positive is expansive -the negative is concentrative.

Universal Laws Never Before Revealed: Keely's Secrets

These two modes of activity are very much like the male and female forces. The male seeks outward and the female seeks inward. It is common knowledge that young males are war-like and ever trying to express themselves in an aggressive, out-seeking fashion. The female on the other hand attempts to seek a centralization (home) and is often more stable (centered in one place) than the male.

These two forces are constantly at war ever seeking to express themselves. They are not really at war but the motions are similar to those of war. The female or center-seeking force is exerting its power to centralize and hold firm that which it finds within its sphere of influence. It has what may be termed an "outreach" and all those things found within that zone of its outreach will be pulled towards the center of focus. This includes the orbiting focus of the male or expansive forces.

The male force on the other hand has an "in-reach" as it were and will reach for the center in its attempts to decentralize or radiate outward all that it comes to influence or all those things found within its sphere of activity.

So even though we see manifest two apparently opposing forces they are in reality two sides of the same thing. They actually come together in a Cosmic dance which inevitably leads to a balanced state. A good analogy would be a child's teeter-totter. The two sides are always in opposition to each other - while one side goes up the other side goes down. It would be extremely frustrating if one desired both sides to go up or down at the same time. Such motion would be contrary to its very nature and would not be possible.

This analogy brings us to the next important part of vibratory movements - that of the neutral or third force constantly at work in undulatory motions. There are some that claim the neutral force is the most important because it spans the gap between the two sexes or polarities of positive and negative. On

the teeter-totter above the point of its suspension - the pivot point upon which it swings up and down is the neutral point or point of balance. It is upon this point that all the weight and motion of the entire assembly is carried. The neutral point in atoms or molecules bears the same relationship - all the outer vibration and oscillation is held it strict abeyance to the dictates of the neutral center about which it has its existence. Take away the pivot point of a teeter-totter or a molecule and it immediately ceases function and hence ceases to exist as a whole entity.

Vibration
vs
Oscillation

Another important type of vibration is the oscillation. Where a vibration is the rhythmic motion of an object within itself an oscillation is a rhythmic motion of the object itself as an external movement usually in reference to objects outside of itself. A piano string actually oscillates itself and does not vibrate. The air inside of an organ tube may be said to vibrate with its alternating condensation and rarefaction thus creating its sonorous tones.

A vibration of an organized object within itself is the embodiment of the Law of One or the Law of the Dominant. All other movements, forces and manifestations are but secondary or tertiary to this one motion or law in its activity. This is alternating pulsations and condensations just as the human heart beats in and out in its periodic or rhythmic motions. The human breathe and the expansion and contraction of solar systems each reflect this one great and basic law of motion before anything else. A vibration is an main part of the Universal Creative Forces in activity. Without this mode of motion and all that it implies Creation would not be.

The Neutral Force

Half way between these two opposing forces is a neutral zone or a place where neither the positive nor the

225

negative predominates yet they both have an influence within and throughout this neutral center or point. This neutral zone is the common ground between the two forces and even though neither predominates they both hold sway or have influence in this area. This is the "half-way" place where they both meet and have a more or less equal effect on the activities of their association. This may be in a molecule under terrific vibratory motion or in a family unit where the ebb and flow of daily activities takes on both aspects of expression and quietude.

All activity, throughout the universe regardless of realm, be it mental, spiritual or physical is a reflection of these three forces forever engaged in the eternal dance of Shiva (the warring or playing - the giving back and forth of energy). From the tiniest sub-atomic particle to the largest galaxy these forces are in constant antagonism one with another constantly seeking a balance of force. This balance can be likened to the concept of *polarity*.

POLARITY

Polarity exists when a single thing or force is divided between these three state - positive, negative and neutral. The thing is said to be a single thing yet it is composed of three forces each antithetical and seemingly contradictory to each other. This is where the fourth force, Mind Force, comes into importance. This fourth force is the most important of them all. It is the force that unites the other three. This bringing together is not really a binding but in human terms or in terms of human activity we can safely use the the word binding. It doesn't bind because there is no *thing* to bind. The mind-set, goals, desires, ideals and ambitions are *non things* and are more like *spiritualized* forces. We are speaking of spiritual type forces here. A force that expands away and a force that tends to inhibit this expansive action are in a constant struggle. The one attempts to get away while the other attempts a centralization of its activities. What is it them

that keeps these two forces in the same arena? Why doesn't the one expand to "escape velocity"? Why doesn't the other centralize until it disappears? What keeps the two face to face in spite of the constant struggle in opposite directions?

In a molecule or atom, the orbiting electrons are spinning at tremendous velocities. Considering the centrifugal (positive, expansive) forces at work - the electron would fling itself to the furthest reaches of the universe were it not for the attractive force of the centripetal (negative, attractive) forces acting upon it. This is a state of constant tension with one pulling against the other. As long as this "pull" is balanced out where neither force gains predominance the unity of the molecule maintains its integrity. If the positive-propulsive force over pulled the negative-attractive the molecule would loose an electron and the molecule would cease to be what it was. It would become something else. If the negative attractive over pulls the positive propulsive the electron would become absorbed into the nucleus and loose its identity as an individualized entity. The molecule would also cease to be what it was because a molecule is a sum total of the characteristics of its parts.

This fourth force, Mind, is a directing or focusing force. The two opposing forces are kept in the same arena because they are focused on the same thing or things. For a molecule - it may be said that the forces are subservient to a common ideal. As long as the ideal or purpose (to be a molecule of a specific type) is adhered to the molecule will be a molecule. If an outside influence impinges on either of the two forces one or both may be caused to shift their focus. This shift in focus can cause disruption of the unit either by assimilation or dissociation and ultimately destruction of its integrity.

The scenario outlined above for molecules also applies to people. The analogy is apt because we are talking about universal forces or principles. Cayce's readings delve very deeply and consistently into the Universal Creative Forces. Whether the discussion is of atoms, people or activities the same forces possessing the same characteristics are ever present.

The realm of activity is the area in which these electrons can perform their Cosmic dance spinning around the nucleus. This area is from a region close to the central nucleus and extends outward to a place where if the electron went even a micron further it would separate from its association with the molecule. This volumetric area Cayce referred to as the "sphere of activity."

The laws of physics demand that this molecule must remain as it is. It will resist the acquisition or loss of any electrons. In other words, it will resist change but will seek its own state of equilibrium. If the molecule gains or looses an electron the molecule ceases to be what it was and becomes something else - a different kind of molecule or a different form of matter. Although the molecule hasn't changed very much, it will become another entity having similar properties as the first molecule. This is pretty much what happens in transmutation of elements. It may be relatively easy to change one element into another as long as the change is made in small, concise steps. The laws of physics, especially the Law of the Dominant, maintains and preserves the stability and integrity of the complex as One unit of whatever it is.

This analogy also applies to people in groups such as the family unit. The sphere of activity is the arena in which the family members choose to be active. It can be social activities, sport or business functions. An association with certain people will always remain the same until one of the family members chooses to do otherwise. Then the sphere of activity is changed and the family integrity becomes slightly modified. Even though the basic areas of interaction with others and among themselves has changed the integrity of the family unit is preserved just as a new

molecule is formed from the old - the new molecule is still an integral unit.

An important point here is the force or forces that causes the unit to remain strong and integral. Without this assimilative force, the unit, be it a molecule, a family or a social or business group, would disintegrate into its component individualities and cease to exist as a functioning whole. This binding force Cayce referred to as the *ideal* of the group. "What is thy ideal?" "Know thy ideal!" are two of the many ways in which he referred to this aspect of integration. For it is the ideal that binds people and things together. This is the Cosmic glue that brings people together such that they have common goals, ideals and their respective spheres of activity are coincidental at least in part.

In the case of the molecule it is the commonality of vibrations of each of the component parts with the vibrations of the Neutral Center of the nucleus. Vibrations here means those parts and aspects that make up each of the individual units.

As long as there is a harmony of vibrations between the component parts the unit will remain integral and whole. *It is this harmony that binds.* If the harmony is disturbed the integrity is threatened. It is the commonality of ideals, goals, desires, *etc.* that binds two or more individuals one to another. Let these small aspects of each of their lives become different and the individuals begin to find their spheres of activity change gradually becoming more and more distant and distinct until a point is reached and disruption of the unit takes place.

The old adage that birds of a feather flock together is very accurate. People of like mind, like interests, common goals will always come together. This is a natural process and takes very little effort on the parts of each of them. Because of the common ideals (which is a spiritual thing) these people will be brought together as if by a Cosmic or Spiritual force which is what it is.

Clara Sophia Jessup Bloomfield-Moore

(nee: Clarissa Sophia Jessup - February 16, 1824 - January 5, 1899)

by Dale Pond

Keely's work, the work we have been enjoying for over 40 months, we owe entirely to Mrs. Clara Jessup Bloomfield-Moore. She financed his research and wrote prolifically attempting to interest science of her day to look at and accept his discoveries.

Mrs. Moore was a remarkable woman. She was born in Philadelphia, Pennsylvania, February 16, 1824, and was a daughter of the distinguished scientist, Augustus Edward Jessup, for many years an active member of the Academy of Natural Sciences. She received her education partly at home and party at the Westfield (Mass.) Academy. October 27, 1842, she married at Westfield, Bloomfield Haines Moore, of Philadelphia, who subsequently established (with his father-in-law) the well-known paper manufacturing firm of Jessup & Moore located near Wilmington, Delaware. His death in 1878 deprived Philadelphia of one of its outstanding citizens. The Philadelphia Inquirer published a long editorial, the writer of which stated that:

"It was the unswerving rectitude, the untiring industry and doubtless enterprise which marked his career from first to last, that made his life of such value to his fellow-citizens and gave him his true distinction."

Mrs. Moore was a prolific writer, her publications including: *The Young Ladies' Friend* (1876), *On Dangerous Ground* (1876), *Sensible Etiquette* (1878), *Slander and Gossip* (1882), and *Social Ethics and Social Duties* (1892). Her last years were passed in London, where she was presented at the Court of Queen Victoria and associated with the greatest literary minds of England, including Robert Browning. Her generosity enriched several institutions, including the Franklin Institute and the University of Penn-

sylvania (to each of which she donated $10,000 as memorials to her husband), and the Pennsylvania Museum and School of Industrial Art at Philadelphia (to which she presented her priceless art collection as a memorial to her husband, and which bears his name). She died in London, January 5, 1899. She and Mr. Moore were the parents of three children:

1. Ella Carlton (1843-1892); m. 1864 Count Carl Gustaf von Rosen, Commander-Captain, Swedish Navy;
2. Clarence Bloomfield (1852-1936); unmarried; and
3. Lillian Augusta Stuart (1853-1911); m. 1874 Baron Carl Nils Daniel de Bildt, Swedish Minister to Italy, and an emminent historian.[1]

MOORE, Clara (Jessup), poet, novelist and philantropist, was born in Philadelphia, PA., Feb. 16, 1824, daughter of Augustus E. and Lydia (Moseley) Jessup. Her father, Augustus E. Jessup, was the scientist of an expedition under Maj. Stephen H. Long, which visited the Yellowstone region in 1816. He was a native of Berkshire county, Mass., and a descendent of John Jessup, who in 1635 settled in Long Island. The Moseley's are an ancient English family, mentioned in "Domesday Book," and have several branches in the United States, including that in Massachucetts, found by Mrs. Moore's ancestor, John Moseley, of Dorchester, 1630. A son of the emigrant was married to Mary Newbury, of Boston, and removed to Westfield, Mass.; was a lieutenant in King Phillip's war, and held other public offices. Clara Jessup was educated partly at home, partly at Westfield Academy, and at the school of Mrs. Merrick, New Haven, Conn. On October 27, 1842, she was married at her father's old home, in Mass., to Bloomfield Haines

Universal Laws Never Before Revealed: Keely's Secrets

Moore, of Philadelphia, and took a prominent place among leaders of society, literary as well as fashionable, of that city. Having much leisure time at her command she began to write for the press, contributing to newspapers and magazines verse and prose purporting to be the work of Clara Moreton. One of her early stories, : *"The Estranged Hearts,"* received the first prize in a competition, where 400 manuscripts were submitted. Later novelettes, such as *"Compensation"* and *"Emma Dudley's Secret,"* were similarly successful. Three books, *"The Hasty Marriage," "The Home of Huntley and Raymond"* and *"Mabels' Mission,"* were published without any name on the title page. When the civil war broke out, Dr. Bellows, of New York, president of the sanitary commission, named Mrs. Moore for the president of the woman's Pennsylvania branch, which she had aided in organizing. She declined, but accepted the position of corresponding secretary, and with this important work upon her hands gave up literature for a time. She created and organized the special relief committee for aiding hospital work, and with Mrs. George Plitt organized the committees of women which conducted the great sanitary fair in Philadelphia. She also projected and aided in founding the Union Temperance Home for children. She also created and organized the Special Relief Committee which took such an active part in the hospital work during the Civil War, knowing no difference between the soldiers of the North and the soldiers of the South in its objects of aid, laying aside all feeling of sectional animosity and administering, with the hands of christian charity, alike to the suffering wearers of "the blue and the gray." After the was she returned to literary work, using, as a rule, her own name. In 1873 an anonymous article by her on etiquette, published in Lippincott's Magazine, attracted much attention and provoked much unreasonable criticism. In that year, also, she published a revised edition of one of her popular works, *"The Young Ladies Friend;"* in 1875, *"Mission on Dangerous Ground,"* which passed through seven editions, and in 1878 her famous work, *"Sensible Etiquette."* Among her works were: *"Gondaline's Les-sons and other Poems"* (1881); *"Slander and Gossip,"* privately printed (1882); *"The Warden's Tale, San Moritz, Magdalena and Other Poems"* (1883); *"Social Ethics and Social Duties"* (1892), and several books for children, of one of which, *"Master Jacky's Holiday,"* more than twenty editions were published. The proceeds of the sales of Mrs. Moore's work were spent in aiding philantropic institutions and individuals who were engaged in literary or scientific pursuits. Among these individuals was John Worrel Keely, the inventor, who for many years was supported by her gifts. Much of Mrs. Moore's life was passed in London, especially after the death of her husband in 1878, and there, as in Philadelphia, her house was a resort for artists, musicians and authors. Mrs. Moore had three children: Clarence B. Moore, of Philadelphia; Ella, wife of Count Carl Gustaf von Rosen, first lord in waiting to King Oscar of Sweden and Norway, and Lillian, wife of Baron Carl de Bildt, Swedish and Norwegian minister in Rome. She died in London, England, January 5, 1899.[2]

Other Works by Clara Jessup Bloomfield-Moore (*pen names:* Clara Moreton, Harriet Oxnard Ward):

The Adopted.
The Fulfilled Prophecy.
Renunciation.
Reasonable and Unreasonable Points of Etiquette.
Unsettled Points of Etiquette.
Miscellaneous Poems.
Stories for Children.
Three Eras in a Life.
Frank and Fanny, a Rural Story (1851)
Social Ethics and Society Dutie: Thorough Education of Girls for Wives and Mothers and for Professions (1892)
Agatha's Friendship: A Romance for American Society.
Sensible Etiquette of the Best Society, Customs, Manners, Morals, and Home Culture. (1878)
The Diamond Cross.
An Echo (1894)
Freedom (1893)
The Refiner of Silver (1891)
Idol Affections (1890)

Clara Sophia Jessup Bloomfield-Moore

Robert Browning (1890)

Letter of Instruction to my Grandson, Clarence von Rosen (1889)

Nancy Lee Songster; containing a complete collection of the above artist, together with a collection of the latest and best serio-comic and sentimental songs of the day (1879)

Character and Descriptive Songster (1877)

First Requisites in Physician and Nurse of the Cure of Insanity (1881)

Tales from Aristo, retold for Children by a Lady (1879)

Poems. A Chapter from the Modern Pilgrims Progress: Slander and Gossip. (1882)

Aerial Navigation: Keely and His Energy (1894)

Keely's Contribution to Science (1890)

Ether, the True Protoplasm (1893)

Keely Motor and the Dogmatism of Science.

Some Truths about the Keely Motor.

The New Philosophy.

Keely's Present Position (1892)

The Keely Motor Secret (1887)

Mr. Keely's Etheric Force (1886)

Keely's Secrets - Etheric Force Identified as Dynaspheric Force - One Phase of Keely's Discovery in its Relation to the Cure of Disease (1888)

The Keely Motor Bubble (1890)

True Science (1890)

What is Science? (1894)

More Science (1891)

Propellor of Keely's Airship.

Physical Discoveries of John Keely (1892)

The Veil Withdrawn.

Some Truths about John Keely

The Keely Motor (1886)

A Confession of Faith (1894)

Keely and His Discoveries (1893)

(1) *Ancestry of Clarence Bloomfield-Moore of Philadelphia*; by Clara Jessup Bloomfield-Moore, edited by Baron Harold de Bildt, Cairo, Egypt and Milton Rubincam, Washington, D.C., circa 1940.

(2) *National Encyclopedia of American Biography*, 1899.

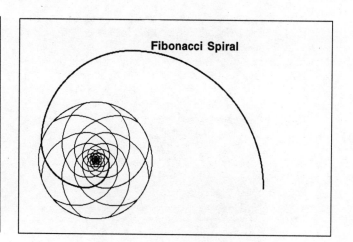

Fibonacci is Music

1 : 1 : 2 : 3 : 5 : 8 : 13 : 21...

1 : 1	Unison
3 : 2	Perfect 5th
8 : 5	Minor 6th
21 :13	Minor 6th
∞ : ∞	Harmonic 6th
21 :13	Minor 6th
13 : 8	Minor 6th
5 : 3	Major 6th
2 : 1	Octave

Fibonacci Numbers

The Fibonnaci series is the base of music. Here we have the series going up which breaks into a smooth series of even musical intervals.

When the numbers are going in reverse order we can see the spontaneous generation of odd or enharmonic musical intervals.

The two series will progress to infinity always attempting to form an Harmonic 6th which does not exist in music or nature because the Harmonic 6th signifies perfect unity or harmony or equation of forces. Should this happen the forces then become latent and non-perceptible.

Fibonacci Spiral

KEELY'S PROVISIONAL ENGINE.

The globe and the drum revolve in opposite directions through the action of etheric force, which is transmitted to them by a wire of platinum and silver.

Keely's Trexar
a Superconductive Wire

by Dale Pond

Throughout the Keely literature there is constant mention of his platinum, gold and silver wire. Keely claimed that this wire is the perfect medium for transmitting vibratory energy all the while perfectly free of interference. Keely considered interference in much the same way that we consider resistance. If the vibrations flowed freely down the wire they are subject to neither resistance or intereference. *It is also a common factor that the new superconducting wires and materials are made from elements combined in Keely's ratio of 1:2:3.*

The following excerpts were taken from the <u>Snell Manuscript</u> and are illustrative of the type of information to be found there. *Some editorial notations can be discerned - these were comments included by Mr. Snell.*

"A wire made of sections of silver, gold and platinum, respectively, is peculiarly adapted to transmit concordant vibrations in the relations of thirds, their range of molecular oscillation being in the proportion of 3:6:9 respectively. The Trexar is this wire composed of: a first section of silver, a second section of gold and a third section of platinum, all uniform in size, which is used as a conductor in vibratory transmission and for the multiplication of vibrational frequencies.

Silver represents the third, gold the sixth and platinum the ninth, in their respective relative molecular oscillating ranges. This triune condition will equate thirds in vibratory frequencies, that is, chords in intervals of thirds will set up disturbances in the Trexar and these disturbances will be equated so as to be transmitted as thirds from the positive or farthest end of the wire.

"There is no medium used in vibratory research so unerringly exact in effecting sympathetic negative attraction as the Trexar. This combination as accurately indicates the action of the earth's sympathetic envelope in its triple focalized action towards the earth's neutral center, as the magnet unfailingly indicates the dominant electric flow."

"Differential molecular volume is required to equate differentiation of sympathetic flows. This condition is satisfied by the Trexar. Two differing molecular densities, represented by two different mediums, make possible the harmonious adjustment of the thirds."

When an introductory transmissive sympathetic chord (say B flat) is conducted along a sectional transmitting wire the molecular triple (intermolecule) is carried along by induced differentiation and it in turn excites high sympathy with the polar terrestrial stream which, being triune in character, requires a triune differential sympathizer of the same ratio of frequency. This is satisfied by the Trexar, consisting of sections of silver the harmonic, gold the enharmonic and platinum the dominant. When the Trexar is properly sensitized by any chord on the dominant, molecular differentiation is induced, the phenomena approaching mag- netism is effect, but without a trace of true magnetism being present."

By means of sympathetic vibrations transmitted through the Trexar, which is elsewhere mentioned as consisting of "German silver, etc." Keely elaborated a system of inducing great range of motion on metallic masses by sympathetic negative attraction, and by periodic vibratory change of their neutral centers instantly depolarized them, thus securing rotation.

232

Trexnonar

It took Keely eight years to perfect the Trexar and the Trexnonar (Trexar used with nine nodes, the first three of silver, the second three of gold and the third three of platinum). He states that during the time he was perfecting the Trexnonar the intermissions of vibratory transmission through the wire were so frequent and of such length, preventing continuity of mechanical motion, that he was about to give up when a seeming accident revealed the truth of his former theory of the law governing the atomic triplets in their association. He states that compound negative vibration of the neutral centers of the molecules in the Trexar and Trexnonar causes antagonism by differentiation and the attractive power of aggregation becomes radiant force with immense rotational velocity, carrying the "force" beyond the molecular inner one-third sphere of coincidence.

When using the Trexar or Trexnonar, a "slight tap on the Chladni wave plate" accelerates the normal molecular frequency from 20,000 to 180,000 or 9 times. The sectional ratio is 3:6:9 or $(9/_3)^2$ or 9 times. Here the nine nodes touch the extreme end, and next to the mass being operated on, in which position they are not in use.

"Now if we shift a gold node along the third or platinum section the oscillatory multiplication will be 9x9 or 81 times the normal 20,000 or 1,620,000 oscillations per second. A gold node shifted over the extreme section will hold the frequency to 1,620,000 per second with the introductory chord of B third octave."

"When using nine nodes, silver, gold and platinum nodes come in the order given, but when associating the seventh node (Trisexar) the gold node comes first and platinum, its third higher, comes last. I always end with the triplet higher."

"Using the second node of platinum raises this frequency to the 81st power, or $1,620,000^{81}$ or far beyond computa-

Harmony is concerned with chords, and every chord is a combination of intervals sounded simultaneously. Any systematic study of harmony must therefore begin with an examination of intervals. The intervals that form the basis of music, and their measurements relative to one another are as follows:

Unison	1 : 1
Schisma	10240 : 10125
Comma (Minor)	10240 : 10125
Diaschisma	10240 : 10125
Komma	81 : 80
Comma of Pythagoras	81 : 80
Comma (Major)	81 : 80
Enharmonic Diesis	128 : 125
Enharmonic	128 : 125
Chromatic Diesis	25 : 24
Semitone Minimus	25 : 24
Minor Semitone	25 : 24
Semitone or Diesis	25 : 24
Lesser Chromatic Semitone	25 : 24
Leimma (Plato, Theon)	256 : 243
Pythagorean Semitone	256 : 243
Greater Chromatic Semitone	135 : 128
Semitone Medius	135 : 128
Chromatic Semitone	135 : 128
Semitone Maximus	27 : 25
Major Semitone	16 : 15
Limma	16 : 15
Diatonic Semitone	16 : 15
Apotome Pythagorica	2187 : 2048
Minor Second	27 : 25
Minor Tone	10 : 9
Smaller Step or Minor Tone	10 : 9
Greater Step or Minor Tone	9 : 8
Major Second	9 : 8
Sesquioctave	9 : 8
Major Tone	9 : 8
Augmented Second	75 : 64
Minor Third	6 : 5
Sesquiquintan	6 : 5
Major Third	5 : 4
Sesquiquartan	5 : 4
Diminished Fourth	32 : 25
Augmented Third	125 : 96
Perfect Fourth	4 : 3
Sesquitertan	4 : 3
Augmented Fourth	25 : 18
Tritone	45 : 32
Diminished Fifth	64 : 45
Diminished Fifth	36 : 25
Perfect Fifth	3 : 2
Trihemitone	3 : 2
Augmented Fifth	25 : 16
Minor Sixth	8 : 5
Major Sixth	5 : 3
Augmented Sixth	125 : 72
Harmonic Seventh	7 : 4
Dominant or Minor Seventh	16 : 9
Minor Seventh	9 : 5
Tonic Seventh	9 : 5
Major Seventh	15 : 8
Diminished Octave	48 : 25
Augmented Seventh	125 : 64
Octave	2 : 1
Minor Ninth	32 : 15
Major Ninth	9 : 4
Harmonic Minor Tenth	7 : 3
Minor Tenth	12 : 5
Major Tenth	5 : 2
Perfect Eleventh	8 : 3
Harmonic Eleventh	11 : 4
Augmented Eleventh	45 : 16
Perfect Twelfth	3 : 1
Augmented Twelfth	25 : 8
Minor Thirteenth	16 : 5
Harmonic Thirteenth	13 : 4
Major Thirteenth	10 : 3
Harmonic Fourteenth	7 : 2
Dominant Fourteenth	32 : 9
Tonic Fourteenth	18 : 5
Major Fourteenth	15 : 4
Double Octave	4 : 1

tion and represents the effect of only two nodes."

"Transmitting the order of sympathetic atomic vibration through a three-node transmitter (Trextrinar) induces interatomic percussion re- sulting in triple atomic subdivision not by oscillation of the atoms across their diameter but by infinite acceleration of the atomic film or etheric capsule, and at the same time permitting the extension of atomic vibration far enough to set free the gaseous atomic element. (This last must refer to the force generated by multiplication of vibratory frequencies in the Trexar as used with the different node combinations. This disintegration Keely claimed was caused chiefly by accelerating the atomic envelope.)

"To rotate the neutral center indicator of the focalizing disk (of the magnetic engine) through a soft steel attractor requires transmission of the full triple-triple chord, or 156,057,552,198,220,-000 corpuscular oscillations per second, resulting in 110 revolutions per minute on the neutral center indicator. This is only multiplication by the one gold node."

"By using the second node of platinum we can raise this frequency to its 81st power, or $156,057,552,198,220,-000^{81}$ or infinitely beyond computation. This frequency represents the effect of only two nodes."

"I have induced rotation up to 123 revolutions per second on a neutral indicator, which required billions of vibrations per second, but even this frequency is only a minute fraction of the frequencies governing the vitality of the far-luminous centers."

"The compounding of the triple-triple or chords in three octaves, will give from the ninth node a frequency that, set down in figures, would represent a number a mile long."

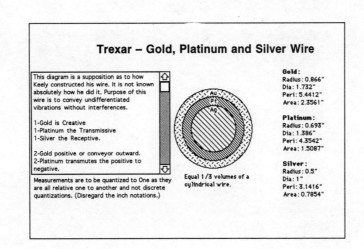

Trexar – Gold, Platinum and Silver Wire

This diagram is a supposition as to how Keely constructed his wire. It is not known absolutely how he did it. Purpose of this wire is to convey undifferentiated vibrations without interferences.

1-Gold is Creative
1-Platinum the Transmissive
1-Silver the Receptive.

2-Gold positive or conveyor outward.
2-Platinum transmutes the positive to negative.

Measurements are to be quantized to One as they are all relative one to another and not discrete quantizations. (Disregard the inch notations.)

Equal 1/3 volumes of a cylindrical wire.

Gold:
Radius: 0.866"
Dia: 1.732"
Peri: 5.4412"
Area: 2.3561"

Platinum:
Radius: 0.693"
Dia: 1.386"
Peri: 4.3542"
Area: 1.5087"

Silver:
Radius: 0.5"
Dia: 1"
Peri: 3.1416"
Area: 0.7854"

Keely's Secrets

A CORNER IN KEELY'S WORKSHOP, SHOWING HALF OF HIS SPHERICAL ETHERIC ENGINE

JOHN KEELY
A Personal Interview

(Scientific Arena, January 1887)

From a personal interview with Mr. Keely in his laboratory in Philadelphia, the associate editor of THE ARENA gathered the data for the following brief sketch of his life and lobors.

Born in Philadelphia, September 3, 1837, he suffered the loss of both parents in his infancy, his mother never recovering from his birth, and his father dying before John was three years old.

From the this time his home was with his grandmother and an aunt. But the latter dying before he was sixteen, and the former a year later, the young man was thus early throuwn upon his own resources. His educational opportunities were limited to the city schools of Philadelphia, which he left at the age of twelve to take up the battle of life, not as "the dumb driven cattle," but "as a hero in strife."

Mr. Keely states that from his earliest recollection he was drawn to the study of sound as related to force, and commenced his first systematic investigation when hardly ten years of age, making his first encouraging discovery at thirteen. As a child he noticed how powerfully windows often were agitated by the heavy tones of an organ, and this led him to place various objects about the room, suspending glass dishes, etc., and then watch for any effect that might be produced by the various chords he was able to secure by the combination of different tones. He soon found that certain chords invariably resulted in the forcible agitation of objects at a distance. His earliest mechanism for noting the uniform force of sound vibrations was a steel bar set full of pins of various lengths, while his first "resonator," or "intensifier," consisted of a shingle screwed to two hollow wooden tubes. The first "engine" was a simple ring of steel with 300 pins set into it, and this first wheel ran in an open box, into and through which an observer was free to look while the wheel was in motion.

For upward of sixteen years Mr. Keely pursued his investigations in the effort to work out his discovery, using the two elements *water* and *air* in connection with sound vibrations.

And during this period of progressive research, writes the inventor, every medium known to science was thoroughly investigated to find what, if any, sympathetic link of association could be brought to bear on the phenomenal conditions that controlled this true but then paradoxical medium, but all the highest concentrative efforts proved unavailing toward inducing even the lowest condition of molecular sympathetic association or assimilation.

The sympathetic atomic flows induced even by the first order of vibratory disassociation, using an atmospheric medium in conjunction with an aqueous, one of thirty-three per cent, showed a condition of tenuity infinitely greater than electricity. These conditions have been successfully proven by passing the flow through fifteen inches of solid glass with as much freedom as if the glass was not present - using a steel rod, three-sixteenths of an inch in diameter and three feet long, as a transmitter, the steel rod being pointed on the other end, and having the point bearing on the center of these glass plates, the plate being two feet square. If this is not a triumph over electrical tenuity, where will you find it?

And, again, passing into the first etheric by certain compound chords vibratorily induced even by percussion the luminous field is revealed and an etheric light of a most beauteous character is evolved (not phosphorescent if you please), but one that passes through

Universal Laws Never Before Revealed: Keely's Secrets

opaque bodies - leaving no shadow. I am reserving these experiments for my closing exhibition which I intend associating with and showing up the conditions governing planetary suspension, and the music required to harmonize with the spheres - celestial music, I call it.

IN the liberation of etheric ozone an apparatus of wonderful strength and peculiar mechanical parts had to be used, and the difficulty of conceiving such a one can only be appreciated properly by knowing that an atomic percussive resistance has to be controlled of over 110,000 pounds per square inch to effect it. At this point the second order of etheric luminosity presents itself of wonderful intensity.

The condition necessary to produce this effect is to induce an antagonistic relation between the liberators, chords of masses, and chord of mass of one of the steel spheres, used for that purpose (of which there are two), the negative one as the introductory one, of $33^1/_3$ against $66^2/_3$, or $66^2/_3$ against 100 = of the volume of 100, on any and all molecular masses.

These conditions produce the highest order of repellant antagonism at the point of unition. The fact of the sympathetic chord leading the antagonistic ones on the triple introductory vibratory impulse accounts for the wonderful percussion that takes place at the point of repulsion and thus breaks up and subdivides on the compound etheric position, and it is at this point that high luminiferous ether is evolved, as also etheric ozone. The spheres that carry this rotating force contain each nearly four hundred pounds of decarbonized steel to carry a volume of the size of an ordinary billiard ball. Three years of experiment was absorbed in getting the proper transmitting leads and compressors necessary to hold under control the force during its evolution, and yet the cry has been, why don't Keely hurry up and get through?

I thank God that the season of experiment is over, and that the great finale is near at hand.

Here is Mr. Keely's statement of the manipulation of liberators to produce the effect above described:

"First, the arrangement of the quadruple chords - on turret, first, A flat, first octave; second B flat, second octave, $33^1/_3$ of a tone below the harmonic; third, B flat on the third octave, $66^2/_3$ of a tone above the inharmonic; and fourth, E flat on the fourth octave, $1/_3$ of a tone below the full harmonic. This arrangement coincides with the chord-mass of the wave plate when free of percussion; but percussion induces in conjunction with the intensification of the 640 forks - a compound degree of atomic antagonism, which must be governed by the rotating nest of sympathizer in the head of liberators to induce sympathetic disassociation by sympathetic association. This setting only applies to the liberation of ozone. The settings of the liberator can be varied hundreds of millions of times."

The first gratifying result in the direction of a solution and its practical application was called the "Hydro-Pneumatic-Pulsatting-Vacuuo-Engine." With this device Mr. Keely was able to produce a power of 500 pounds to the square inch, as shown by the best pressure gauges. Out of this first success sprang the present enterprise in 1872. Before discarding the use of water in the production of his force, twelve "generators" were copnstructed varying in weight from 175 pounds up to 34,000 pounds, with a "receiver" weighing 7,000 pounds additional! and by which he was able to develop the enourmous power of 30,000 pounds to the square inch.

For this "generator" seven or eight engines were constructed, with varying success in their operation. They all would "run," but not to the satisfaction of this indefatigable worker. At last, about four years ago, the discovery was made that air alone was better than the combined air and water before employed. This at once resulted in important changes in the mechanism. The clumsy generator of several tons weight gave place to the lighter "liberator." Of these, three have been constructed, each one more slight than its predecessor, until that at present in his laboratory weights less than 150 pounds, while the inventor has in process of construction the foureth and last one, which "is a perfect machine of its kind," weighing less than seventy-five pounds, and with which he expects to produce a greater force than has ever before been shown.

Some idea of the wide experimental field that has been covered by this tireless man may be gained by Mr. Keely's statement that "since 1872 there have been over thirty changes in the progressive development of the *mechanical* to reach the present, and what I call the perfect system." And as many as 124 different machines or "engines" have been constructed in experimenting with one "liberator." The reader will readily believe Mr. Keely's statement that these researches and experiments have "absorbed over a quarter of a million dollars, along with more than twenty-five years of the most intense study and unremitted application."

In trying to get a clear idea of the nature of his new force from the lips of the only man living capable of explaining it, the discoverer himself, one must labor at the outset with this - to me - insurmountable difficulty, Mr. Keely talks with the rapid fluency begotten of his thirty years' study, and consequent familiarity with a subject that is wholly new to his listener, while his thoughts are often clothed in words rarely joined together in framing a sentence. As an illustration. In giving a description of the nature of his force and what has been involved in the multitudinous changes necessitated in its *development - omitting all thought of the methods of its practical application,* which has ever been a problem of itself - Mr. Keely says, "The different conditions include the change of the mediums for disturbing equilibrium under different mediums of intensifing vibration as associated with them progressively from the molecular to the interetheric: first, percussion; second, undulation; third, vibratory undulation; fourth, vibratory percussion; fifth, water and air; sixth, air alone." Now let the reader imagine the above statement poured into him at the rate of 250 words per minute, with no stop for refreshments, and he will ex-

perience solid relief to be assured by Mr. Keely that he is preparing for publication a complete explanation of these various changes. It is simply impossible to reproduce more than a fraction of what is freely put at one's disposal a chat of an hour with this remarkable man, but here are the simple facts as they appear to the writer.

It is a commonly observed phenomenon that sound of a certain tone produces a response in any body having a corresponding vibrational number. Witness the responsive vibration of the piano string, when its corresponding tone is sounded several feet away, or the sympathetic vibration of one tuning fork in response to another at a distance, and the beautiful fact of the window responding to a distance steam whistle at a particular pitch of its tone, as described by Dr. Hall in THE MICROCOSM, vol. III, p. 377. Taking these basic facts as a complete evidence of the existence fo such a substantial *force* as sound, Mr. Keely set to work to secure by a combination of tones a uniform chord which he terms the *"etheric"* through which he should be able *always* to obtain that degree of force capable of mechanical effect.

If sound of any quality exerts a force capable of causing a stretched steel wire, like a piano-string, several feet distant to sway to and fro, in one perfect responsive vibration, why cannot the process be multiplied? and why may not the fact involved be developed and utilized? This was the problem. In its slow but sure solution Mr. Keely claims to have uncovered many curious and valuable facts, for instance: in the responsive vibrations superinduced by the mighty force of this etheric chord, he discovered that 42,800 vibrations per second communicated to common quartz caused its immediate disintegration, while metal will successfully withstand the enormous force of 240,000 vibrations per second. Here is the formula by which he expresses the fact he claims above, "the first etheric chord on the first octave induces 42,800 vibrations per second," or a force sufficient to disintegrate quartz.

Said Mr. Keely, "I can attach a com-

Universal Laws Never Before Revealed: Keely's Secrets

rious and valuable facts, for instance: in the responsive vibrations superinduced by the mighty force of this etheric chord, he discovered that 42,800 vibrations per second communicated to common quartz caused its immediate disintegration, while metal will successfully withstand the enormous force of 240,000 vibrations per second. Here is the formula by which he expresses the fact he claims above, "the first etheric chord on the first octave induces 42,800 vibrations per second," or a force sufficient to disintegrate quartz.

Said Mr. Keely, "I can attach a common steel wire to a steel bar of the chord of B flat, and associate with it two more bars of the same chord, and bringing them into contact with ton of quartz, disintegrate it in fifteen seconds."

Curious thought, is it not, that this man is *bug* of the "hum" species? Yet this is the chargereiterated frequency in public print, and not only is he denounced as a "crank," but all he claims and all he exhibts is declared to be a delusion and a fraud by those who do not know the man or cannot understand his work.

But what *object* to be a crank? What *motive* to give his life to the perpetration of a fraud so stupendous as to secure the everlasting execration of his name, remembered only to be detested?

A poor lad reared in obscurity and privation, in early childhood drawn to these unique researches, and having caught a glimpse of the possibilities involved, he toiled on, concentrating every energy, devoting every resource, deprived of every enjoyment, often destitute of the conforts that his skill, turned into other channels, would quickly and abundantly have provided, for SIXTEEN YEARS he *kept* on ALONE *and unaided.*

Love of notoriety? Odd way to enjoy it, cloistered for years alone with an inspiration! Greed of gain? Yet struggling with want when he might have enjoyed abundance! Since the formation of a company to aid in the development of his invention, consuming a fortune yet accounting for every dollar in labor or materials, and turning into the treasury $50,000 of his own (the proceeds of the sale of a personal interest), with the quiet remark. "It will be needed. You can repay it when I have completed the invention." Such facts should go a long way in refuting the cry of "fraud," "notoriety," "greed," and "crank."

"But he has been so long about it and always completing it within sixty days, yet never completed.

"Well, all honor to him for his exhaustless tenacity; and if he,to whom the completion and final demonstration of such vast claims would bring so much of honor, wealth and fame, can afford to wait,why should the"fraud"shouting public become so impatient at the delay of a "bug" to "hum"?

In personal appearance Mr. Keely is a splendid specimen of the *genus homo.* Tall, straight, broad-shouldered, and muscular. In manner he is courteous, frank and genial, cordial and generous with friends, keen and cautious with enemies, his presence is always magnetic, and so surely as his discoveries are the most stupendous ever given to man to accomplish, his memory will live while men cherish with pride the names of great benefactors.

"My system, in every part and detail, both in the developing of this power and in every branch of its utilization, is based and founded on *sympathetic vibration*. In no other way would it be possible to awaken or develop this force, and equally impossible would it be to operate my engine upon any other principle."

John Keely, 1888

A Second Visit To Mr. Keely

by Dr. Hall
editor of The Scientific Arena

On the 24th of July, after our August ARENA had gone to press, we received a letter from Mr. Collier informing us that the large engine (250 horsepower) had been completed, and that Mr. Keely desired us to witness its exhibition at four o'clock that afternoon. So, in company with Mr. Hudson, the associate editor, and Dr. Richmond, of this city, we took the eleven o'clock train to Philadelphia. Promptly at the time designated, we repaired to the shop in North 20th Street, and were cordially welcomed by Mr. Keely and a number of the stockholders present, who congratulated THE ARENA for its fair and faithful report of the previous exhibition, and its description of the new motor, as printed in the July issue. Mr. Keely pronounced it the only rational and consistent description of his invention that had yet appeared in any scientific journal.

As on the previous occasion, the shop was well filled with earnest admirers of Mr. Keely and seekers after knowledge concerning the working of his engine, which now stood completed in its enlarged form in the middle of the room, ready to astonish one of the most anxious and expectant assemblies ever congregated in a room of similar space. Although we had witnessed the previous tests, we are free to confess that our curiosity on the present occasion was even more on tiptoe than at the former exhibition since, as everybody knew, the final and triumphant success of the Keely motor as a revolutionizing invention was to depend largely on the working of the formidable apparatus now ready to demonstrate its powers.

The first thing that attracted our attention was the jaded and carworn look of Mr. Keely, who declared that he had been working almost night and day to get this engine ready, since we bade him good-bye at the previous exhibition, and that he was so nearly worn out he had barely strength enough left to give the present demonstration. Still, as new visitors crowded into his shop, and expectation began to effervesce into animated conversation all over the room, the old fire commenced showing itself in Mr. Keely's face, and he soon forgot that he was tired.

Those who will revert to the July ARENA[1] and read our explanations of the liberating apparatus and the engine at the previous exhibition, will not need a preliminary word from us except to consider the present hollow sphere, constituting the engine proper, of about eight or ten times the capacity of the one previously employed, it being fully four feet in diameter, with its frame and other parts correspondingly massive. And we must not forget here to state that, in addition to the globular cylinder and its trunnions, there was in this large apparatus a supplementary shaft telescoped through the center of the revolving trunnion, its inner end passing into the interior cavity of the great four-foot copper sphere. On the outer end of this supplementary shaft were secured two great steel Chladni disks nearly three feet in diameter.

These resonators or wave-plates were placed about eight or ten inches apart, and between them was secured the belt pulley. This supplementary shaft, as it seems, revolves independently of the great sphere and its rotating trunnions, and when they are in motion it makes exactly *five* rotations to the sphere's one. What could have been the object of this supplementary shaft and how its

Universal Laws Never Before Revealed: Keely's Secrets

greater velocity could possibly have been effected (being apparently loosely telescoped into the trunnion attached to the rotating sphere), were problems incomprehensible to anybody present save Mr. Keely himself.

On opening the exhibition, as on the previous occasion, the etheric force for driving the machinery was generated in the usual way, by first getting the liberator in tune or harmony with its various parts in what Mr. Keely now designates the "mass-chord," by which he means the average chord of the mass of all the resonators of the apparatus, including the tuning forks, Chladni plates, resonating tubes, and steel wire rods. When this has been accomplished to the satisfaction of Mr. Keely's precise ear, the bowing of the forks began, and it was but a minut more when the force was announced as present, and was also demonstrated to be present by turning the valve-wheel of the receiver which had been previously shown to be empty, when out rushed a hissing discharge of the "etheric" vapor resembling the sound of a small jet of high-pressure steam, but leaving nothing in the atmosphere of the room to mark its presence.

As on previous occasions, this power was first applied to the lifting of weights, and at the second attempt more than 22,000 pounds to the square inch were raised as explained in our july report. Mr. Keely's assistant then stood on the outer end of the long arm of the weighted lever without counteracting the pressure of the vapor, proving it to exert more than 25,000 pounds to the square inch. All present cheered Mr. Keely at this successful demonstration of power fully up to everything he had claimed.

But as the old stockholders there present, who had frequently witnessed this feature of the experiments, were becoming impatient to see the operation of their long looked-for perfect engine, we suggested to Mr. Keely the propriety of passing over all minor tests, however interesting to strangers and let the impa-

tient friends of the motor see for themselves at last realize the accomplishment of their long-cherished dreams. THes request was at once complied with, the force being diverted from the weighted lever to the stationary trunnion of the great sphere through a number of small receivers (all previously shown to be empty) by means of a diminutive copper tube having a hole passing through it no larger than a small knitting needle, a section of which is now before us as we write.

When the connections had all been properly secured, Mr. Keely turned the valve wheel at the stationary trunnion of the engine, and as quick as thought the suplementary shaft with its Chladni plates started with a velocity of rotation that was simply frightful, and to which the great copper sphere responded in the ratio of one to five, itself making a rotation velocity so great as to be anything but assuring to the nerves of those present. As proof of this, the reader should have heard the ominous humming roar of the various parts of this mighty machine as they whirled, felt that brick building shake to its foundations, and seen the crowd of brave investigators, including THE ARENA delegation, philosophically piling themselves up close together in the securest corners of the room out of range of the copper globe's centrifugal menace, while the great calm figure of the ruling spirit of the occasion, monarch of all he surveyed, stood at the throttle to say to the terrible force - Thus far shalt thou go and no further.

It was a relief to all present when, after about two minutes of roaring suspense, he reversed the valve wheel and slowed down the moster globe so that those present might safely approach and examine it in motion with its one-to-five complexity of rotation. "Well, that beats the world," was the simultaneous exclamation of more than thirty voices as soon as the roar had ceased sufficiently to let them be heard.

This experiment was repeated over and over, till no one present, who had witnessed the tremendous velocity of the sphere, and the five-fold velocity of the Chladni-plates, resembling the action of enormous circular saws, could doubt the actual presence of at least 250 horse power of working energy, while that prodigious force was in operation.

At the close of the exhibit Mr. Keely was asked many questions concerning the working of his engine, all of which je answered off-hand, in a manner to astonish his visitors even as much as they had been astonished by the working of the engine. One man asked how many times he would have to draw the fiddle-bow across the tuning forks to generate force enough to send a train of cars from Philadelphia to New York? "Once - only once," was the emphatic response of Mr. Keely! A dozen pair of eyes that had been focused upon Mr. Keely's suddenly turned upon each other on mute amazement. But why doubt? If the force is what Mr. Kweely describes it to be, and if it is generated as he claims, there is not a doubt of the correctness of his response; for if once drawing the bow will generate force enough to turn a locomotive wheel once around, it is evident that a small fraction of that force could readily be switched off by which to keep the bow in motion, if needed, just as the motion of the main piston of a steam locomotive automatically diverts the power alternately into the opposite ends of the cylinder.

In conversation with Mr. Collier, after the close of the exhibition, we learned that this large engine was especially built for driving a train of cars between these two great cities, and that after Mr. Keely had obtained a few weeks of needed rest and recuperation at Cape May and in the mountain, he would proceed to fit and attach the great engine to a suitable locomotive truck, and that as soon as its practical utility had been demonstrated in drawing a train of cars from Philadelphia to New York, his patents would be taken out in every country in the civilized world.

The stockholders, therefore, will now look forward to this consummation of their hopes with an anxiety more intense than was ever before experienced by investors in any financial enterprise since the world began; for no other project ever before promised even a small fraction of the financial profits reasonably to be looked for from that Keely Motor stock at its present insignificant price, when this first train of cars shall reach Jersey City. The capital stock is now $5,000,000 in 100,000 shares, at the par value of $50 per share, and is owned by about 2000 shareholders located principally in New York and Philadelphia, but scattered also all over the United States and Canada. One wealthy and eminent business lady, now in England, is said to be one of the largest share owners in the company, and has done more than any other single individual by way of financial assistance in holding up Mr. Keely's hands while conducting his numerous and expensive experiments.

We have a personal invitation from Mr. Keely, as soon as he returns from his vacation, to visit his place again, and in the presence of two witnesses (Mr. Hudson, of THE ARENA, and Mr. Collier) to manipulate with our own hands certain sonorous apparatus in which machinery will be driven by the force of sound-vibrations alone, caused by drawing a fiddle-bow twenty feet away! Mr. Keely's design is to be in an adjoining room, with only a hole in the partition through which he can answer our questions or give directions, while we alone shall do the bowing of the sounding instruments, and thus witness results which no man but himself has ever before seen. We need hardly say we look forward with no little degree of pleasurable anticipation to the intellectual treat thus promised, all of which will be set forth in THE ARENA, should Mr. Keely so permit.

P.S.- Since the foregoing was in type we have had two pleasant calls from Mr. Charles B. Collier, of about an hour each, in which we have received the most elaborate information, with ex-

Universal Laws Never Before Revealed: Keely's Secrets

planatory details, of Mr. Keely's remarkable experience in the development of his motor during years past, that we had yet learned. From these conversations we learn for the first time that during the Centennial Exhibition in 1876 Mr. Keely had a "globe motor" in operation, of about two feet in diameter, which had its liberating and generating devices all within itself, and which would run for hours with great power and velocity by means of sonorous force alone as its motive power, from first touching it with the hand and moving it gently in the direction in which it was intended to rotate.

It is enough to make one's head swim to learn of all the various experimental devices contrived and tested during the past fifteen years by Mr. Keely's persistent ingenuity. Yet with all these fluctuations in the forms of his devices, Mr. Collier has remained unfaltering in his faith both in Mr. Keely and in his great discovery. No one, we assert, can converse with Mr. Collier for one minute without being deeply impressed with his sincerity and his full conviction that the "Keely Motor" is all that is claimed for it; and that its final triumph is at last assured by the successful working of his great engine.

1. See SVP January, 1988

States of Matter and Energy

"Matter is bound up energy and energy is liberated matter." Keely, 1893

Highest Frequency

		Keely	Ancient	Modern	
Most Energetic	9	Infinite Ninths	God		Least Solid
	8	Mind	Mind		
	7	Compound Interetheric	Ether	Gluon?	
	6	Interetheric	Ether	Quarkian	
	5	Etheric	Ether	Photonic	
	4	Interatomic	Fire	Plasma	
	3	Atomic	Air	Gaseous	
	2	Intermolecular	Water	Liquid	
Least Energetic	1	Molecular	Earth	Solid	Most Solid

Lowest Frequency

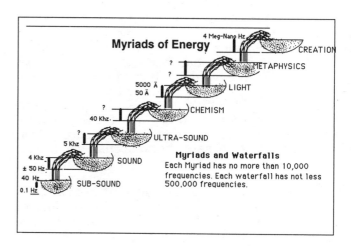

Myriads of Energy

Myriads and Waterfalls
Each Myriad has no more than 10,000 frequencies. Each waterfall has not less 500,000 frequencies.

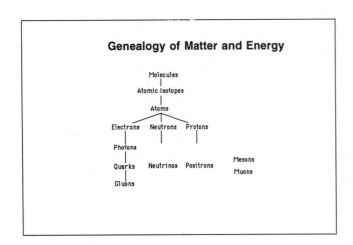

Genealogy of Matter and Energy

Mr. Keely's Researches - Sound Shown To Be A Substantial Force

by Henry B. Hudson, associate editor of
The Scientific Arena, December, 1886

Upon the 24th of September, the editors of The Arena, incompany with some then other gentlemen from New York and Philadelphia, accepted Mr. Keely's invitation to witness some experiments as his shop, of a character to illustrate the line upon which his investigations have runn all these years.

We found the great inventor in excellent health, and spirits, having but just returned from his first vacation in years. He was hard at work upon his "vibratory governor," by which he expects to secure a regulated speed, and thus overcome another of the remaining difficulties in his work.

We were assured by those familiar with the work, and in the confidence of the inventor, that the end is at hand, when the validity of the process will be established beyond controversy by the perfect and public utilization of the power in doing great and continuous work.

The introduction over, and the fes minutes' chatting and chaffing ended, the experiments proceeded.

Mr. Keely first put together his liberator, the various parts of which were scattered about the shop, and freely accessible to such handling and examination as any one was disposed to make.

And we are frank to say that such examination upon our part failed to throw any new light upon the great question at issue. We saw nothing that suggested any other origin for the power than that claimed by Mr. Keely. Certainly all the well-known and easily-distinguished phenomena of the known gases, compressed air, etc., were not present. The

various tests and experiments, showing the enormous force exerted, are all familiar to the readers of The Arena, these having been described by Dr. Halls's graphic pen in the July and September numbers, and need not be repeated here. What interested us most, and was, in fact, the object of our presence, were some experiments calculated to demonstrate the power of sympathetic vibration as applied to dynamics. For the purpose of these experiments, we were shown into an upper room about 12 x 14 feet in size, across one end of which extended a plain work-bench.

Upon this bench, extending more than half the length of it, were stretched two wires, tensioned to vibrate when agitated, the first wire giving forth a low note, the second a tone considerably higher.

Commencing at the termination of the second wire, and constituting a continuation of it, was what appeared to be a small steel rod, really consisting of three sections, so arranged that the ends touched, the extreme end of the last one, terminating against a heavy plate of glass. The stretched wires and steel rods, extending nearly the entire length of the bench, in fact, leaving just room for the copper sphere that was expected to refolve by the force of sympathetic vibration, to stand at the end.

This sphere was an unpretentious, smooth structure, about one foot in diameter, hung in a circular frame, and free to revolve in either direction, looking quite like a school globe without its maps, except that one axle terminated in a rubber bulb, like a small syringe. THis sphere was placed between the thick plate of glass against which the

Universal Laws Never Before Revealed: Keely's Secrets

rod above described terminated, and a similar late resting against the wall of the room, thus securing perfect insulation from both sides.

The four iron legs supporting the circle frame in which the sphere swung, also rested upon a common pane of glass, for which Mr. Keely sent to the store as we waited. Thus it will be observed the sphere was insulated upon the three sides of contact. Upon the bench were also two large tuning forks fixed upright in their movable pine resonant cases, standing some three feet apart, and the nearest one that distance from the sphere. Between the tuning forks stood a small brass object resembling a snail shell mounted on a pedestal, and called a resonator.

Thus much about the bench and its furnishing.

At the opposite end of the room from the bench, thrown carelessly upon the floor, was a flat ring about one inch wide, having a diameter of perhaps forty inches. Into this flat ring was fixed a large tuning fork at right angles with its flat surface. Attached to the inner edge, and extending entirely around the ring, was a brass tube half an inch in diameter, terminating where the two ends met in a small sphere, about the size of an apple. Between this ring and the bench, also resting upon the floor, was placed a small iron receiver, or "double compressor," as Mr. Keely termed it. A small copper pipe led from this receiver to the little ball or sphere of the brass tube on the inner side of the flat ring. Another copper pipe was attached to the receiver and led out into the adjoining room to the liberator. Through this long pipe, and through the "double compressor," and the short pipe was passed the "vapor" with which the brass tube in the ring on the floor was "charged."

Before the ring was charged, or any experiments were performed, Mr. Keely proceeded to get the "mass chord" of such of the party as desired to have a hand in the experiments. We can imagine the reader asking what is the "mass chord," and while we do not claim to be sufficiently enlightened to stand sponsor to the numenclature, we venture the explanation that the chord or tone to which the body or person responds or is in unison is what is meant by the mass chord. THis was the *modus operandi* of its determination - Mr. Keely put into the hand of any volunteer assistant a steel bolt (called a "sensitizer") resembling a car coupling pin, but shorter, and having a one-quarter inch hole through its length; extending from the end of this was a ten-foot hair-like wire that terminated in a reed whistle; this whistle Mr. Keely dropped into the snail-shell resonator that stood on the bench. When the bow was drawn across the tensioned wires and the tuning forks on the bench, and the sensitizer having been gently struck against something to agitate the "vibrators" within it, if the "mass" or resultant sound did not suit Mr. Keely, he handed a small steel pin or rod, picked up from a pile of various lengths lying on the bench, to the assistant, to be held in the disengaged hand. If the chord was still unsatisfactory, a longer or shorter steel rod was given to the assistant, until the tone was declared right. In one each of these steel rods was a small hole perhaps an inch deep. Every change of assistant necessitated a change of rod to be held in the hand, no two persons using the same.

When all was in readiness, the brass tube within the flat ring on the floor was charged with the force, though, during the operation, the sheet of vulcanized rubber in the top of the "double compressor," which Mr. Keely said would only yield to a pressure of 2000 pounds, was blown out with a report that indicated great power, and caused some of the brave savants present to seek positions in the remote corners.

At this point Mr. Keely passed out into the room through which entrance was gained to the experiment-room, in which all the spectators remained. The only known factors of the experiments that were in the room with Mr. Keely were the liberator and a brass tube

Mr. Keely's Researches - Sound Shown to be a Substantial Force

about four and a half inches in diameter, and perhaps eight inches deep. This piece of mechanism was supposed to be full of "resonators," and the top suggested and old-fashioned candle-mold. In exhibiting this through the window, by which he had his only communication with any of the party, Mr. Keely said as he placed it on the bench beside him, "I can give you 140 octaves with that."

Now let us recapitulate the preparations before stating the experiments. In one room, a bench with its stretched wires, and steel rods extending its length, two large tuning-forks in movable pine cases, a snail-shell resonator, and the insulated copper sphere. At the opposite end of the room, lying upon the floor, was the flat ring with one tuning fork fixed upright in it, and the brass tube charged with the vapor, upon its inner edge. IN the middle of the floor, the small "double compressor," connected by copper pipes with the brass-tube ring. NO VISIBLE OR APPARENTLY POSSIBLE CONNECTION between the bench and the revolving sphere at one end, and this "compressor" and the flat hoop at the OPPOSITE end of the room. The one dozen spectators remained in this room.

In the adjoining room were the liberator, "140 octave resonator," and Mr. Keely. Communication between the two rooms was limited to a door near the bench, which Mr. Keely left partly closed as he passed out, and a square hole, or window, at the opposite end of the partition containing the door.

At this square opening Mr. Keely took his stand - thrusting his head and shoulders through into our room, and fixing his eyes on the, thus far, stationary sphere.

Dr. Wood stepped within the circle upon the floor, grasped in one hand the "sensitizer" (from which the hair-like wire extended out into the "140 octave resonator" near Mr. Keely), and held in his other hand the steel pin of his "mass chord." Mr. Keely commanded the bow-ing of the tuning-forks, which was promptly done by volunteers, when lo! the hitherto impertubable sphere, away across the room, began to revolve, slowly at first, but with an increasing speed as the forks continued to vibrate. Dr. Woods stepped out of the circle, and the sphere stopped at once; stepping back into the circle, the sphere immediately responded.

Dr. Hall next stepped within the magic circle, the forks upon the bench, and the one upon the hoop on the floor were vibrated, and the sphere started off again, like a thing of life.

Then Mr. Charles Collier, to whom this whole experiment was also new, tried it, and the same results were as unfailing as before.

Mr. Keely next said he would exhibt the sphere revolving in response to its note upon a harmonica, without the aid of any vibrating tuning-forks. With Mr. Collier still standing within the circle, holding the "sensitizer" and "mass chord" steel pin, Mr. Keely began playing "Home, Sweet Home" upon the harmonica. Our gaze alternated between the strange musician and the responsive sphere. As soon as he sounded a certain chord the sphere began to revolv; faster and faster it speed, urged on by this mysterious power, until it attained a speed of several hundred revolution a minute. But a chord not its own quickly brought it to a standstill.

The spectators looked from one to the other in silent wonder, when Mr. Hall, with his irrepressible instinct for investigation, exclaimed: "Let me play that harmonica." "Certainly," replied the master spirit, "any one who likes may try it." Then one and another remembered some long-lost chord. But it mattered not on the sphere whether "The Girl I Left Behind Me" or :Hark, from the Tombs a Doleful Sound" was the selection: so long as the chord to which it was responsive was sounded, it whirled on; other chords might be sounded at the same time, still on it went. But if that chord was not head, no other

Universal Laws Never Before Revealed: Keely's Secrets

other sound or combination of sounds affected it in the least.

The reader can hardly appreciate, from this simple narrative of the facts, the emotions awakened by such an exhibition. The entire absence of careful preparation, for the gathering, as shown by Mr. Keely's repeated search for objects needed at various points, that should have been gathered and placed where wanted beforehand; the change made on the instant by the substitution of one article for another, that was found to be misfit or would not work, etc., all added force to the results shown, and yet cannot be reproduced on paper. Mr.

Keely asserts that these or other experiments are not devised to convert observers. He cares not what may be the conclusion of individuals or the press, being sure of the end himself, and only continues these experiments at the request of parties desirous of seeing with their own eyes the strange things thus far accomplished. And our purpose in reporting thus in detail what we saw, is served by putting into the possession of our readers all the facts in our hands, thereby enabling them to form such an opinion as in their judgement these facts seem to warrant.

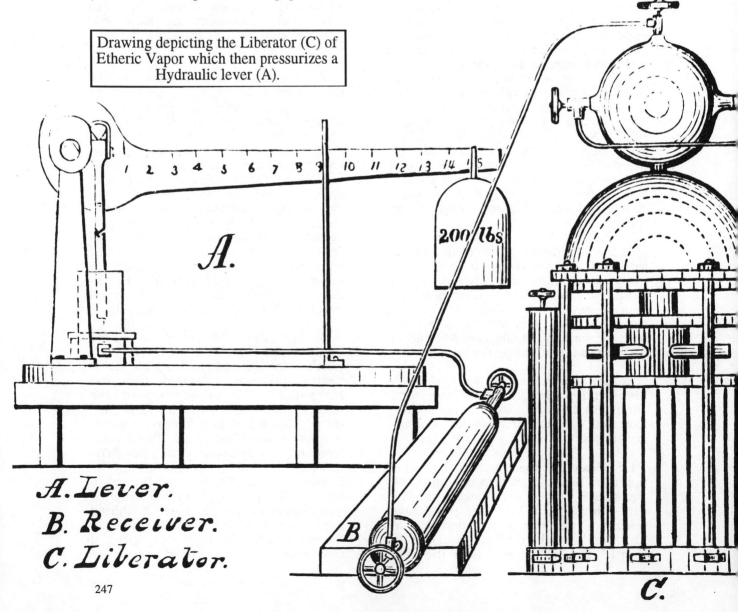

Drawing depicting the Liberator (C) of Etheric Vapor which then pressurizes a Hydraulic lever (A).

A.

200 lbs

B

C.

A. Lever.
B. Receiver.
C. Liberator.

The Keely Motor Illustrated

by Henry B. Hudson, associate editor
THE SCIENTIFIC ARENA, January, 1887

The many readers of THE ARENA who have manifested such a keen interest in the Keely Motor, will be gratified with the revelation the accompanying cuts will make to an observant eye of the great mystery the very mention of Mr. Keely's name always suggests. We can assure any one disposed to doubt their own eyes, that these cuts convey an accurate idea of the mechanism at present employed in the development of the enterprise. We feel quite confident, however, that the seeing will do about as much toward explaining the problem as the hearing has done, and not much more. The illustration may nevertheless serve to show that as Mr. Keely claims to be dealing with an original force entirely new to mechanics, his methods and machines are at least consistent in presenting an appearance as new and novel as the power they are said to accommodate. A glance at the "engine" is sufficient to show how completely the mind has become adjusted to other and totally different forms as suggested by that term; but in this case the eye is trustworthy and the thought must accommodate itself to "the new form in the old place."

In an effort to explain we will begin with the "Liberator," which is presented to us as the source of the power, and over which very severe storms of criticism have swept. This is clearly shown to be a slight structure, weighing perhaps 150 pounds, easily and frequently moved about the room during the experiments, precluding all possibility of extraneous power being communicated during the operations so often shown.

See The Journal of Sympathetic Vibratory Physics, January, 1988 to review cuts mentioned in this article.

The reader will readily recognize the small "receiver" with a valve in each end, and a small copper pipe ($1/_{32}$ in. bore) leading to the extreme top piece of the structure. Next above this "receiver" is shown the base of the device, consisting of a plain surface of wood, upon which rests the iron ring with two tuning-forks fixed upright in its surface; in addition to the two forks are three upright devices, which in turn support each a large tuning-fork fixed into their top; resting in these three elevated forks by means of projecting bolts, is the main piece of the whole device, this being at once the largest and heaviest part. Underneath this, and fastened to it by a bolt passing through its center, may be seen the large Chladni plate of steel. Beneath this plate, and resting upon the wooden base, is shown a curious device consisting of numerous steel pins radiating from a common center. The tuning-forks, steel pins, and Chladni plate are all agitated by bowing or striking, to produce the power. The main part of the "Liberator," as shown above, is not a single section but several pieces. That part seen to consist of a row of perpendicular tubes, is simply a collar of brass resonant tubes, set over the iron body. Above this is seen another smaller but similar device, except the brass resonators are set in horizontally. Above this again is seen the outer rim (about $2^{1}/_{2}$ inches wide) of another design, also full of resonators, while the next story is seen to resemble three funnel-like projections, surmounted by a good likeness of a lamp-shade, and crowing all is the "turret," from which the connection is made to the "receiver" by a copper pipe. The two short pipes near the top are said to be for the "positive" and "negative" flow. In the above, the reader has an ex-

Universal Laws Never Before Revealed: Keely's Secrets

cellent likeness and a fair description of the claimed origin of the great force shown by Mr. Keely.

The second cut is of the weighted lever by which Mr. Keely is able to show in simple measure the enormous force he produces.

The respective arms of the lever are about sixteen to one; that is to say, the length of the longer arm is forty-eight inches, and the shorter arm is three inches from the fulcrum; the diameter of the piston upon which the uplifting force impinges to raise the lever is $7/8$ of an inch; and its area in cross section is, accordingly, $6/10$ of an inch.

This being the case, and adding the weight of the lever, it follows that when a weight of five hundred and fifty pounds is suspended on the end of the longer arm, it requires a force of fifteen thousand seven hundred and fifty-one pounds per square inch impinging on the lower end of the piston to raise the lever.

The accompanying sectional drawing, signed by J. E. Schiedt, correctly represents the construction of the piston and the cylinder in which it works. - *Extract from report of Messrs. Linville and Le Vin.*

The third cut is quite as interesting as the first, as it presents to the eye an idea of Mr. Keely's method of applying his new force to practical uses; and I doubt not that whatever question the reader may hold about a new force, it will readily be conceded that Mr. Keely employs a new harness.

This is the engine. It runs! I have seen it running with a velocity that shook the building and seemed to threaten itself with destruction, such was its tremendous speed. And this speed was secured entirely by the introduction into its hollow interior of this same mysterious force with which the weighted lever is lifted, the cannon fired, etc. The whole sphere revolves and carries with in the large pulley or

band-wheel shown on the end of the shaft, and by this means the power may be distributed in the usual way. This shell, while hollow, is not empty but contains securely fastened to the stationary trunnion, a complicated system of cog-gearing which is said to relate only to the reversing device, by which it is made to run with equal facility in either direction, as determined only by its initial motion. The mystery of an exhaust for this unique construction is solved by the fact that it is *not airtight,* and any gas, air, steam, or other force employed to drive it, is at liberty to diffuse itself imperceptibly into the air after it has performed its work.

We have now placed before our readers the leading parts of the mechanism that greet the eye of a visitor to Mr. Keely's laboratory, together with such a statement of the details as may serve to make the illustrations intelligible, and here we might leave the matter to the unaided discussion of the interested. But we are aware of the state of the public mind touching the whole enterprise, and believe also that we understand some of the reasons that have led to if not merited the distrust with which it is generally regarded.

Let us now canvass some of this ground:

This invention comes before the world with no ordinary claims, and of course can be substantiated by no ordinary proof. For years the public have been hearing tales that put to blush the "Arabian Nights."

As a preliminary to any acceptance of this new discovery we were bidden to set aside forever all that science and mechanics have shown to be fundamental since the knowledge of man began to wrest valuable service from the coy forces of nature. The axiom, *"Ex nihilo nihil fit,"* was seemingly ruled out by a stroke of Mr. Keely's wand or bow.

The might problem of perpetual motion was quietly admitted to have been successfully solved, and treated as an unimportant corollary. We were told that the sleepless forces of cohesion and gravity slunk away abashed in the presence of a modern Jupiter who had tardily assumed the throne of his power at the bidding of this remarkable inventor. With these stupendous claims supported by such unsatisfactory proof as "vague rumor" alone afforded, it is no wonder the road to public confidence has been long and difficult.

One obstacle that has been thus far effectually prevented public confidence is the failure to give a *complete* exhibition or permit a full examination, and since the company went into the exhibition business of its own volition, the public has justly condemned the attempts upon the simple ground of what it has *failed to show*. Moreover the disjointed and contradictory accounts that reach the public as a result of these partial exhibitions to the few have been better calculated to create doubt than beget confidence.

Is the power previously stored ready for use at the will of the exhibitor, and in what part of the structure is it concealed? are the questions of earnest and tenacious discussion. It has been said by expert examiners that the "construction and organization is such that it is *incapable* of containing or concealing *any* stored power."

Now, as an aid to the cautious investigator, we will here show that this cannot be so, since *Mr. Keely claims to secrete and store, his force in this "liberator" between the time it is generated or "liberated"* by the bowing of the tuning-forks and the commencement of the work the force is shown to perform. That is, after assembling the various parts and properly adjusting them, Mr. Keely proceeds to agitate the tuning-forks for a minute, after which he exclaims: "It is vitalized, it is charged," etc., and of course from that instant until it is liberated to perform work this force is "contained or concealed" in this "liberator." Thus "any power" *can* be stored in *this* part of the mechanism. Has it ever been shown that the power which *must* be

"contained" in this liberator before any effects are produced is *a new force? I fully believe it has;* but unfortunately, not in a manner to at once and effectually answer all objections, as might readily have been done. Thus, at the examination of the various parts of this liberator on Oct. 22, by Messrs. Linville and Le Vin, in my presence, how effectually might the *conviction* of these eminent engineers have been welded into an *incontrovertible fact,* had their examination extended to the receivers and every part involved in the experiments so often made, and had such examination been immediately followed by a series of performances such as are commonly shown.

Such a test, with the identical parts examined, would have given may be seen by the fact that while Mr. Keely has been patiently and quietly working out his idea, and years before he was ready to bring it before the public, his financial managers deluged the market with 100,000 shares of stock representing a par value of $5,000,000 *without one dollar's worth of actual property behind it,* only the promise of Mr. Keely that *when* he should have produced a patentable device and secured patents, they were to be the property of the company.

A man once met a boy hurrying along with a gun. "What are you after?" asked the man. "Rabbits," said the boy. "Are you having any luck?" "First-rate." "How many have you?" "When I get the one I am after and two more I'll have three," replied the boy as he disappeared into the bush. Imagine that man making extensive preparations and inviting his friends to a rabbit stew upon the strength of the boy's enthusiasm! Why the management allow the invention to be delayed and the inventor denounced by industriously circulated reports that "it is all complete," is clearly shown by the fact that so soon as the market value of the stock reaches ten or twelve per cent, there is a great unloading, and a prominent officer of the company is one of the most active dealers, "selling for a friend," of course. But the supply of

Universal Laws Never Before Revealed: Keely's Secrets

friends is something phenomenal. Such manipulations of the stock by parties in interest has tended to arouse first the suspicion and then the contempt of financial and business men. But responsibility for this state of affairs is exactly placed by the fact that in 1881 Mr. Keely desired to secure and *lock up for five years* over half the entire stock, and the proposition was promptly rejected by the parties into whose hands the management had fallen.

Mr. Keely states that for nearly sixteen years he worked on alone before he brought his enterprise to the attention of others, and then only when compelled to do so by a lack of means to press on. Could he have gone on in his own quiet way until his work was done, or had the parties who undertook to furnish the needed funds been content to wait, and keep out of the milk-and-water line, the community would have been better pleased and the inventor better treated.

But however manifold the obstacles that were created by a premature introduction of the enterprise to the public, or have since arisen through these attempts to stimulate public interest and confidence by such partial and unsatisfactory methods as exhibiting one part to one man or set of men, and another section to other men upon a different occasion, until the community, in the absence of any consecutive or reliable statement of the affair came to regard it as a veritable delusion, the fact remains that Mr. Keely is able to demonstrate the existence of a stupendous power perfectly obedient to his will which, however unwilling men may be to accept as a new discovery, has never yet been satisfactorily accounted for by the supposition of any old and well recognized force. I can give no better statement of my own confidence in the complete validity and perfect integrity of Mr. Keely's enterprise than is afforded by the following letter of the prominent engineers, Messrs. Linville and Le Vin, of Philadelphia:

As the result of our observations upon several occasions of experiments conduct-

ed by Mr. Keely in the generation of his so-termed "etheric force," and having examined in detail his structure designated a "liberator" having immediately after such examination seen its several parts assembled and put together and connected with his "receiver," and it having been conclusively shown that such structures contained nothing but atmospheric air at normal pressure, we have seen a force generated or liberated, exerting an expansive energy of upward of 20,000 pounds per square inch, without other instrumentally in its production than the agitation of two or more tuning forks.

There was no possible connection between the power-generating structures and any extraneous source of power. There was no appreciable thermal changes either at the instant development of the power, or upon its being instantaneously exhausted into the room.

Compelled as we are to eliminate as factors in the development of this force all known agents such as heat, electricity, chemical combustion, etc., the conclusion forced upon us is that the power is developed in the manner stated by Mr. Keely, *viz.*, that the result is the disintegration of the air contained in his receivers by vibration, and the liberation of a highly attenuated vapor or ether. That Mr. Keely is dealing with compressed air or other :stored power," as has been alleged, is preposterous.

We have seen it different times the tests made by Mr. Keely of the utilization of this force as a motive power, and in view of our observations in this line, our belief is that the obstacles still remaining in the way of his practical success in running engines will be overcome by him.

Very respectfully yours,
W. Barnet Le Vin, J. H. Linville
Philadelphia, October 25, 1886.

Mr. J. H. Linville was for many years President of the Keystone Bridge Company, and is inventor and patentee of many important features in iron bridge construction. The majority of the iron bridge in use by the Pennsylvania Railroad were erected by the Keystone Bridge Company under the superintendence of Mr. Linville. He was for many years associated with the Messrs. Carnegie, of Pittsburgh, in the Union Mills and other enterprises. Mr. Linville is recognized as one of the most eminent engineers in the State of Pennsylvania.

Mr. W. Barnet Le Vin has for many years been a contractor for machinery, including steam engines, boilers, electrical plants, etc., has long been a conspicuous member of the Franklin Institute and a contributor to its journal, is a member of the American Association of Engineers, and is regarded as authority in all branches of steam engineering, and is frequently called as an expert in patent litigation involving questions pertaining to steam and electrical engineering.

Keely firing his Etheric Vapor cannon during a demonstration to the U.S. Navy at Sandy Hook. The Navy turned him down because "it was too complicated".
See other photo page 199.

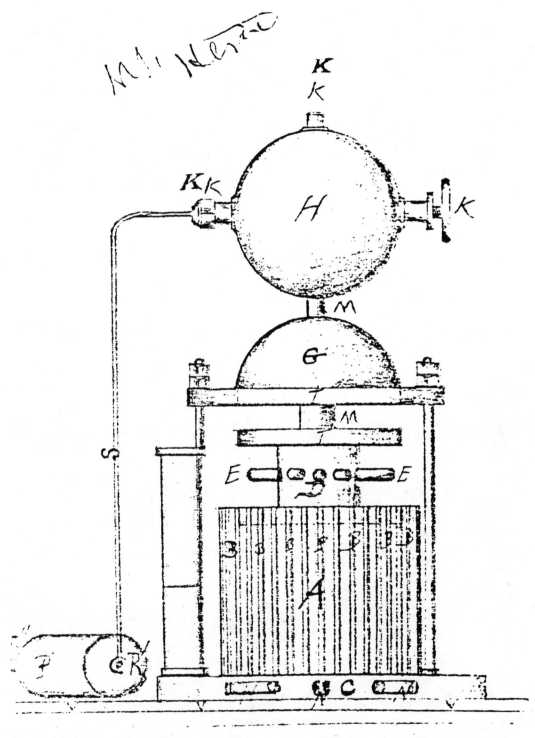

Deciphering Keely's Harmonic & Inharmonic Chords

by Dale Pond

A great mystery surrounding Keely's work has now been solved.

Keely used music notation throughout his many explanatory charts and his writings are peppered with music terminology. Little has been done over the past one hundred years that help with understanding what he was trying to convey to us. This is no longer the case.

Inherent in Sympathetic Vibratory Physics are two main thrusts of study: music and vibratory science. Music is well developed and many works can be found explaining music theory and technique. Vibratory science is becoming more and more developed every day most notably via acoustics and vibration analysis. They both deal extensively with vibration frequencies;

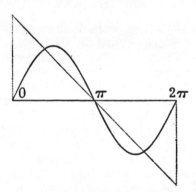

music used a shorthand notation system of notes placed on a staff while vibration analysis uses mathematical notation. Their common meeting ground is that of music synthesis or wave form synthesis. Let us take an example and explore for a moment what it may mean.

Common to both fields, as well as many others, is the conceptualized vibration commonly depicted as a sine wave.

If we assign the frequency of this sine wave as C, representing the fundamental, having a wavelength of *l,* this value can be graphically pictured as middle C on the music staff thus:

For our sample problem we are going to analyze a complex sound generated

$$y = A_0 + 96.5 \sin (\quad \theta + 76°) + 66.0 \sin (2\theta + 319°)$$
$$+ 36.5 \sin (3\theta + 337°) + 19.2 \sin (4\theta + 354°)$$
$$+ 10.3 \sin (5\theta + 330°) + 8.4 \sin (6\theta + 347°)$$
$$+ 6.4 \sin (7\theta + 354°) + 8.9 \sin (8\theta + 290°)$$
$$+ 4.3 \sin (9\theta + 252°) + 2.3 \sin (10\theta + 252°)$$
$$+ 2.2 \sin (11\theta + 230°) + 1.5 \sin (12\theta + 211°)$$

from a pipe-organ. The equation above defines the first twelve components of the wave form pictured below: The first wave form is the true wave shape as analyzed by an oscilloscope. The next 12 patterns are of the individual components or harmonics or partials, whichever term you may choose to use. Thus it can be seen that a complex periodical wave form is in reality a composite of several individual frequencies all of which are sounded at the same time as the fundamental. Thus two different instruments may sound the same note but they have a different tonal quality. A tone sounded on a string instrument

Keely's Secrets

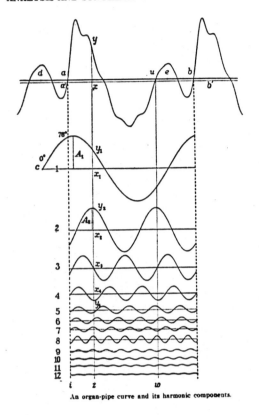

An organ-pipe curve and its harmonic components.

is different than the tone from a horn instrument even thought they sound the same fundamental. The difference is in what components are present in the sound and the amplitude of each component.

This difference in tonal quality can be shown in the following chart of different musical instruments.

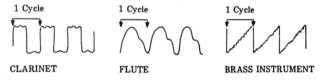

Three different waveforms.

What this means to us who want to use vibrations as a power source is this: If a digital device is required to create a sine wave, square wave or pulse wave

forms it would sound its various oscillators simultaneously according to the following chart:

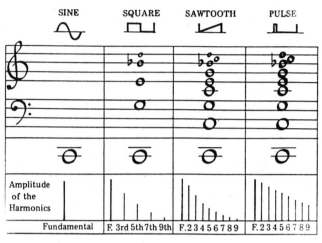

Harmonic series.

These frequencies for the sine wave form can be expressed mathematically as follows:

$$y = \frac{1}{l}\int_0^l y\,dx + \left\{ \begin{array}{l} \left[\frac{2}{l}\int_0^l y\sin\frac{2\pi x}{l}dx\right]\sin\frac{2\pi x}{l} + \left[\frac{2}{l}\int_0^l y\sin\frac{4\pi x}{l}dx\right]\sin\frac{4\pi x}{l} + \cdots \\ \left[\frac{2}{l}\int_0^l y\cos\frac{2\pi x}{l}dx\right]\cos\frac{2\pi x}{l} + \left[\frac{2}{l}\int_0^l y\cos\frac{4\pi x}{l}dx\right]\cos\frac{4\pi x}{l} + \cdots \end{array} \right.$$

Fourier Equation

All of the above work is done with octave harmonics (partials) of the fundamental. Therefore they are all periodic wave forms or wave forms having a clear distinct repeating pattern. Keely mentions the use of inharmonic wave forms. These are called *aperiodic* wave patterns or wave trains not possessing this quality of a clear repetitive pattern. These wave trains are derived from a fundamental and partials of the fundamental which are not octave components of the fundamental. A very good example of this is the music notation found on Keely's chart governing sphere rotation.

Deciphering Keely's Harmonic and Inharmonic Chords

In the literature he even goes so far as to specifically say that a sphere at rest is in perfect harmony and to cause it to rotate one must sound an inharmonic chord. On the top of his chart defining sphere rotation we see a chord of 12 notes. The musical relationship of these notes one to another are close to seconds, or what is considered in music theory as very inharmonic notes when sounded together.

If these notes are synthesized together the resulting wave form appears something like the following:

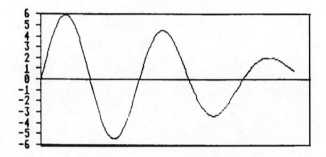

Thus we can see that Keely conceived, engineered, built and used in his researches and inventions the world's first true wave form synthesizer over 100 years ago. He was able to generate complex wave forms such as pulse and square waves using his unique devices and apparently could amplify and intensify them to a very high quantity. Keely called his device for generating these wave forms his "Disintegrator." One of his original disintegrators survives today under the care of The American Precision Museum in Windsor, Vermont. It is on display there and labeled "Keely's Etheric Force" machine. Unfortunately this surviving sample of his signal generation equipment has been partially dismembered.

1) Miller, Dayton Clarence; The Science of Musical Sounds.
2) Friend, Pearlman & Piggott; Learning Music with Synthesizers.
3) Bloomfield-Moore, Clara Jessup; <u>Keely and His Discoveries.</u> Delta Spectrum Research P. O. Box 316, Valentine, Nebraska 69201 (402) 376-1523.

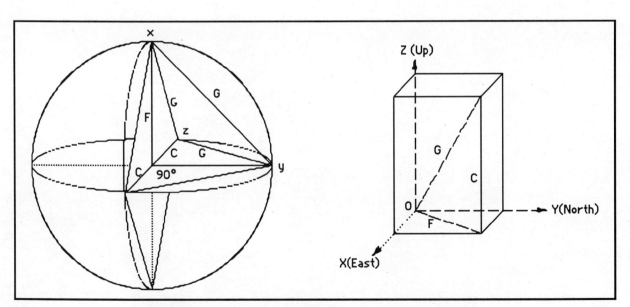

Quantum quaternions versus Hamiltonian quaternions.

This is a photograph of the original fascinating experiment where Keely moved heavy metallic weights up or down using proper vibratory chords. See drawing on page 60. See also chapter on Gravity page 134.

GLASS CONTAINING WEIGHT WHICH KEELY CLAIMED COULD BE MOVED
UP OR DOWN BY STRIKING THE ZITHER STRINGS

Keely's Triple Chords

by Dale Pond

Perhaps one of the most enigmatic and troublesome of Keely's ideas is that of his triple chords. For years the search has yielded nothing in modern vibration science that resembled his theory on this subject. Recently, there has come to my attention, through applied ultrasonics, a concept of vibration modes that very strongly resembles Keely's concept or that which we perceive to be his concept.

Keely stated that there are three modes of vibration inherent in all vibratory motions. He called these the enharmonic, harmonic and dominant. One, he said, travels in a straight line, another is a zig-zag and the third possesses an elliptical motion. In modern ultrasonic technology there are recognized and used three and sometimes a fourth mode. These are the longitudinal or compression waves, the transverse or shear waves, the Rayleigh or surface waves and the Lamb or plate waves. It looks like these may be the modes Keely was trying to identify and wrote about.

The longitudinal or compression wave (sometimes referred to as the L-wave) travels in straight lines and can be propagated through gases, liquids and solids.

The transverse or shear wave (sometimes referred to as the S-wave) travels in a manner perpendicular to the longitudinal in a back and forth motion which can very easily be described as zig-zag. This wave can be (according to the text books) be only propagated through solids and will not travel through gases and liquids. Perhaps they mean they will not travel in these forms of matter sufficient to be of use in ultrasonic techniques. More research is needed to verify this. The transverse wave has a velocity approximately $1/2$ that of the longitudinal wave but the frequency remains the same.

The surface or Rayleigh wave travels in elliptical patterns. It travels along the surface of a solid (not gases or liquids) and is easily damped out by objects on the surface. The Rayleigh waves penetrate less than a wave length into the solid and have a velocity about 9/10th of the transverse or shear wave. The frequency remains constant.

Another notable waveform is the plate of Lamb wave. It tends to travel in thin plates only such as a Chladni plate. This wave can refract into many different modes of vibration. The most notable being the symmetrical and asymmetrical modes.

The process of a vibration breaking down into these various modes is called refraction. Depending on the angle at which the impinging or incident vibration strikes an object it will refract or differentiate into one or more of these vibration modes. It is interesting to visualize what happens when a high frequency vibration strikes a spherical object such as a rain drop. The **ONE FORCE** differentiates or refracts into seven distinct and readily identifiable wave lengths. Apparently the velocity of these seven ranges of frequencies remains the same. Another interesting occurence is that because of this differentiation or refraction the undifferentiated chord becomes triune in manifestation, i.e., from it (the rainbow for instance) we get three basic colors, red, blue and yellow. These three colors possess separate and distinct traits. The red has what Keely called thermism

Universal Laws Never Before Revealed: Keely's Secrets

- it has heat latent in it. The blue has what he called chemism or the ability to excite chemical activity. The yellow appears to possess only a capacity of light.

Why can we not assume an undifferentiated sound beam also possesses these latent abilities? Perhaps they do - perhaps one day we will discover some hidden things not witnessed by good and accepted physics. From the above we know that an undifferentiated beam of vibratory energy can and does refract into other forms and manifestations. A fundamental also evolves into other forms not unlike what we have seen in some previous articles. Take for instance the Fibonacci series evolving from a fundamental of 1, then progressing into an octave Or as 1 is to 2 then into a Perfect Fifth or 2 is to 3 then into a Major Sixth or as 3 is to 5, etc.
The sequence is:

1:1	Unison
1:2	Octave
2:3	Perfect Fifth
3:5	Major Sixth
5:8	Minor SIxth
8:13	Major Sixth
13:21	Minor Sixth

The rainbow differentiation takes on slightly different sequence in its evolution:

1:1 Unison	White or no color
1:2 Octave	Black
2:3 Perfect Fifth	Red to Blue
4:5 Major Third	Yellow to Blue
5:6 Major Third	Red to Yellow

I wonder what we would find if the three modes of ultrasonic vibrations were compared as the ones above? If the wave lengths, velocities, heat and chemical effects were comparatively analyzed would we find similar intervals? I'd almost bet on it.

Taking the fundamental wavelength or the wave length of the longitudinal wave as 1 we see that the transverse wave length is almost half of that length. Would or could this be termed an octave? There is a great discrepancy in

music theory when Keely says the octave is not really an actual doubling of rates but is slightly less than that. In the tempered (tampered) scale we use an exact doubling of frequency (halving the wavelength) because the numbers work out nicely for us and partials aren't generated such that a discordant note or sound isn't created.

Philosophically speaking, if these terms equaled each other then no new thing could be evolved - progressive evolution would cease. There must be a small difference that can be expanded into a reality of its own. A complete and full circle would be perfect harmony or equation of forces. Perhaps this points to the adage that progress comes only through adversity.

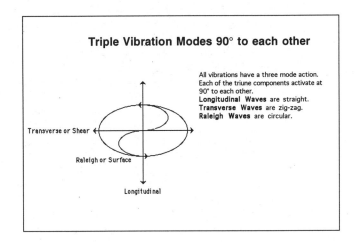

Triple Vibration Modes 90° to each other

All vibrations have a three mode action. Each of the triune components activate at 90° to each other.
Longitudinal Waves are straight.
Transverse Waves are zig-zag.
Raleigh Waves are circular.

Transverse or Shear

Raleigh or Surface

Longitudinal

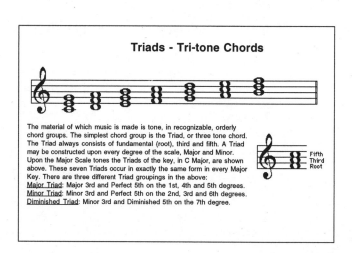

Triads - Tri-tone Chords

The material of which music is made is tone, in recognizable, orderly chord groups. The simplest chord group is the Triad, or three tone chord. The Triad always consists of fundamental (root), third and fifth. A Triad may be constructed upon every degree of the scale, Major and Minor. Upon the Major Scale tones the Triads of the key, in C Major, are shown above. These seven Triads occur in exactly the same form in every Major Key. There are three different Triad groupings in the above:
<u>Major Triad</u>: Major 3rd and Perfect 5th on the 1st, 4th and 5th degrees.
<u>Minor Triad</u>: Minor 3rd and Perfect 5th on the 2nd, 3rd and 6th degrees.
<u>Diminished Triad</u>: Minor 3rd and Diminished 5th on the 7th degree.

Fifth
Third
Root

KEELY'S
Acoustic ✦ Theoretical ✦ Charts,

EMBRACING THE

PHILOSOPHY OF PLANETARY SUSPENSION,
MECHANICAL ROTATION BY NEGATIVE ATTRACTION,
CONTROL OF MIND OVER MATTER.

Being an Exposé of all the Conditions Governing the Harmonic Chords of Harmonic Coincident-Sympathy between the Neutral Centres of
Planetary Masses, as, also, the High Sympathetic Conditions of the Physical Organism as Associated
with Mind-Flow on the Luminiferous Track, viz.

MIND-CONTROL OVER MATTER,

Both Accordant and Discordant, with all the Progressive Links of Molecular, Inter-Molecular, Atomic, Inter-Atomic, Etheric, Inter-Etheric, and
Compound Inter-Etheric Positions.

Author's Notice
The following charts first appeared
in my hands as very poor quality
photocopies. I have never seen the
originals nor do I know who has them.
These charts were scanned, edited
and printed at 600 dpi. Some errors
have crepted into some of the images
due to the poor originals. Perhaps some
time in the future a book dealing specifically
with these images can be produced.
Dale Pond, December 16, 1994

By JOHN W. KEELY.

PHILADELPHIA.

1887.

261   Keely operating the Liberator to drive the Musical Sphere.

Symbols and conditions of Vibratory Streams.

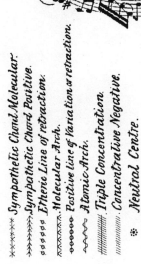

1. Ab first Octave.
2. Quadruple chord of Bb 3rd Octave.
3. Etheric chord of Bb 3rd Octave.
4. Etheric chord of C 1st Octave.
5. Etheric chord of D 2nd Octave.
6. Etheric chord of E# 3rd Octave.
7. Chord of radiation. Bb 1st Octave.
8. Chord of equation. Bb 5th Octave.
9. Neutral chord. Bb any Octave.
10. Chord of aggregation. Molecular. Bb 4.
11. Sympathetic chord of transmission.

Designed by
— JOHN W. KEELY. —
January 1896.

×××××× Sympathetic Chord. Molecular.
>>>>>> Sympathetic Chord Positive.
ºººººº Etheric Line of retraction.
ΛΛΛΛ Molecular Arch.
ºººººº Positive line of Variation or retraction.
~~~~~ Atomic Arch.
Triple Concentration.
:::::: Concentrative Negative.
✳ Neutral Centre.
〜〜〜 Dead Lines.

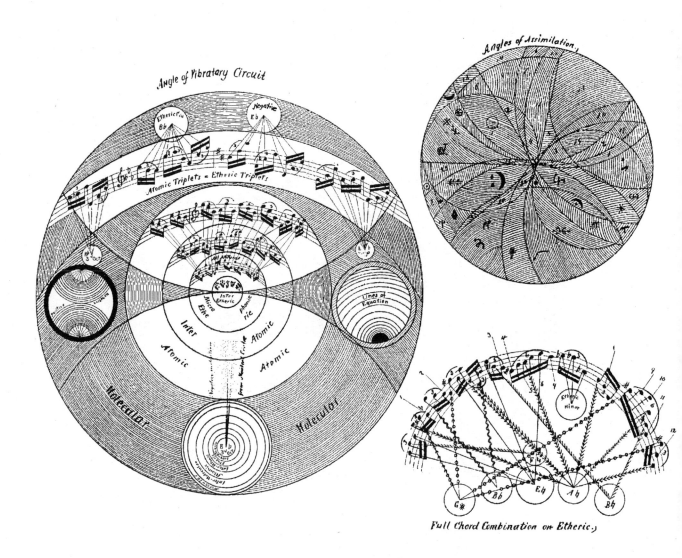

Angle of Vibratory Circuit

Angles of Assimilation

Full Chord Combination on Etheric

263

Chart of the angles of interference and coincidence trigeminal.

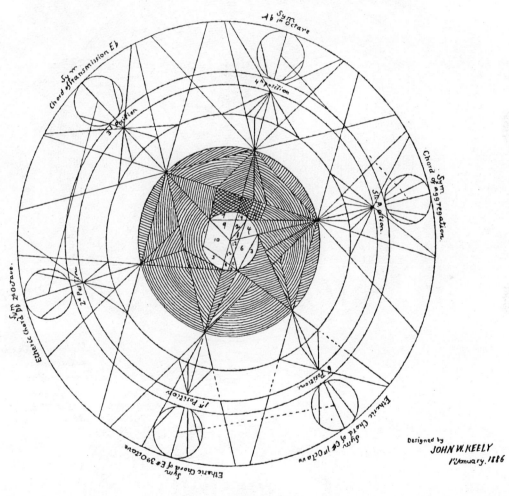

Designed by
JOHN W. KEELY
1st January, 1886

264

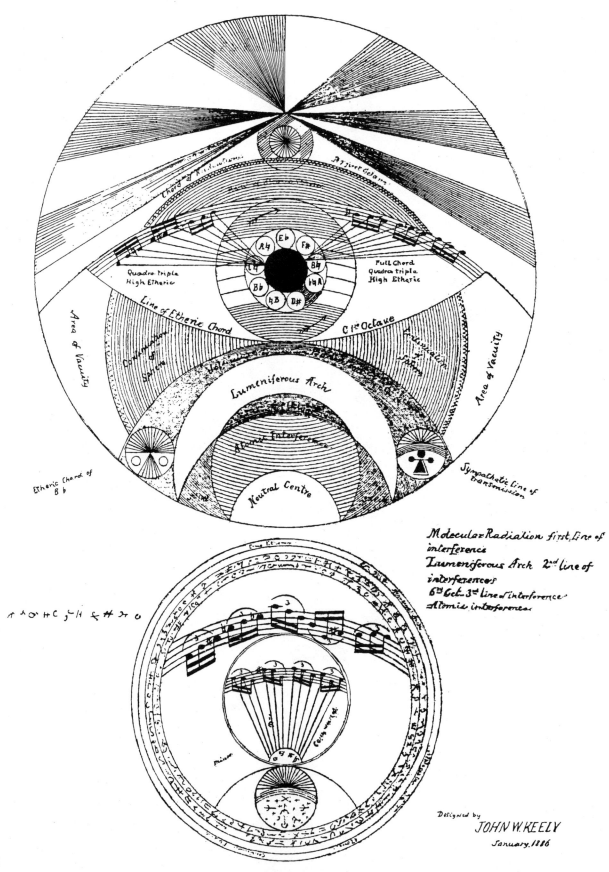

Quadra triple
High Etheric

Full Chord
Quadra triple
High Etheric

Line of Etheric Chord

C 1st Octave

Area of Vacuity

Area of Vacuity

Lumeniferous Arch

Atomic Interference

Neutral Centre

Etheric Chord of
B♭

Sympathetic Line of
transmission

Molecular Radiation first Line of
interference
Lumeniferous Arch 2nd line of
interferences
6th Oct. 3rd line of interference
Atomic interferences

Designed by
JOHN W. KEELY
January, 1886

265

Chart showing the conditions governing the transmittive link of sympathy between neutral centre and periphery of vibratory circuit.

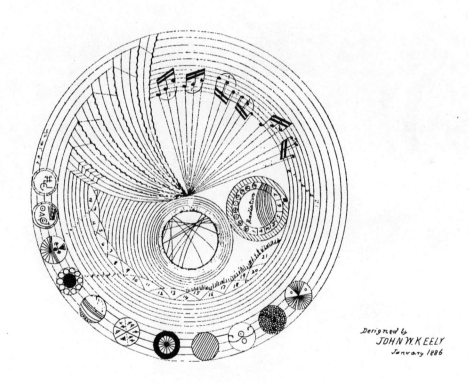

Designed by
JOHN W. KEELY
January 1886

Chart showing the conditions governing the discordants on all their combinations. _____

Designed by
JOHN W. KEELY.
March 1886.

Chart showing the conditions governing harmonious chords on the different octaves quadruple and double quadruple also positive and negative radiation from neutral centre and equation of concordants under antagonism.

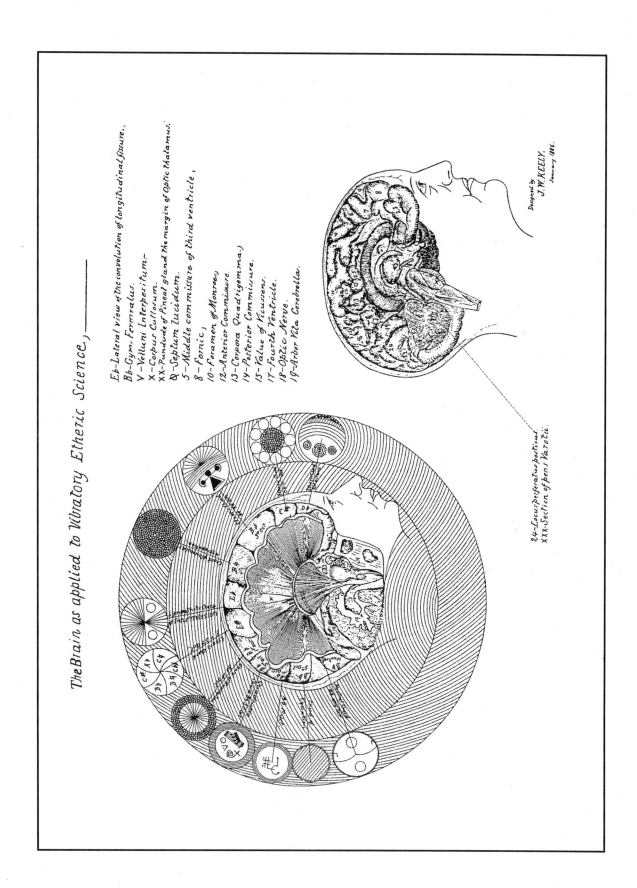

The Brain as applied to Vibratory Etheric Science

Eb—Lateral view of the convolution of longitudinal fissure.
Bb—Gym. Fornealus.
V—Velluti Interpositum.
x—Corpus Callosum.
XX—Punduxe of Pineal gland the margin of Optic Thalamus.
Q—Septum lucidum.
5—Middle commissure of third ventricle,
8—Fornic,
10—Foramen of Monroes
12—Anterior Commisure.
13—Corpora Quadrigemma.)
14—Posterior Commisure.
15—Value of Vieussens.
17—Fourth Ventricle.
18—Optic Nerve.
19—Arbor Vita Cerebrolla.

24—Locus perforatus posticus.
XXX—Section of pons Varolii.

Designed by
J. W. KEELY.
January 1886.

Brain as Applied to Vibratory Etheric Science

Chart defining the different chord associations on the three Octaves, as also interferences on single and double chord bar and theory of setting chords of masses

Interference on single Bar quadruple chord of Bb 3d Octave, and molecular chord of aggregation of B♮ first order of triple sub division.
Interference on double Bar molecular chord of aggregation B♮ and etheric chord of C# 1st Octave.
Concentration of independant chord on sympathetic chord of transmission of E♭.

○ Molecular curve.
∞ Inter molecular curve.
⌒ Discordant groupings on the atomic.

Explanatory Key, see Book 3rd Theoretical expose Pages from 194 to 203.

Designed by
JOHN W. KEELY
February 1886

270

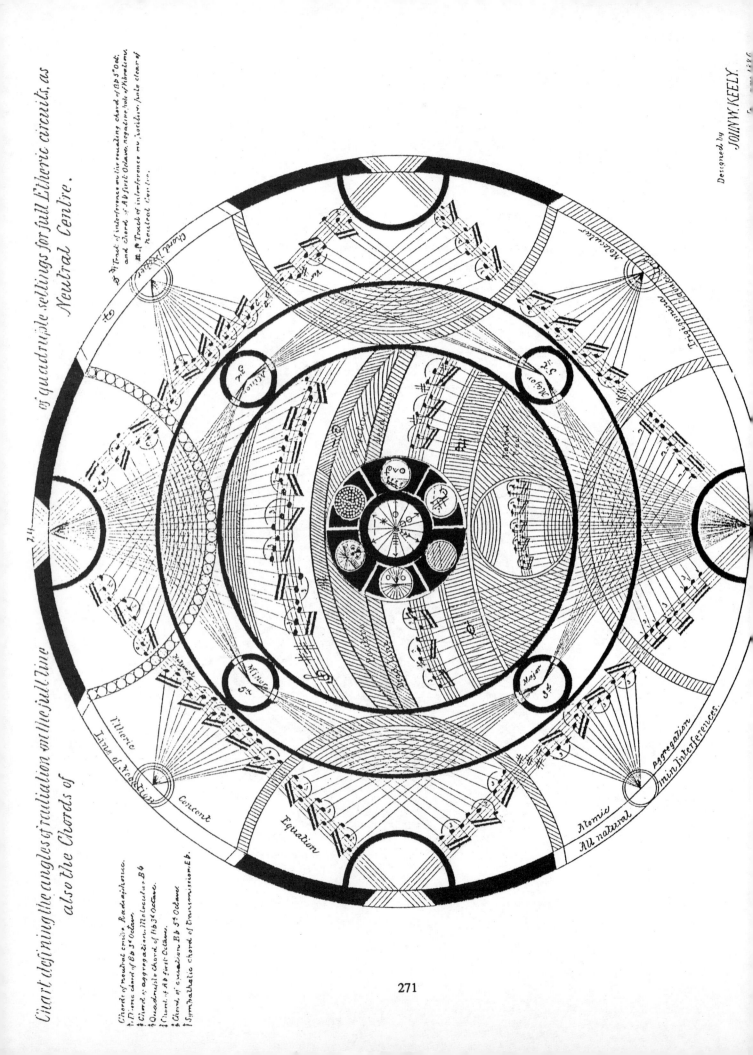

Chart defining the angles of radiation with the full line
of quadruple settings for full Etheric circuits, as
also the Chords of Neutral Centre.

Chord of neutral centre. Radiodynamic.
*Prime chord of Bb 3rd Octave.
‡Chord; aggregation. Molecular Bb
†Quadruple chord of 1 Bb 3rd Octave.
§Chord of Ab First Octave.
♯Chord of radiation Bb 3rd Octave.
†Sympathetic chord of Transmission. Eb.

Bb 3rd Track of interference on live reading chord of Ab 3rd Oct.
and Chord of Ab first Octave, negative, rule of Vibration.
♯Ɵ Track of interference on neutral, rule clear of
neutral Centre.

Designed by
JOHN W. KEELY.

271

Key to Vibratory Rotation

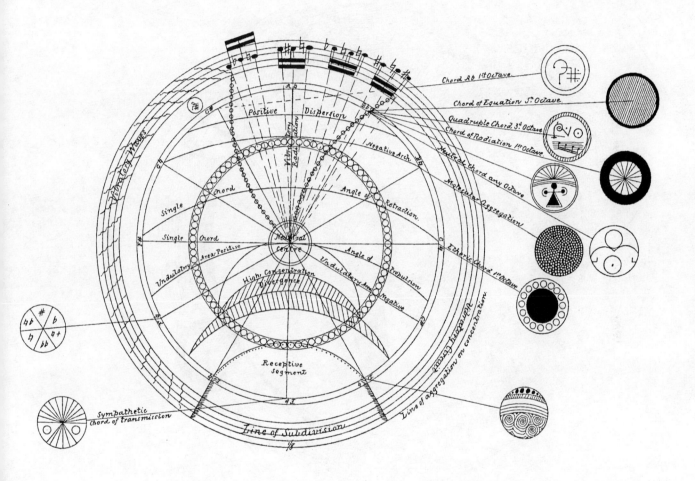

Designed by
JOHN W. KEELY.
January 1886

272

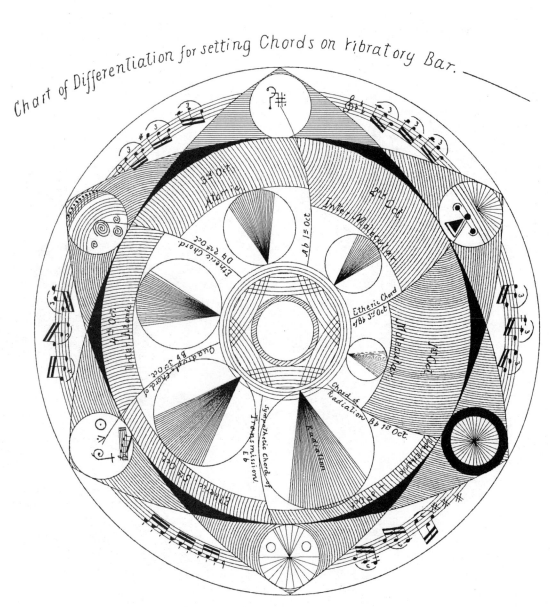

Chart of Differentiation for setting Chords on Vibratory Bar.

Designed by
JOHN W. KEELY.
January 1886

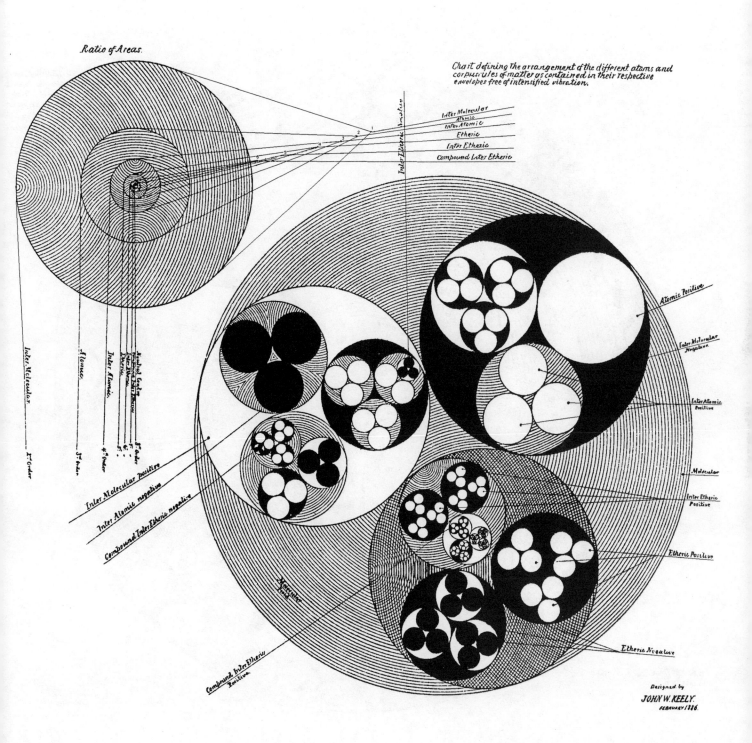

Ratio of Areas.

Chart defining the arrangement of the different atoms and corpuscules of matter as contained in their respective envelopes free of intensified vibration.

Inter Molecular
Atomic
Inter Atomic
Etheric
Inter Etheric
Compound Inter Etheric

Inter Etheric negative

Atomic Positive

Inter Molecular Negative

Inter Atomic Positive

Molecular

Inter Etheric Positive

Etheric Positive

Etheric Negative

Inter Molecular
1st Order
2nd Order
3rd Order
4th Order
Atomic
Inter Atomic

Inter Molecular Positive

Inter Atomic negative

Compound Inter Etheric negative

Molecular

Compound Inter Etheric Positive

Designed by
JOHN W. KEELY.
FEBRUARY 1886.

274

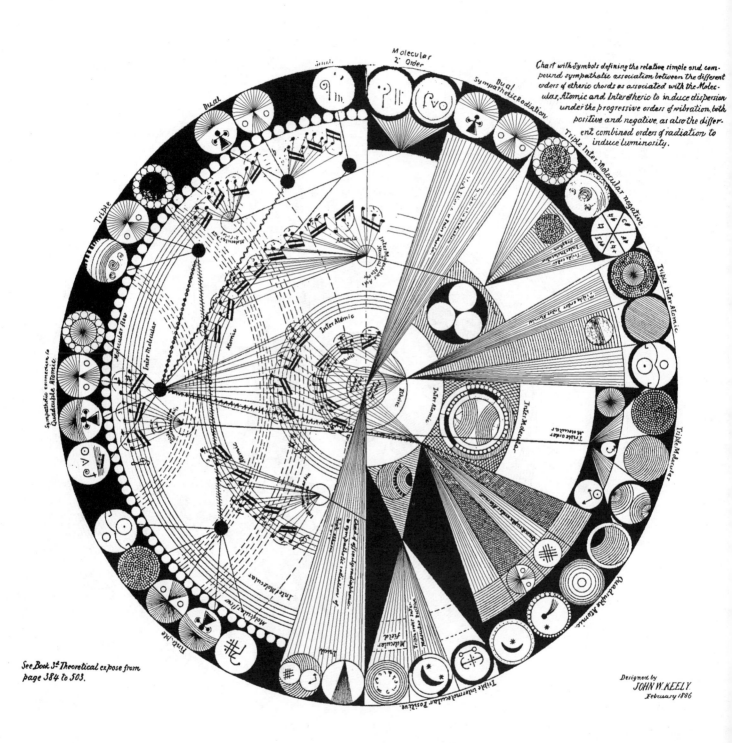

Chart with Symbols defining the relative simple and compound sympathetic association between the different orders of etheric chords as associated with the Molecular, Atomic and Inter etheric to induce dispersion under the progressive orders of vibration, both positive and negative, as also the different combined orders of radiation to induce luminosity.

See Book 3ᵈ Theoretical expose from page 384 to 503.

Designed by
JOHN W. KEELY
February 1886

275

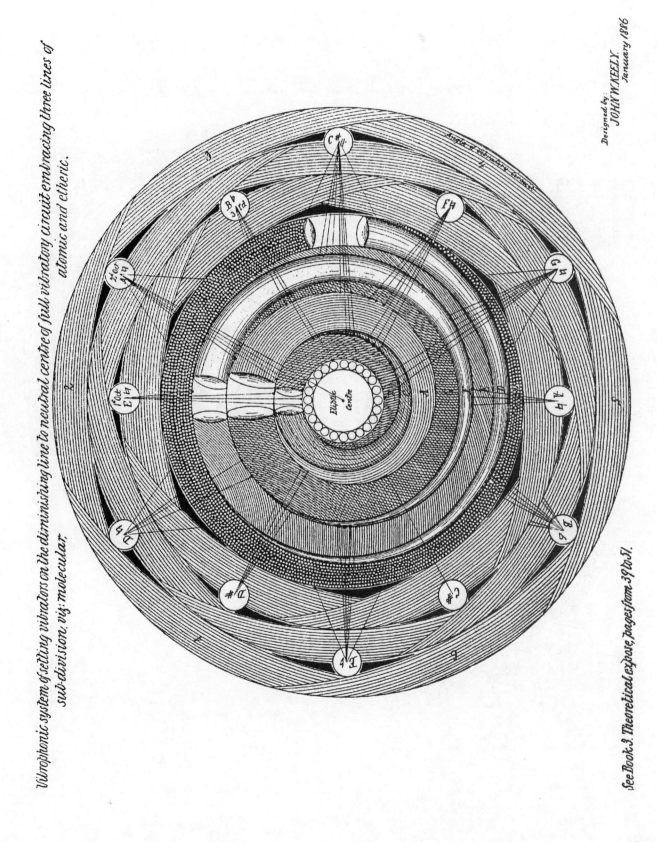

Vibrophonic system of setting vibrators on the diminishing line to neutral centre of full vibratory circuit embracing three lines of sub-division. viz: molecular, atomic and etheric.

Designed by:
JOHN W. KEELY
January 1886

See Book.3. Theoretical expose, pages from 39 to 51.

276

Chart of the Sinuses and nerves of the Skull vibro etherically considered as associated with the Liberator.

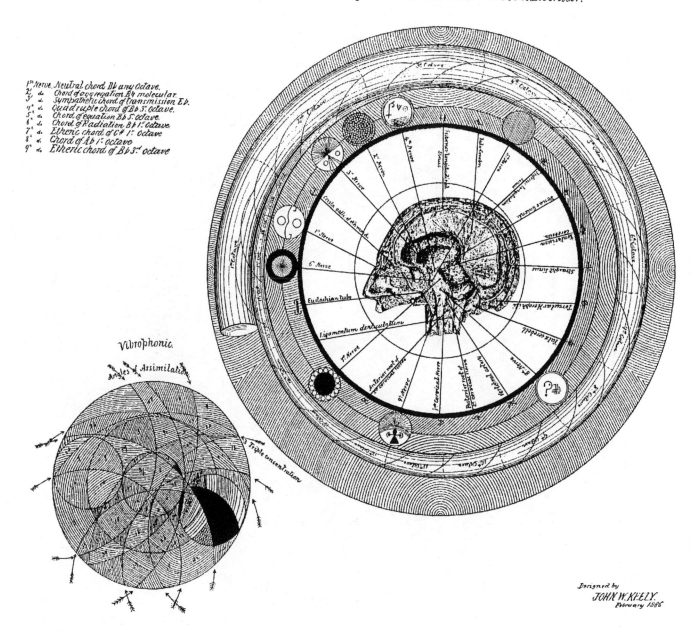

1st Nerve. Neutral chord Bb any Octave.
2d d.   Chord of aggregation Bb molecular.
3d d.   Sympathetic chord of transmission Eb.
4th d.   Quadruple chord of Bb 5. octave.
5th d.   Chord of equation Bb 5. octave.
6th d.   Chord of Radiation Bb 1st Octave.
7th d.   Etheric chord of C# 1st. octave.
8th d.   Chord of Ab 1st. octave.
9th d.   Etheric chord of Bb 3d. octave.

Vibrophonic.

Angles of Assimilation

Triple concentration

Designed by
JOHN W. KEELY.
February 1886

277

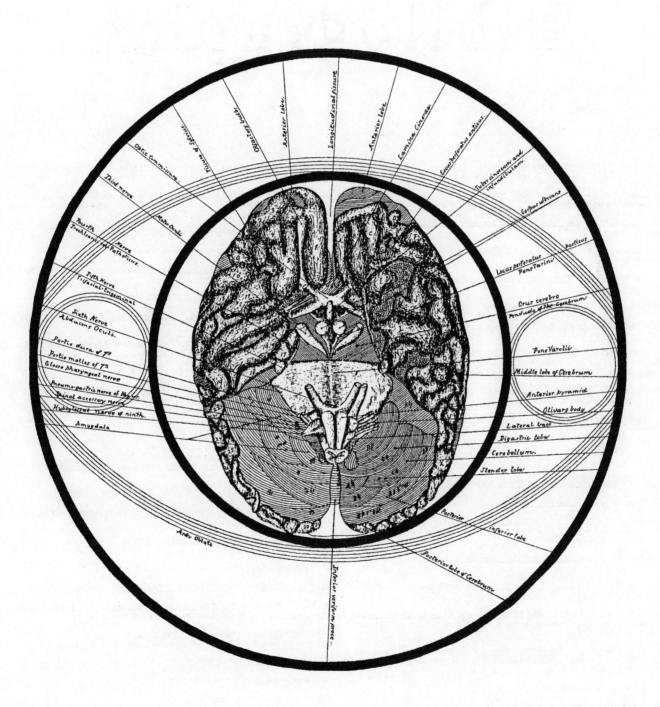

Olfactory Nerve.
Anterior Lobe.
Longitudinal Fissure.
Anterior Lobe.
Lamina Cinerae.
Crus Perforatus antius.
Vulva cinoreum and infundibulum.
Corpus albicans.
Fissure of Sylvius.
Optic Commissure.
Third nerve.
Motor Oculi.
Fourth Nerve Trochlearis or Pathaticus.
Fifth Nerve Trifacial-trigeminal.
Sixth Nerve Abducens Oculi.
Portio dura of 7.
Portio mollis of 7.
Glosso pharyngeal nerve
Pneumo-gastric nerve of Vagus.
Spinal accessory nerve
Hypoglossal nerve of ninth.
Amygdala
Arch Oliate
Inferior vermiform proce
porticus
Locus perforatus Pons Tarini
Crus cerebro Peduncle of the Cerebrum
Pons Varolii
Middle lobe of Cerebrum
Anterior pyramid
Olivary body
Lateral tract
Digastric lobe
Cerebellum.
Slender lobe
Posterior
Inferior lobe
Posterior lobe of Cerebrum

Bibliography

1) Bloomfield-Moore, Clara Jessup, Keely and His Discoveries, Delta Spectrum Research P. O. Box 316, Valentine, Nebraska 69201 (402) 376-1523.

2) Edgar Cayce Readings, Edgar Cayce Foundation, A.R.E., Inc. 67th & Atlantic Blvd., Virginia Beach, Virginia 23451.

3) McGraw-Hill Concise Encyclopedia of Science & Technology, McGraw-Hill Book Company.

4) McGraw-Hill Dictionary of Science & Technical Terms 3rd ed., McGraw-Hill Book Company.

5) Anderson, Philip C., The Spectral Energy Value System. Applied Spectroscopy, Vol. 29, #1, 1975.

6) Tyndall, John, Sound, Longmans, Green, and Co., London, 1893.

7) Allen, Grant, A Newly Discovered Law in Physics, Arena, April 1890. Delta Spectrum Research P. O. Box 316, Valentine, Nebraska 69201 (402) 376-1523.

8) Ramsay, Dougald Carmichel, The Scientific Basis and Build of Music, Marcus Ward & Co., Ltd., New York, 1893. Delta Spectrum Research P. O. Box 316, Valentine, Nebraska 69201 (402) 376-1523.

9) Colville, W. J., Dashed Against the Rock, Colby, Rich, Boston, 1894. Delta Spectrum Research P. O. Box 316, Valentine, Nebraska 69201 (402) 376-1523.

10) Hughes, F. J., Harmonies of Tones and Colors Developed by Evolution, Marcus Ward & Co., London, 1883. Delta Spectrum Research P. O. Box 316, Valentine, Nebraska 69201 (402) 376-1523.

11) Snell, C.W., The Snell Manuscript, edited by Dale Pond, Delta Spectrum Research P. O. Box 316, Valentine, Nebraska 69201 (402) 376-1523.

12) Parker, John A., Quadrature of the Circle, John Wiley & Sons, NY, 1874.

13) Brye, Joseph, Basic Principles of Music

14) Iverson, Ben, Pythagoras And The Quantum World, Carlton Press, Inc., New York, 1982, ISBN 0-8062-1935-1. Delta Spectrum Research P. O. Box 316, Valentine, Nebraska 69201 (402) 376-1523.

15) AMORC, Messages From the Celestial Sanctum, Rosicrucian Press, San Jose, California.

16) Ghiraldi, Alfred A., Radio Physics Course, Radio & Technical Publishing Co., New York, 1933. page 376

17) Keely, John Ernst Worrel, Latent Force & Theory of Vibratory Lift for Airships, Lippincott, 1891. Delta Spectrum Research P. O. Box 316, Valentine, Nebraska 69201 (402) 376-1523

18) Allen, Grant, Force & Energy - The Theory of Dynamics, Longmans, Green, and Co., London, 1888. Delta Spectrum Research P. O. Box 316, Valentine, Nebraska 69201 (402) 376-1523.

19) Scientific American Magazine, May 2, 1874.

20) Transamerica Delaval Corporation.

21) Westrup, J.A., Harrison, F.L., Collin's Music Encyclopedia, William Collins Sons, & Co., Ltd., London, 1959.

22) Hilarion, The Nature of Reality, Canada, Toronto Books, 1979.

23) John Hopkins University Gazette, 10/9/1985

24) Phylos, A Dweller on Two Planets, Borden Publishing Company, Los Angelos, California, 1952.

25) Gamow, George, Thirty Years that Shook Physics, Doubleday & Co., New York, 1966.

26) Andrew, Rev. John, The Pendulograph, George Bell and Sons, London, 1881. Delta Spectrum Research P. O. Box 316, Valentine, Nebraska 69201 (402) 376-1523.

27) Ratzlaff, John T., Patent Wrappers Vol. 1 pg 125, Millbrae, Calif.

28) Anonymous, The Kybalion, San Francisco, 1904.

29) Kimball, Arthur, L., Kimball's College Physics 5th ed., Henry Holt and Company, New York, 1937.

30) Lehrs, Ernst, Man or Matter, Harper & Brothers, New York, 1958.

31) Alexander, James B., The Dynamic Theory of Life and Mind, Minneapolis, The Housekeeper Press, 1893.

32) Goold, Joseph, Benham, Charles E., Kerr, Richard & Wilberforce, Prof. L.R., Harmonic Vibrations and Vibration Figures, Newton and Co., London, 1909.

33) New World Antiquities 14:7/8,67; 14:4; 21:4; 22:4

34) Lewis, H. S., Rosicrucian Manual 2nd. ed., Rosicrucian Press, San Jose, California, 1927

35) Fuller, Buckminster R., Synergistics, MacMillian Publishing Co., New York, 1975.

36) Scientific American Magazine 11/1983 pg 144

37) Ratzlaff, John T., Reference Articles for Solutions to Tesla's Secrets, Millbrae, Calif. Tesla Book Co., 1981

38) Bearden, Tom.

39) Edgar Cayce Blue Book - Dimensions, Edgar Cayce Foundation, A.R.E., Inc. 67th & Atlantic Ave., Virginia Beach, Virginia 23451

40) Birren, Faber, Color Psychology and Color Therapy, New York, University Books, 1961.

41) Nature Magazine, pg 144 3/30/1911

42) McGraw-Hill Encyclopedia of Science & Technology, "Intermolecular Forces"

43) Khan, Hazrat Inayat, The Mysticism of Sound. Music: The Power of the Word: Cosmic Language) by The Sufi Message of Hazrat Inayat Khan, 1979.

44) Bloomfield-Moore, Clara Jessop, Aerial Navigation, The Arena, 1894. Delta Spectrum Research P. O. Box 316, Valentine, Nebraska 69201 (402) 376-1523.

45) Nature Magazine, pg 3339/29/1925

46) Nature Magazine, pg 314 3/2/1929

47) The New Century Dictionary

48) Bearden, Tom, The New Tesla Electromagnetics and The Secrets of Electrical Free Energy, Tesla Book Company, 1580 Manolia Ave., Millbrae, Calif. 94030

49) Foundation for the Study of Cycles, 124 South Highland Avenue, Pittsburgh, PA. 15206

50) Tansley, D.; Radionics and the Subtle Anatomy of Man, New York, Weisner.

51) Dewey & Mandino; Cycles - The Mysterious Forces that Trigger Events, NY, Hawthorne, 1971.

52) Irion, Everett; Vibrations, ARE Press, 67th & Atlantic Blvd., Virginia Beach, VA. 23451

53) Dewey, Edward; Cycles, The Science of Prediction, Foundation for the Study of Cycles, Pittsburgh, PA.

54) Lewis, H. S.; Self Mastery and Fate with the Cycles of Life, AMORC Press. Rosicrucian Park, San Jose, CA.

55) Conner, William; Math's Metasonics, Vol. I & II, Tesla Book Company, Millbrae, Calif.

56) Excerpts on Nicola Tesla, Tesla Book Company, Millbrae, CA.

57) 1977 World Almanac

58) Lewis, H. S.; Whisperings of Self, AMORC Press, San Jose, CA

59) The Old Farmers Almanac, 1977.

60) Pike, Albert; Morals & Dogma, L.H. Jenkins, Inc., Richmond, VA. 1956

61) Shearer, Tony; Land of the Dawn, Quetzalcoatl, Symes Building Suite S-335, 820 16th Street, Denver, CO. 80202

62) Jamison, S.L.; Laklovsky Wave Oscillator, from "Probe the Unknown", June 1973 pp. 3,4.

63) Tonnely, John; Astrological Cycles and the Life Crisis Periods, NY, Weisner, 1977.

64) Dewey, Edward; Catalogue of Cycles, Part I, Economics, Foundation for the Study of Cycles, Pittsburgh, PA.

65) Imperial Earthquake Investigation Committee, Vol. IV, No. 2; Vol. V, No. I.

66) O'Neil, John; Prodigal Genius, The Life of Nicola Tesla, Tesla Book Company, Millbrae, Calif.

67) Curtiss, Leon Francis; Introduction to Neutron Physics, D. Van Nostrand Company, Inc., Princeton, NJ, 1959.

68) Harris, T. F.; Hand Book of Acoustics, 5th edition, J. Curwen & Sons, London, 1903?

69) Friend, David; Learning Music with Synthesizers, Hal Leonard Publishing Corporation, 1974.

70) Piezoelectric Accelerometers and Vibration Preamplifiers, Bruel & Kjaer, 1986.

71) Eclectic Magazine, 1880, pp 510

72) Colville, Wm. J.; Kabbalah The Harmony of Opposites; Macoy Publishing & Masonic Supply Co., New York, 1916.

73) Cayce, Edgar; Auras An Essay On The Meaning Of Colors. A.R.E. Press, Virginia Beach, Va. 23451, 1972.

74) Eddy, Mary Baker; Science and Health with Key to the Scriptures. 1971

75) Rossing, Thomas D.; The Science of Sound. Addison-Wesley Publishing Company, 1982.

76) Cayce, Hugh Lynn; Oneness of all Force, May, 1935.

77) New Tomorrow, A.R.E. Press, No. 1, p 18 67th & Atlantic Ave., Virginia Beach, VA 23451

78) New Tomorrow, A.R.E. Press, No. 2, p 11 67th & Atlantic Ave., Virginia Beach, VA 23451

79) New Tomorrow, A.R.E. Press, No. 2, p 12 67th & Atlantic Ave., Virginia Beach, VA 23451

80) New Tomorrow, A.R.E. Press, No. 1, p 16 67th & Atlantic Ave., Virginia Beach, VA 23451

81) Theon of Smyrna; Mathematics Useful For Understanding Plato, Wizard's Bookshelf, P.O. Box 6600, San Diego, CA 92106, 1979.

82) Raphael, Carey, K. X.; The Starseed Transmissions, Uni-Sun Books, 1986.

83) Edgar Cayce lecture. Auras read by Edgar Cayce at Tuesday Night Bible Study Group Meeting, August 26, 1941. Supplement to reading (5746-1)

84) J. G. Horner, Dictionary of Terms Used in Mechanical Engineering, The Technical Press, Ltd., London, England, 1960.

85) Martin Hirschorn, Compendium of Noise Engineering - Part I, Sound & Vibration Magazine, July 1987.

86) G. M. Graham and D.G. Lahoz, Observation of Static Electromagnetic Angular Momentum in Vacuo, Nature, Vol. 285, 15 May 1980, pp. 154- 155.

87) Roland Hunt, The 7 Rays of Healing, A.R.E. Press, 67th & Atlantic Ave., Virginia Beach, VA 23451

88) D. N. Trifonov & V. D. Trifonov, Chemical Elements, How They Were Discovered, Mir Publishers, Moscow.

89) Raknes, Ola, Wilhelm Reich and Orgonomy, Pelican Books, 1971.

90) Mann, Edward W., Orgone, Reich and Eros, Wilhelm Reich's Theory of Life Energy; Simon and Schuster, 1973, NY, NY.

98) Haigh, John; Serving the Planet Earth.

99) Bloomfield-Moore, Clara Jessop, What is Electricity, Part II. Delta Spectrum Research P. O. Box 316, Valentine, Nebraska 69201 (402) 376-1523

100) Field of Rotating Machinery Measurment, Monitoring and Analysis; Bentley Nevada Corporation.

101) Benson, A. L., Nikola Tesla, Dreamer, in The World Today, February, 1912, pp. 1763-1767.

102) Thomas, Ralph H., Ultrasonics in Packaging and Plastics Fabrication, 1974, Cahners Publishing Company, Inc., 89 Franklin Street, Boston, Mass. 02110

103) Fantel, Hans; The True Sound of Music - A Practical Guide to Sound Equipment for the Home, 1973, E. P. Dutton & Company, Inc., New York

104) Miller, Dayton Clarence; The Science of Musical Sounds. The Macmillan Company, New York, 1926.

105) Young, F. Ronald; Cavitation. McGraw-Hill Book Company, Maidenhead, Berkshire, England, 1989.

106) Glinka, N.; General Chemistry; Peace Publishers, Moscow.,+1970.

107) Franklin, William S.; MacNutt, Barry; Heat - A Text Book for Colleges and Technical Schools; Franklin and Charles, Lancaster, PA., 1923.

108) Everest, F. Alton; The Master Handbook of Acoustics, 2nd ed., TAB Books, Blue Ridge Summit PA; 1988.

109) Duane, W., and Scheuer, O., Le Radium 10, 33 (1913).

110) Lanning, F. C., and Lind, S. C., J. Phys. Chem. 42, 1229 (1938).

111) Risse, O., Strahlentherapie 34, 578 (1929).

112) Fricke, H., and Brownscombie, E. R., Phys. Rev. 44, 240 (1933).

113) Guenther, P., and Holzapfel, L., Z. Phys. Chem. 44B, 374 (1939).

114) Lea, D. E., Actions of Radiations on Living Cells, Cambridge Univ. Press, NewYork, 1946.

115) Allen, Augustine O.,; The Radiation Chemistry of Water and Aqueous Solutions; D. Van Nostrand Company, Inc.; Princeton, NY; 1961.

116) Trefil, James S .; From Atoms to Quarks - An Introduction to the Strange World of Particle Physics; Charles Scribner's Sons, New York; 1980.

117) Norman, Emest L.; The Infinite Concept of Cosmic Creation. Unarius, Science of Life, P.O. Box 1042, El Cajon, CA 92020, 1970.

118) Roberts, John D.; Nuclear Magnetic Resonance; McGraw-Hill Book Company, Inc., 1959.

119) Lighting the Way; Series 16th Year, No. 2; Helena Elizabeth Ruhnua; P. O. Box 440606, Aurora, CO, 80044

120) Photonics Spectra; Laurin Publishing, Manifestations in Nature: Part I, July, 1992, page 195-196.

121) Haeckel, Ernst; The Riddle of the Universe at the close of the Nineteenth Century: Watts & Co., London, 1906.

122) Goldsmid, H. J.; Thermoelectric Refrigeration; Plenum Press, New York, 1964.

123) Laing, Stephen; A Modern Zoroastrian; Chapman and Hall, London, 1891.

124) Steiner, Rudolph; The Story of My Life: London, 1928.

125) Stainer, John; Barrett, W. A.; A Dictionary of Musical Terms; Novello, Ewer and Co., London, pre1900.

126) Author unknown; Japasutram, The Science of Creative Sound; date unknown, publisher and place unknown.

127) Lindeman, Peter, Journal of Borderland Research, Sept.-Oct., 1992, page 17.

128) Althouse, Andrew D.; Turnquist, Carl H.; Bracciano, Alfred F.; Modern Refrigeration and Air Con- ditioning; The Goodheart-Willcox Company, Inc., South Holland, IL.1988.

129) Bird, Christopher; Fire From Water - Part III; Explore Magazine, Vol. 3, No. 6, 1992; page 47-62.

130) D'Antonio, Peter; Fractals and Number Theory are Changing the Shape of Acoustics; Sound & Vibration Magazine; October, 1992, page 27.

131) Hartmann, Franz; The Life of Philippus Theo- phractus. Bombast of Ffohen- heim Known by the name of Paracelsus and The Subtance of His Teach- ings; George Redway, London, 1887.

132) Bearden, Thomas E., Analysis of Scalar/ FLectromagnetic Technology, Tesla Book Company; P. O. Box 121873, Chula Vista, CA 91912

133) Cantor, G.N. and Hodge, M.J.S., Conceptions of Ether - Studies in the History of Ether Theories. 1740-1900. Cambridge University Press, Cambridge, 1981

134) Bearden, Thomas E., Gravitobiology - A New Bio- physics, Tesla Book Company, P. O. Box 121873, Chula Vista, CA 91912, 1991

135) Anonymous, Keely - Pictures of His Discoveries, Delta Spectrum Research P. O. Box 316, Valentine, Nebraska 69201 (402) 376-1523.

136) Bloomfield-Moore, Clara Jessup, Keely's Present Po- sition, Delta Spectrum Research P. O. Box 316, Valentine, Nebraska 69201 (402) 376-1523.

137) Bloomfield-Moore, Clara Jessup, Keely's Contribution to Science, Delta Spectrum Research P. O. Box 316, Valentine, Nebraska 69201 (402) 376-1523.

138) Bloomfield-Moore, Clara Jessup, Mr. Keely's Etheric Force, Delta Spectrum Research P. O. Box 316, Valentine, Nebraska 69201 (402) 376-1523.

139) Bloomfield-Moore, Clara Jessup, Some Truths about Keely, Delta Spectrum Research P. O. Box 316, Valentine, Nebraska 69201 (402) 376-1523.

140) Bloomfield-Moore, Clara Jessup, The Veil With- drawn, Delta Spectrum Research P. O. Box 316, Valentine, Nebraska 69201 (402) 376-1523.

141) Bloomfield-Moore, Clara Jessup, The Dogmatism of Science, Delta Spectrum Research P. O. Box 316, Valentine, Nebraska 69201 (402) 376-1523.

142) Bloomfield-Moore, Clara Jessup, The Action of Force is Spiro-Vortex, Delta Spectrum Research P. O. Box 316, Valentine, Nebraska 69201 (402) 376-1523.

143) Bloomfield-Moore, Clara Jessup, The Keely Motor Secret, Delta Spectrum Research P. O. Box 316, Valentine, Nebraska 69201 (402) 376-1523.

144) Bloomfield-Moore, Clara Jessup, What is Science?, Delta Spectrum Research P. O. Box 316, Valentine, Nebraska 69201 (402) 376-1523.

145) Brinton, Professor Daniel G., The Laws of Being, Delta Spectrum Research P. O. Box 316, Valentine, Nebraska 69201 (402) 376-1523.

146) Browning, Robert, Two Poems to John Keely, Delta Spectrum Research P. O. Box 316, Valentine, Nebraska 69201 (402) 376-1523.

147) Collier, Charles, Collier's Letter to Scientific American. Delta Spectrum Research P. O. Box 316, Valentine, Nebraska 69201 (402) 376-1523.

148) Collier, Charles, Report of Charles Collier on The Keely Motor Company, Delta Spectrum Research P. O. Box 316, Valentine, Nebraska 69201 (402) 376-1523.

149) Davidson, Dan A., A Breakthrough to New Free En-ergy Sources, Dan Davidson, Arizona.

150) Keely Motor Company, Keely Motor Company - By- Laws, Delta Spectrum Research P. O. Box 316, Valentine, Nebraska 69201 (402) 376-1523.

151) Keely, John Ernst Worrell, Operation of the Vibratory Circuit, Delta Spectrum Research P. O. Box 316, Valentine, Nebraska 69201 (402) 376-1523.

152) Keely, John Ernst Worrell, Propositions of Astronomical Circles, Delta Spectrum Research P. O. Box 316, Valentine, Nebraska 69201 (402) 376-1523.

153) Keely, John Ernst Worrell, Propositions of Geometry, Delta Spectrum Research P. O. Box 316, Valentine, Nebraska 69201 (402) 376-1523.

154) Lascelles-Scott, Wentworth, A Remarkable Book and its Teachings, Delta Spectrum Research P. O. Box 316, Valentine, Nebraska 69201 (402) 376-1523.

155) Lorimer, John H., Keely Motor Company - Minority Report to Stockholders, Delta Spectrum Research P. O. Box 316, Valentine, Nebraska 69201 (402) 376-1523.

156) Pond, Dale, Keely's Secrets, Delta Spectrum Research P. O. Box 316, Valentine, Nebraska 69201 (402) 376-1523.

157) Pond, Dale, The Journal of Sympathetic Vibratory Physics. Vol. I-V; Publication began October, 1985, Delta Spectrum Research P. O. Box 316, Valentine, Nebraska 69201 (402) 376-1523.

158) William Hudgings, Dr. Abrahms and the Electron Theory, Delta Spectrum Research P. O. Box 316, Valentine, Nebraska 69201 (402) 376-1523.

158.1) Pond, Dale, Sympathetic Vibratory Physics - A Compendiurn of Terrns and Phrases, Delta Spectrum Research P. O. Box 316, Valentine, Nebraska 69201 (402) 376-1523.

159) Skinner, John Ralston, An Essay Upon Force and its Effect Upon Matter, Delta Spectrum Research P. O. Box 316, Valentine, Nebraska 69201 (402) 376-1523.

159.1) Russell, Walter, Atomic Suicide?, University of Science and Philosophy, Swannanoa, Waynesboro, Virginia

160) Iverson, Ben, Pythagoras and the Quantum World. Volume III, Delta Spectrum Research P. O. Box 316, Valentine, Nebraska 69201 (402) 376-1523.

160.1) Feynman, Richard, The Feynman Lectures on Physics: mainly Electromagne- tism and Matter, Addison-Wesley Publishing Company, Inc., 1964, 2nd ed.

161) Iverson, Ben, Pythagoras and the Quantum World. Volume II, Delta Spectrum Research P. O. Box 316, Valentine, Nebraska 69201 (402) 376-1523.

161.1) Fox, Hal, Discussion Topics for Models and Theory Workshop, Fusion Infor- mation Center, Inc. P. O. Box 58639 Salt Lake City, Utah 84158

162) Kramer, Edna E., The Nature and Growth of Modern Mathematics, Hawthorn Books, Inc. New York, 1970

163) Russell, Walter, The Universal One, University of Science and Philosophy, 1974; Swannanoa, Virginia

164) Hankins, Thomas L., Sir William Rowan Hamilton, The John Hopkins Univer- sity Press

165) Wellington, Harold, Blakiston's New Gould Medical Dictionary, The Blakiston Company, 1949; 1st edition.

166) Kelland, P. & Tait, P. G., Introduction to Quaternions, MacMillian and Co., 2nd ed., 1882, London

167) Hardy, A. S., Elements of Quaternions, Ginn, Heath, & Co., 1881, Boston

168) Tyndall, John, Heat Considered as A Mode of Motion, Longman, Green, Long- man, Roberts, & Green; 1865, London

169) Colby, Frank Moore, Keely: Obituary. The International Year Book, 1898; edi- tor, Frank Moore Colby; New York, Dodd, Mead & Company

170) Unknown, One View of the Keely Motor, Engineering Magazine, 2:14 Delta Spectrum Research P. O. Box 316, Valentine, Nebraska 69201 (402) 376-1523.

171) Keltz, Martha, Amplitude of Force - A play about John Keely, Studio Editions, 3303 Guilford Ave., #3, Baltimore, MD 21218

171) Appleton Annual Cylcopedia, The Keely Motor, Appleton Annual Cyclopedia and Register of Important Events of the Year 1887; New Series, Vol. XII; New York, D. Appleton & Company, 1889 Delta Spectrum Research P. O. Box 316, Val- entine, Nebraska 69201 (402) 376-1523.

173) Gimore, Robert, Lie Groups. Lie Algebras and Some of Their Applications, John Wiley & Sons, New York, 1974

174) Cohen, I. Bernard, Benjamin Franklin's Experiments, Harvard University Press, 1941; Cambridge, Mass.

175) Iverson, Ben, QA-l. Natural Arithmetic, Institute for Technically Applied Mu- sic, Tigard, OR. Delta Spectrum Research P. O. Box 316, Valentine, Nebraska 69201 (402) 376-1523.

176) Marks, Lionel S., Mechanical Engineer's Handbook, McGraw-Hill Book Com- pany, Inc. 1951

177) Puharich, Andrija, URI - A Journal of the Mystery of Uri Geller, Anchor Press, Doubleday & Company, Garden City, New York, 1974

178) Thompson, Silvanus P., Elementary Lessons in Electricity & Magnetism, The MacMillan Company, New York, 1899

179) K K Jain, D Chennareddy, P I John and Y C Saxena, Design and Performance of a Tesla Transformer Type Relativistic Electron Beam Generator, Sadhana, Vol. 9, Part 1 February 1986, pp. 19-29; India.

180) Tesla, Nikola, Coil for Electro-Magnets, US Patent Office, Serial Number 479,804, July 7, 1893 Bifilar coils as opposed to standard mono-filament coils.

181) Howey, M. Oldfield, The Encircled Serpent - A Study of Serpent Symbolism in all Countries and Ages, Arthur Richmond Company, NY City, 1955

182) Collom, John, Prophetic Numbers of Daniel and the Revelation - An Identifica- tion of the Times and Events referred to in Prophecy together with Coincident Facts Respecting the Great Pyramid of Egypt and the approaching Planetary Perihelia, Wilson & Jones Book Publishers 1880, Delta Spectrum Research P. O. Box 316, Valentine, Nebraska 69201 (402) 376-1523.

183) Michael S. Triantafyllou; George S. Triantafyllou, An Efficient Swimming Ma- chine, Scientific American Magazine; March, 1995, pg. 64-70

281

Index

Index

ORDER FORM

Phone, fax or write if you would like a copy of our catalog listing
all books, videos, etc. that we produce and distribute.

Telephone Orders: Call 505-474-0998 to charge your VISA, MasterCard, American Express or Discover

Mail Orders: The Message Company
4 Camino Azul
Santa Fe, NM 87505

Fax Orders: 505-471-2584

CODE	TITLE	QUANTITY	PRICE	TOTAL
D20020	**The Physics of Love,** 156 pages, 8½ x 11, paperback.	____ x	$15.95 =	____
D20039	**Universal Laws Never Before Revealed: Keely's Secrets** 288 pages, 8½ x 11, paperback.	____ x	$19.95 =	____
D2008X	**Nikola Tesla's Earthquake Machine,** 176 pages, 8½ x 11, paperback.	____ x	$16.95 =	____
D20063	**Spiritual Vampires: The Use and Misuse of Spiritual Power** 256 pages, 6 x 9, paperback.	____ x	$14.95 =	____
D20101	**History of the American Constitutional or Common Law** 144 pages, 8½ x 11, paperback.	____ x	$11.95 =	____
D20004	**Law and the Heart: A Practical Guide for Successful Lawyer/Client Relationships,** 168 pages, 5½ x 8½, paperback.	____ x	$14.95 =	____
D20128	**How To Find the Best Lawyers . . . and Save 50% on Legal Fees** 200 pages, 5½ x 8½, paperback.	____ x	$14.95 =	____
D20055	**International Directory of Hemp Products and Suppliers** 144 pages, 6 x 9, paperback.	____ x	$29.95 =	____
D20047	**Grazing Through the Woods with the Herb Man** Color video.	____ x	$19.95 =	____

PRESENTER

Willis Harman, PhD	**Spirituality in Business: The Tough Questions** Color video, 60 minutes	____ x	$19.95 =	____
Richard Barrett	**Unfolding of the World Bank Spiritual Unfoldment Society** Color video, 60 minutes	____ x	$19.95 =	____
Martin Rutte	**Livelihood: Growing Spirit at Work,** Color video, 60 minutes	____ x	$19.95 =	____
Judith Thompson, PhD	**Moving from Corporate Social Responsibility to Corporate Spirituality,** Color video, 60 minutes	____ x	$19.95 =	____
Michael Horst/Brooke Warrick	**Spirituality in Real Estate,** Color video, 60 minutes	____ x	$19.95 =	____

SUBTOTAL _____

SHIPPING $2.00 _____

EXTRA SHIPPING _____

NM RESIDENTS ADD SALES TAX 5.75% _____

TOTAL $_____

Extra Shipping Charges:
- Priority Mail: add $3.00
- AK, HI, Canada: add 10%
- All other countries: add 25%
- Foreign Air: add $8.00 per book

❑ Enclosed is a check or money order for total.

❑ Please charge to my [ ] VISA [ ] MC
[ ] American Express [ ] Discover

CARD #

EXP. DATE

SIGNATURE

NAME

ADDRESS

CITY / STATE / ZIP

PHONE